D0234739

Introduced by the multi-talented raconteur, Peter Ustinov, THE LAUGHTER OMNIBUS is a wildly funny collection of humorous stories from some of the twentieth century's best known writers and comedians.

As Groucho Marx himself might have said on receiving such a book,

'From the moment I picked it up until I laid it down, I was convulsed with laughter. Some day I intend reading it.'

# The Laughter Omnibus

Introduction by Peter Ustinov

HEADLINE

The publisher wishes to thank
Gigi Joly for her help

The Comedy Collection Copyright © 1989 Michael O'Mara
Books Limited

First published in 1989
by Michael O'Mara Books Limited

First published in paperback in 1990
by HEADLINE BOOK PUBLISHING

10 9 8 7 6 5 4

All rights reserved. No part of this publication may be
reproduced, stored in a retrieval system, or transmitted,
in any form or by any means without the prior written
permission of the publisher, nor be otherwise circulated
in any form of binding or cover other than that in which
it is published and without a similar condition being
imposed on the subsequent purchaser.

All characters in this publication are fictitious
and any resemblance to real persons, living or dead,
is purely coincidental.

ISBN 0 7472 3460 4

Printed and bound in Great Britain by
Cox & Wyman Ltd, Reading, Berkshire

HEADLINE BOOK PUBLISHING
A Division of Hodder Headline PLC
338 Euston Road
London NW1 3BH

# Contents

# *Introduction*

## Peter Ustinov

Comedy is merely tragedy which has gone awry; tragedy is merely comedy which has gone awry. This, known by at least one person as Ustinov's Law, was formulated during a half century of theatrical First Nights which shall be nameless for no other reason than that the names in question have slipped gracefully into oblivion. However, the lawmaker insists that the principle can be applied even to the greatest works of art.

Paradox is a vital element in man's eternal search for Truth, which any thinking student of the human condition must ardently hope he never finds. What would man do with the Truth once he found it? He could only fumble with it. Messiahs are there to be waited for, not to arrive. For the satirist to castigate the follies of the world is all well and good so long as the talent is there, and so long as the sting of the whip causes no lasting laceration. That would be tantamount to destroying his own livelihood and about as intelligent as a bee complaining about the existence of flowers in the garden.

M'lud the judge may well express his deepening horror at every new crime brought to his attention, but even he must realise that without crime, he would be out of a job, and be forced to turn his talents to something constructive. Once we recognise that the whole structure of justice, with its pomp and majesty, is based on the foundation of all that is sordid, and depends on the criminal, the reprehensible, for its very *raison d'être,* we may safely explore further along the same, well-marked track.

Today there is a great inflation in the possibilities of

corruption due to the privatization of practically everything, including private life, now in the public sector. A study of the cheaper media outlets is enough to convince us that criminals are merely the patsies who get caught, the scapegoats, whereas the cleverer miscreants get titles. Scandals occur through oversights as on those occasions, usually skilfully avoided, when those with titles, or at least fortunes, get caught.

All this is the pretext for several books in this century of the middle man, and all the publisher asked for was a brief preface. Enjoy to the full the glittering series of failed tragedies contained in this volume. They will certainly sharpen the appetite for an acuter observation of life's paradoxes, the source of all laughter and tears, mix to taste, and keep within the reach of children. The sooner they learn, the better.

*Part One*

# THE WAR BETWEEN THE SEXES

Bigamy is having one wife too many.
Monogamy is the same thing.

**Anon.**

# *The Dangerous World of Relationships*

## Miles Kington

Having survived innumerable liaisons, many a tragic affair, several lifelong romances, five marriages and a very long evening with a female Romanian architect, I think I may be said to have an average experience of relationships. And the golden truth I have learnt about relationships, whether they are with the opposite sex, the same sex, a pet or even a house plant, is that they do not come to grief on the big things like love, money, ambition and sex so often as on the small things like personal habits, attitudes, prejudices and sex.

This is because people rush blindly into relationships without doing adequate research. Oh yes, they establish that they're in love; that they enjoy each other's company; that they have the same attitude to life, television and Woody Allen; that they think this is a wonderful relationship which is going to last for ever and ever. Well, that's the basic requirement, the very least you need. What they *haven't* found out is what the other person thinks about party games, puddings, bending paperbacks back as you read them and throwing old newspapers away. The really crucial things, in fact.

Many a wonderful relationship has been ruined because two otherwise well-suited people were totally incompatible in the little matter of, say, temperature. I know one couple whose marriage, has, against all the odds, survived the fact that he likes a sheet and blanket at night and she likes four blankets, a duvet and socks. It has survived long enough for their children to be now starting university. At last they can break loose and do some travelling. The only trouble is – and it looks likely to wreck the marriage – he can only go north and she has to go to the tropics.

So if you are thinking of combining with someone in the near future and expect them to say those magic words: 'Would you care to initiate a relationship with me?' for heaven's sake make sure you are compatible first. Make them fill in a questionnaire; hold an informal audition; talk to their parents; *but find out first.*

To help you, I have mapped out the areas in which most relationships are later found floating upside down, without a crew and with all the lifeboats gone.

1. Listening to music. Most people don't listen to music completely without reaction, except music critics. They tap feet, click fingers or nod in time with the music. Or, of course, very nearly but not quite in time with the music. Some people hum along, just audibly. A few people sit motionless for up to fifteen minutes, then say loudly: 'Ye-eah!' I myself have an appalling habit of clicking my teeth in complicated rhythms. It's quite inaudible when there's music playing, but when I'm remembering a favourite record, all people can hear is tuneless grinding of molars, unaware that I'm really bashing out the most exotic rhythmic patterns. I'm thinking of making the big switch to electric dentures.

Anyway, remember that where you now watch your loved one enthralled by a record and think how wonderful it is to see someone so enraptured, you will one day say to yourself: 'If he doesn't stop swaying backwards and forwards with his eyes shut, I shall scream till the neighbours come.' Ask him to stop *now.*

2. The world is divided into people who like party games, and those who would rather die than get involved. One from the first camp should not live with one from the second camp. The same is roughly true of community singing, wearing fancy dress and putting your hand up when volunteers from the audience are asked for.

3. Money. The world is also divided into people who feel sick if they get into debt, and people who don't know what it's like to be without an overdraft. If you are one of each, you could still make it, but for God's sake have separate bank accounts.

4. Nightwear. Some people always put it on, some never. I don't think it's anything to do with sensuality; it's another facet of the hot v cold problem. But you've both got to decide to do the same thing. If one person sleeps with nothing on, the other person is going to feel perpetually overdressed, which is something we shouldn't have to worry about after we've got undressed. A friend of mine once had a brief liaison with a girl with very poor circulation who wore a dressing gown in bed. 'Nothing wrong with that,' he said, 'except that every time she turned over things fell out of her pockets. I hurt myself badly on a hairbrush one night.' I personally think girls in pyjamas are rather attractive, but that's my problem.

5. Throwing things away. Some do, some don't. If the two types live together, you sooner or later find one partner routinely going through the waste paper baskets and dustbins to find what the other is trying to get rid of. If you feel now a flash of irritation when your partner says: 'You never know when it might come in useful,' your relationship is already doomed.

6. Arguments. An argument should ideally take place in order to get at the truth, but unfortunately a lot of people (mostly men, I'm afraid) argue to win, and will go on backing a half-baked idea until the other person bursts into tears or throws something. Unfortunately, in the early stages of relationships, when the sun is shining, there aren't any arguments and it's hard to know how things will turn out. Better provoke an argument early on, just to see how it goes.

7. Does he like the countryside? Do you hate it? Or vice versa? Then call it off now.

8. Some people skip starters in order to leave room for the pudding. Others order every course except the pudding. Put one of each kind together, and most of your meals will be spent with one partner staring into space. Unless, of course, you compromise by both having every course, in which case laying the foundations for a very overweight middle-aged couple.

9. Sex. Not as important as eating, but still quite important. A New Yorker once told me: 'A good sex life takes up less than five percent of your time; a rotten sex life traps up all your time.' I can't better that. She then added reflectively: 'My mother told me that.'

10. Funny stories. Why is it that so many partnerships sort themselves out sooner or later into a double act, consisting of one person telling stories badly and the other correcting them the whole time? Because they didn't get it sorted out right at the beginning. It's one of the facts of life that we find ourselves telling stories more often than we have a stock of stories for; therefore we start telling the same anecdotes over and over again. The other person must understand this, and at least hope that the anecdotes improve with age. *Don't interrupt.* Realise humbly that you don't do it any better either.

There is one exception to all this; the person who believes that stories are funnier if you say everything three times, like this: 'It was a lovely day, blue sky, not a cloud to be seen. And this man, just an ordinary bloke, some fellow or other, was strolling along, just walking down the street, minding his own business when suddenly, out of the blue, from nowhere . . .' Or, if it's personal reminiscence: 'I remember one time we were staying in this hotel in Brussels, ordinary Belgian hotel, usual continental pension . . .'

People like that should not have a relationship with anyone.

●

I can see from your utter misery, from your eagerness to misunderstand each other, and from your thoroughly bad temper, that this is the real thing.

**Peter Ustinov,** *Romanoff and Juliet,* 1957

My boyfriend and I broke up. He wanted to get married, and I didn't want him to.

**Rita Rudner**

Marriage is not a word but a sentence.

**Anon.**

Never go to bed mad. Stay up and fight.

**Phyllis Diller**

I never knew what real happiness was until I got married. And by then it was too late.

**Max Kauffmann**

Some people ask the secret of our long marriage. We take time to go to a restaurant two times a week. A little candlelight, dinner, soft music and dancing. She goes Tuesdays, I go Fridays.

**Henry Youngman**

*'Maybe you don't have charm, Lily, but you're enigmatic.'*

I like two kinds of men: domestic and foreign.

**Mae West**

When women go wrong, men go right after them.

**Mae West**

I did a picture in England one winter and it was so cold I almost got married.

**Shelley Winters**

I told my wife the truth. I told her I was seeing a psychiatrist. Then she told *me* the truth: that she was seeing a psychiatrist, two plumbers and a bartender.

**Rodney Dangerfield**

# *Is it Time for a Degree in Sex?*

## Jilly Cooper

Pondering rather gloomily this week on the merits of sex education for eleven-year-olds, I ask myself where's it all going to end? Will our children be taking sex at O-Level in a few years' time, with *Portnoy's Complaint* and *Lady C.* as set books? And how will they cope with their practicals? And will pupils who show no aptitude for sex have to give it up at thirteen?

Enough fuss, too, is made about public school boys having the edge over grammar school boys when it comes to landing the posh jobs. But imagine the furore when girls with first-class honours in sex keep getting promoted over rivals who can only boast a first in geography?

And consider the headaches of being a parent. If in future years I tick my son off for chatting up the girl next door all day, he'll just tell me he's doing his homework, or perhaps he'll turn accusingly to my husband and ask: 'What did you do in the sex war, Daddy?'

I begin to wonder how my generation ever managed without a proper sex education. I was lucky, of course. I lived in the country and there were always foals being born and cows being mated. But I still got in a muddle: I couldn't sort out geldings and mules, and having read abut racehorses like Blue Peter being at stud, I assumed for years that Stud must be the name of a very chi-chi Old Horses' Home.

Occasionally, when we were wandering round the garden, my mother, much embarrassed and frenziedly tugging off roseheads, would try and tell me the odd fact of life. Usually I knew it already, and helped her along. A friend reported that when her mother tried to tell her about sex she kept getting bits wrong.

Having devoured *Gone With the Wind* at an early age, I thought I knew all about pregnancy, and when I went away to school, my favourite game after lights out was to enact the birth scene from *Green Dolphin Country* with my friend Jennifer Snooky. One of us played the doctor, which only involved brow-mopping and tugging, and the other took the far more coveted part of the woman in labour, grunting and groaning so realistically that invariably the dormitory prefect woke up.

But if we knew how babies came out, we were very hazy about how they got in. We didn't get on to Reproduction until the Fifth Form, and even then they skated round the subject for weeks, telling us about saddles or worms, rabbits and fish eggs. Finally, on the week scheduled for human reproduction I caught chicken-pox, and by the time I'd recovered they'd moved on to reptiles, which perhaps accounts for my muddled thinking ever since.

My husband claims he first learnt about reproduction at prep school when his form were straggling along the sands one Sunday afternoon and suddenly a boy called Stuart piped up: 'I say, chaps, I know how babies are made.'

All around there were cries of: 'Go on, Stuart. Tell us.'

'The man lies on top of the woman,' said Stuart portentously, 'and is excused into her.'

Back at St Trinian's, I remember, we learnt a bit from the Bible, Leviticus and Song of Solomon in particular. But we were totally mystified by homosexuals. Someone once asked our poor divinity mistress what Our Lord thought about them and she replied: 'He feels very sorry for them.' Which didn't get us much further.

What exactly had poor Oscar Wilde done? We gleaned inadequate information from Marlowe and stirring boys' school books like *The Hill* and *The Loom of Youth*. Chaucer, of course, taught us a lot about everything, so did Shakespeare, and we giggled like mad over a bowdlerised version of *Othello*, which changed strumpet to trumpet to produce the immortal line: 'She played the trumpet in my bed.'

Dictionaries were a dead loss. You looked up intercourse, it said coition; you turned to coition, it said intercourse. A prostitute was defined as a whore, a whore as a harlot, a harlot as a prostitute. How we went round the gooseberry bush.

First-aid books were more rewarding. You learnt about fringe subjects like emetics and bowels and venereal diseases, which I'd always thought were something you caught in the spring, tra-la. There was one splendid chapter on having a baby at home which made it sound just like a teenage fruit-cup party: 'Take two large jugs and a large enamel bowl.'

And yet, and yet, this feverish pursuit of sexual knowledge had nothing to do with love as it first struck me at the age of eleven. I fell deeply in love with a prefect called Angela Wallis who played third man at lacrosse and looked like Reggie Bosanquet. How chastely and undemandingly I adored her, giving her my sweet ration every month, filling her locker with bluebells in the summer and hazel nuts in the autumn.

The fact that she didn't deign to speak to me once in two years did nothing to diminish my passion, but at thirteen, feeling a guilty thrill of infidelity, I suddenly switched to men. In quick succession Budge Patty, Richard Todd, Brian Close, Louis MacNeice, John Carol Case became the object of my undying affection.

Often I cried myself to sleep at the sheer impossibility of any of them loving me back – but if Budge Patty or any of the others had actually turned up and tried to seduce me behind the squash courts, I should have died of horror and shame.

Obviously there is a divergence when one is eleven between theory and practice. But I find it sad that sex seems to be taught today with such earnestness and lack of humour, and everyone seems to have forgotten words like joy, magic, affection and – most important of all – love.

●

*'You're going a bit far, Miss Blanchard.'*

Telegram to Hollywood agent Leland Hayward on his elopement with his beautiful client Margaret Sullavan from Walter Wanger:

CONGRATULATIONS ON GETTING THE OTHER NINETY PER CENT.

●

## *The Perfect Husband*

He tells you when you've got on too much lipstick.
And helps you with your girdle when your hips stick.

**Ogden Nash**

## *On Her Husband*

His beard is much like rusty wire,
His pimples black as tow,
His lips like parchment curled by fire,
His forehead wondrous low.

His squinting, staring, goggling eyes
Poor children to affright,
His nose is double Roman size
And sheds a purple light.

His oven-mouth wide open stands,
With teeth like rotten peas;
His brick-dust neck, his flour sack hands,
His chest all bit with fleas.

His ears might draw a galleon,
His belly holds a rick,
No roasted ox can match his bum
For broadness, fat and thick.

Thus have you heard my husband praised,
And yet no flattery used;
Pray tell me, is he not of worth?
Let him not be abused.

**Anon.**

●

*'You wait here and I'll bring the etchings down.'*

*'I love the idea of there being two sexes, don't you?'*

# *The Pickwick Papers*

## Charles Dickens

*Descriptive of a very important proceeding on the part of Mr Pickwick; no less an epoch in his life, than in this history*

Mr Pickwick's apartments in Goswell Street, although on a limited scale, were not only of a very neat and comfortable description, but peculiarly adapted for the residence of a man of his genius and observation. His sitting-room was the first floor front, his bed-room the second floor front; and thus whether he were sitting at his desk in the parlour, or standing before the dressing-glass in his dormitory, he had an equal opportunity of contemplating human nature in all the numerous phases it exhibits, in that not more populous than popular thoroughfare. His landlady, Mrs Bardell – the relict and sole executrix of a deceased custom-house officer – was a comely woman of bustling manners and agreeable appearance, with a natural genius for cooking, improved by study and long practice into an exquisite talent. There were no children, no servants, no fowls. The only other inmates of the house were a large man, and a small boy; the first a lodger, the second a production of Mrs Bardell's. The large man was always home precisely at ten o'clock at night, at which hour he regularly condensed himself into the limits of a dwarfish French bedstead in the back parlour; and the infantine sports and gymnastic exercises of Master Bardell were exclusively confined to the neighbouring pavements and gutters. Cleanliness and quiet reigned throughout the house; and in it Mr Pickwick's will was law.

To any one acquainted with these points of the domestic

economy of the establishment, and conversant with the admirable regulation of Mr Pickwick's mind, his appearance and behaviour on the morning previous to that which had been fixed upon for the journey to Eatanswill, would have been most mysterious and unaccountable. He paced the room to and fro with hurried steps, popped his head out of the window at intervals of about three minutes each, constantly referred to his watch, and exhibited many other manifestations of impatience, very unusual with him. It was evident that something of great importance was in contemplation, but what that something was not even Mrs Bardell herself had been enabled to discover.

'Mrs Bardell,' said Mr Pickwick at last, as that amiable female approached the termination of a prolonged dusting of the apartment—

'Sir,' said Mrs Bardell.

'Your little boy is a very long time gone.'

'Why it's a good long way to the Borough, Sir,' remonstrated Mrs Bardell.

'Ah,' said Mr Pickwick, 'very true; so it is.'

Mr Pickwick relapsed into silence, and Mrs Bardell resumed her dusting.

'Mrs Bardell,' said Mr Pickwick, at the expiration of a few minutes.

'Sir,' said Mrs Bardell again.

'Do you think it's a much greater expense to keep two people, than to keep one?'

'La, Mr Pickwick,' said Mrs Bardell, colouring up to the very border of her cap, as she fancied she observed a species of matrimonial twinkle in the eyes of her lodger; 'La, Mr Pickwick, what a question!'

'Well, but *do* you?' inquired Mr Pickwick.

'That depends—' said Mrs Bardell, approaching the duster very near to Mr Pickwick's elbow, which was planted on the table; 'that depends a good deal upon the person, you know, Mr Pickwick; and whether it's a saving and careful person, Sir.'

'That's very true,' said Mr Pickwick, 'but the person I have in my eye (here he looked very hard at Mrs Bardell) I think possesses these qualities; and has, moreover, a considerable knowledge of the world, and a great deal of sharpness, Mrs Bardell; which may be of material use to me.'

'La, Mr Pickwick,' said Mrs Bardell; the crimson rising to her cap-border again.

'I do,' said Mr Pickwick, growing energetic, as was his wont in speaking of a subject which interested him, 'I do, indeed; and to tell you the truth, Mrs Bardell, I have made up my mind.'

'Dear me, Sir,' exclaimed Mrs Bardell.

'You'll think it very strange now,' said the amicable Mr Pickwick, with a good-humoured glance at his companion, 'that I never consulted you about this matter, and never mentioned it, till I sent your little boy out this morning – eh?'

Mrs Bardell could only reply by a look. She had long worshipped Mr Pickwick at a distance, but here she was, all at once, raised to a pinnacle to which her wildest and most extravagant hopes had never dared to aspire. Mr Pickwick was going to propose – a deliberate plan, too – sent her little boy to the Borough, to get him out of the way – how thoughtful – how considerate!

'Well,' said Mr Pickwick, 'what do you think?'

'Oh, Mr Pickwick,' said Mrs Bardell, trembling with agitation, 'you're very kind, Sir.'

'It'll save you a good deal of trouble, won't it?' said Mr Pickwick.

'Oh, I never thought anything of the trouble, Sir,' replied Mrs Bardell; 'and, of course, I should take more trouble to please you then, than ever; but it is so kind of you, Mr Pickwick, to have so much consideration for my loneliness.'

'Ah, to be sure,' said Mr Pickwick; 'I never thought of that. When I am in town, you'll always have somebody to sit with you. To be sure, so you will.'

'I'm sure I ought to be a very happy woman,' said Mrs Bardell.

'And your little boy—' said Mr Pickwick.

'Bless his heart,' interposed Mrs Bardell, with a maternal sob.

'He, too, will have a companion,' resumed Mr Pickwick, 'a lively one, who'll teach him, I'll be bound, more tricks in a week, than he would ever learn in a year.' And Mr Pickwick smiled placidly.

'Oh you dear—' said Mrs Bardell.

Mr Pickwick started.

'Oh you kind, good, playful dear,' said Mrs Bardell; and without more ado, she rose from her chair, and flung her arms round Mr Pickwick's neck, with a cataract of tears, and a chorus of sobs.

'Bless my soul,' cried the astonished Mr Pickwick; – 'Mrs Bardell my good woman – dear me, what a situation – pray consider – Mrs Bardell, don't – if anybody should come—'

'Oh, let them come,' exclaimed Mrs Bardell, frantically; 'I'll never leave you – dear, kind, good, soul;' and, with these words, Mrs Bardell clung the tighter.

'Mercy upon me,' said Mr Pickwick, struggling violently; 'I hear somebody coming up the stairs. Don't, don't, there's a good creature, don't.' But the entreaty and remonstrance were alike unavailing: for Mrs Bardell had fainted in Mr Pickwick's arms; and before he could gain time to deposit her on a chair, Master Bardell entered the room, ushering in Mr Tupman, Mr Winkle, and Mr Snodgrass.

Mr Pickwick was struck motionless and speechless. He stood with his lovely burden in his arms, gazing vacantly on the countenances of his friends, without the slightest attempt at recognition or explanation. They, in their turn, stared at him; and Master Bardell, in his turn, stared at everybody.

The astonishment of the Pickwickians was so absorbing, and the perplexity of Mr Pickwick was so extreme, that they might have remained in exactly the same relative situations until the suspended animation of the lady was restored, had it not been for a most beautiful and touching expression of filial affection on the part of her youthful son. Clad in a tight suit of corderoy, spangled with brass buttons of a very considerable size, he at first stood at the door astounded and uncertain; but by degrees, the impression that his mother must have suffered some personal damage, pervaded his partially developed mind, and considering Mr Pickwick as the aggressor, he set up an appalling and semi-earthly kind of howling, and butting forward with his head, commenced assailing that immortal gentleman about the back and legs, with such blows and pinches as the strength of his arm, and the violence of his excitement, allowed.

'Take this little villain away,' said the agonised Mr Pickwick, 'he's mad.'

'What *is* the matter?' said the three tongue-tied Pickwickians.

'I don't know,' replied Mr Pickwick, pettishly. 'Take away the boy – (here Mr Winkle carried the interesting boy, screaming and struggling, to the further end of the apartment). – Now help me, lead this woman down stairs.'

'Oh, I am better now,' said Mrs Bardell, faintly.

'Let me lead you down stairs,' said the ever gallant Mr Tupman.

'Thank you, Sir – thank you;' exclaimed Mrs Bardell, hysterically. And down stairs she was led accordingly, accompanied by her affectionate son.

'I cannot conceive—' said Mr Pickwick, when his friend returned – 'I cannot conceive what has been the matter with that woman. I had merely announced to her my intention of keeping a man servant, when she fell into the extraordinary paroxysm in which you found her. Very extraordinary thing.'

'Very,' said his three friends.

'Placed me in such an extremely awkward situation,' continued Mr Pickwick.

'Very;' was the reply of his followers, as they coughed slightly, and looked dubiously at each other.

This behaviour was not lost upon Mr Pickwick. He remarked their incredulity. They evidently suspected him.

'There is a man in the passage now,' said Mr Tupman.

'It's the man I spoke to you about,' said Mr Pickwick, 'I sent for him to the Borough this morning. Have the goodness to call him up, Snodgrass.'

Mr Snodgrass did as he was desired; and Mr Samuel Weller forthwith presented himself.

'Oh – you remember me, I suppose?' said Mr Pickwick.

'I should think so,' replied Sam, with a patronising wink. 'Queer start that 'ere, but he was one too many for you, warn't he? Up to snuff and a pinch or two over – eh?'

'Never mind that matter now,' said Mr Pickwick hastily, 'I want to speak to you about something else. Sit down.'

'Thank'ee, Sir,' said Sam. And down he sat without farther bidding, having previously deposited his old white hat on the landing outside the door. 'Ta'nt a werry good 'un to look at,' said Sam, 'but it's an astonishin' 'un to wear; and afore the brim went, it was a wery handsome tile. Hows'ever it's lighter without it, that's one thing, and every hole lets in some air, that's another – wentilation gossamer I calls it.' On the delivery of this sentiment, Mr Weller smiled agreeably upon the assembled Pickwickians.

'Now with regard to the matter on which I, with the concurrence of these gentlemen, sent for you,' said Mr Pickwick.

'That's the pint, Sir,' interposed Sam; 'out vith it, as the father said to the child, ven he swallowed a farden.'

'We want to know, in the first place,' said Mr Pickwick, 'whether you have reason to be discontented with your present situation.'

'Afore I answers that 'ere question, gen'l'm'n,' replied Mr Weller, '*I* should like to know, in the first place, whether you're a goin' to purwide me vith a better.'

A sunbeam of placid benevolence played on Mr Pickwick's features as he said, 'I have made up my mind to engage you myself.'

'Have you though?' said Sam.

Mr Pickwick nodded in the affirmative.

'Wages?' inquired Sam.

'Twelve pounds a year,' replied Mr Pickwick.

'Clothes?'

'Two suits.'

'Work?'

'To attend upon me; and travel about with me and these gentlemen here.'

'Take the bill down,' said Sam, emphatically. 'I'm let to a single gentleman, and the terms is agreed upon.'

'You accept the situation?' inquired Mr Pickwick.

'Cert'nly,' replied Sam. 'If the clothes fits me half as well as the place, they'll do.'

'You can get a character of course?' said Mr Pickwick.

'Ask the landlady o' the White Hart about that, Sir,' replied Sam.

'Can you come this evening?'

'I'll get into the clothes this minute, if they're here,' said Sam with great alacrity.

'Call at eight this evening,' said Mr Pickwick; 'and if the inquiries are satisfactory, they shall be provided.'

With the single exception of one amiable indiscretion, in which an assistant housemaid had equally participated, the history of Mr Weller's conduct was so very blameless, that Mr Pickwick felt fully justified in closing the engagement that very evening. With the promptness and energy which characterised not only the public proceedings, but all the private actions of this extraordinary man, he at once led his new attendant to one of those convenient emporiums where gentlemen's new and second-hand clothes are provided, and the troublesome and inconvenient formality of measurement dispensed with; and before night had closed in, Mr Weller was furnished with a grey coat with the 'PC' button, a black hat with a cockade to it, a pink striped waistcoat, light breeches and gaiters, and a variety of other necessities, too numerous to recapitulate.

'Well,' said that suddenly-transformed individual, as he took his seat on the outside of the Eatanswill coach next morning; 'I wonder vether I'm meant to be a footman, or a groom, or a game-keeper, or a seedsman. I looks like a sort of compo of every one on 'em. Never mind; there's change of air, plenty to see, and little to do; and all this suits my complaint uncommon, so long life to the Pickvicks, says I.'

●

*'In bed he just lies there'*

*'It's our* own *story exactly! He bold as a hawk, she soft as the dawn.'*

# *The Inimitable Jeeves*

## P. G. Wodehouse

### *The Pride of the Woosters is Wounded*

If there's one thing I like, it's a quiet life. I'm not one of those fellows who get all restless and depressed if things aren't happening to them all the time. You can't make it too placid for me. Give me regular meals, a good show with decent music every now and then, and one or two pals to totter round with, and I ask no more.

That is why the jar, when it came, was such a particularly nasty jar. I mean, I'd returned from Roville with a sort of feeling that from now on nothing could occur to upset me. Aunt Agatha, I imagined, would require at least a year to recover from the Hemmingway affair: and apart from Aunt Agatha there isn't anybody who really does much in the way of harrying me. It seemed to me that the skies were blue, so to speak, and no clouds in sight.

I little thought . . . Well, look here, what happened was this, and I ask you if it wasn't enough to rattle anybody.

Once a year Jeeves takes a couple of weeks' vacation and biffs off to the sea or somewhere to restore his tissues. Pretty rotten for me, of course, while he's away. But it has to be stuck, so I stick it; and I must admit that he usually manages to get hold of a fairly decent fellow to look after me in his absence.

Well, the time had come round again, and Jeeves was in the kitchen giving the understudy a few tips about his duties. I happened to want a stamp or something, and I toddled down the passage to ask him for it. The silly ass had left the kitchen door open, and I hadn't gone two steps when his voice caught me squarely in the eardrum.

'You will find Mr Wooster,' he was saying to the substitute chappie, 'an exceedingly pleasant and amiable young gentleman, but not intelligent. By no means intelligent. Mentally he is negligible – quite negligible.'

Well, I mean to say, what!

I suppose, strictly speaking, I ought to have charged in and ticked the blighter off properly in no uncertain voice. But I doubt whether it's humanly possible to tick Jeeves off. Personally, I didn't even have a dash at it. I merely called for my hat and stick in a marked manner and legged it. But the memory rankled, if you know what I mean. We Woosters do not lightly forget. At least, we do – some things – appointments, and people's birthdays, and letters to post, and all that – but not an absolute bally insult like the above. I brooded like the dickens.

I was still brooding when I dropped in at the oyster-bar at Buck's for a quick bracer. I needed a bracer rather particularly at the moment, because I was on my way to lunch with Aunt Agatha. A pretty frightful ordeal, believe me or believe me not, even though I took it that after what had happened at Roville she would be in a fairly subdued and amiable mood. I had just had one quick and another rather slower, and was feeling about as cheerio as was possible under the circs, when a muffled voice hailed me from the north-east, and, turning round, I saw young Bingo Little propped up in a corner, wrapping himself round a sizeable chunk of bread and cheese.

'Hallo-allo-allo!' I said. 'Haven't seen you for ages. You've not been in here lately, have you?'

'No. I've been living out in the country.'

'Eh?' I said, for Bingo's loathing for the country was well known. 'Whereabouts?'

'Down in Hampshire, at a place called Ditteredge.'

'No, really? I know some people who've got a house there. The Glossops. Have you met them?'

'Why, that's where I'm staying!' said young Bingo. 'I'm tutoring the Glossop kid.'

'What for?' I said. I couldn't seem to see young Bingo as a

tutor. Though, of course, he did get a degree of sorts at Oxford, and I suppose you can always fool some of the people some of the time.

'What for? For money, of course! An absolute sitter came unstitched in the second race at Haydock Park,' said young Bingo, with some bitterness, 'and I dropped my entire month's allowance. I hadn't the nerve to touch my uncle for any more, so it was a case of buzzing round to the agents and getting a job. I've been down there three weeks.'

'I haven't met the Glossop kid.'

'Don't!' advised Bingo, briefly.

'The only one of the family I really know is the girl.' I had hardly spoken these words when the most extraordinary change came over young Bingo's face. His eyes bulged, his cheeks flushed, and his Adam's apple hopped about like one of those india-rubber balls on the top of the fountain in a shooting-gallery.

'Oh, Bertie!' he said, in a strangled sort of voice.

I looked at the poor fish anxiously. I knew that he was always falling in love with someone, but it didn't seem possible that even he could have fallen in love with Honoria Glossop. To me the girl was simply nothing more nor less than a pot of poison. One of those dashed large, brainy, strenuous, dynamic girls you see so many of these days. She had been at Girton, where, in addition to enlarging her brain to the most frightful extent, she had gone in for every kind of sport and developed the physique of a middle-weight catch-as-catch-can wrestler. I'm not sure she didn't box for the Varsity while she was up. The effect she had on me whenever she appeared was to make me want to slide into a cellar and lie low till they blew the All-Clear.

Yet here was young Bingo obviously all for her. There was no mistaking it. The love-light was in the blighter's eyes.

'I worship her, Bertie! I worship the very ground she treads on!' continued the patient, in a loud, penetrating voice. Fred Thompson and one or two fellows had come in, and McGarry, the chappie behind the bar, was listening with his ears flapping. But there's no reticence about Bingo. He always reminds me of the hero of a musical comedy who takes the centre of the stage, gathers the boys round him in a circle, and tells them all about his love at the top of his voice.

'Have you told her?'

'No. I haven't the nerve. But we talk together in the garden most evenings, and it sometimes seems to me that there is a look in her eyes.'

'I know that look. Like a sergeant-major.'

'Nothing of the kind! Like a tender goddess.'

'Half a second, old thing,' I said. 'Are you sure we're talking about the same girl? The one I mean is Honoria. Perhaps there's a younger sister or something I've not heard of?'

'Her name is Honoria,' bawled Bingo reverently.

'And she strikes you as a tender goddess?'

'She does.'

'God bless you!' I said.

'She walks in beauty like the night of cloudless climes and starry skies; and all that's best of dark and bright meet in her aspect and her eyes. Another bit of bread and cheese,' he said to the lad behind the bar.

'You're keeping your strength up,' I said.

'This is my lunch. I've got to meet Oswald at Waterloo at one-fifteen, to catch the train back. I brought him up to town to see the dentist.'

'Oswald? Is that the kid?'

'Yes. Pestilential to a degree.'

'Pestilential! That reminds me, I'm lunching with my Aunt Agatha. I'll have to pop off now, or I'll be late.'

I hadn't seen Aunt Agatha since that little affair of the pearls; and, while I didn't anticipate any great pleasure from gnawing a bone in her society, I must say that there was one topic of conversation I felt pretty confident she wouldn't touch on, and that was the subject of my matrimonial future. I mean, when a woman's made a bloomer like the one Aunt Agatha made at Roville, you'd naturally think that a decent shame would keep her off it for, at any rate, a month or two.

But women beat me. I mean to say, as regards nerve. You'll hardly credit it, but she actually started in on me with the fish. Absolutely with the fish, I give you my solemn word. We'd hardly exchanged a word about the weather, when she let me have it without a blush.

'Bertie,' she said, 'I've been thinking again about you and how necessary it is that you should get married. I quite admit that I was dreadfully mistaken in my opinion of that terrible, hypocritical girl at Roville, but this time there is no danger of an error. By great good luck I have found the very wife for you, a girl whom I have only recently met, but whose family is above suspicion. She has plenty of money, too, though that does not matter in your case. The great point is that she is strong, self-reliant and sensible, and will counterbalance the deficiencies and weaknesses of your character. She has met you; and, while there is naturally much in you of which she disapproves, she does not dislike you. I know this, for I have sounded her – guardedly, of course – and I am sure that you have only to make the first advances—'

'Who is it?' I would have said it long before, but the shock had made me swallow a bit of roll the wrong way, and I had only just finished turning purple and trying to get a bit of air back into the old windpipe. 'Who is it?'

'Sir Roderick Glossop's daughter, Honoria.'

'No, no!' I cried, paling beneath the tan.

'Don't be silly, Bertie. She is just the wife for you.'

'Yes, but look here—'

'She will mould you.'

'But I don't want to be moulded.'

Aunt Agatha gave me the kind of look she used to give me when I was a kid and had been found in the jam cupboard.

'Bertie! I hope you are not going to be troublesome.'

'Well, but I mean—'

'Lady Glossop has very kindly invited you to Ditteredge Hall for a few days. I told her you would be delighted to come down tomorrow.'

'I'm sorry, but I've got a dashed important engagement tomorrow.'

'What engagement?'

'Well – er—'

'You have no engagement. And, even if you had, you must

put it off. I shall be very seriously annoyed, Bertie, if you do not go to Ditteridge Hall tomorrow.'

'Oh, right-o!' I said.

It wasn't two minutes after I had parted from Aunt Agatha before the old fighting spirit of the Woosters reasserted itself. Ghastly as the peril was which loomed before me, I was conscious of a rummy sort of exhilaration. It was a tight corner, but the tighter the corner, I felt, the more juicily should I score off Jeeves when I got myself out of it without a bit of help from him. Ordinarily, of course, I should have consulted him and trusted to him to solve the difficulty; but after what I had heard him saying in the kitchen, I was dashed if I was going to demean myself. When I got home I addressed the man with light abandon.

'Jeeves' I said, 'I'm in a bit of difficulty.'

'I'm sorry to hear that, sir.'

'Yes, quite a bad hole. In fact, you might say on the brink of a precipice, and faced by an awful doom.'

'If I could be of any assistance, sir—'

'Oh, no. No, no. Thanks very much, but no. I won't trouble you. I've no doubt I shall be able to get out of it by myself.'

'Very good, sir.'

So that was that. I'm bound to say I'd have welcomed a bit more curiosity from the fellow, but that is Jeeves all over. Cloaks his emotions, if you know what I mean.

Honoria was away when I got to Ditteredge on the following afternoon. Her mother told me that she was staying with some people named Braythwayt in the neighbourhood, and would be back next day, bringing the daughter of the house with her for a visit. She said I would find Oswald out in the grounds, and such is a mother's love that she spoke as if that were a bit of a boost for the grounds and an inducement to go there.

Rather decent, the grounds at Ditteredge. A couple of terraces, a bit of lawn with a cedar in it, a bit of shrubbery, and finally a small but goodish lake with a stone bridge running across it. Directly I'd worked my way round the shrubbery I spotted young Bingo leaning against the bridge smoking a cigarette. Sitting on the stonework, fishing, was a species of kid whom I took to be Oswald the Plague-Spot.

Bingo was both surprised and delighted to see me and introduced me to the kid. If the latter was surprised and delighted too, he concealed it like a diplomat. He just looked at me, raised his eyebrows slightly, and went on fishing. He was one of those suspicious striplings who give you the impression that you went to the wrong school and that your clothes don't fit.

'This is Oswald,' said Bingo.

'What,' I replied cordially, 'could be sweeter? How are you?'

'Oh, all right,' said the kid.

'Nice place, this.'

'Oh, all right,' said the kid.

'Having a good time fishing?'

'Oh, all right,' said the kid.

Young Bingo led me off to commune apart.

'Doesn't jolly old Oswald's incessant flow of prattle make your head ache sometimes?' I asked.

Bingo sighed.

'It's a hard job.'

'What's a hard job?'

'Loving him.'

'Do you love him?' I asked, surprised. I shouldn't have thought it could be done.

'I try to,' said young Bingo, 'for Her sake. She's coming back tomorrow, Bertie.'

'So I heard.'

'She is coming, my love, my own—'

'Absolutely,' I said. 'But touching on young Oswald once more. Do you have to be with him all day? How do you manage to stick it?'

'Oh, he doesn't give much trouble. When we aren't working he sits on that bridge all the time, trying to catch tiddlers.'

'Why don't you shove him in?'

'Shove him in?'

'It seems to me distinctly the thing to do,' I said, regarding the stripling's back with a good deal of dislike. 'It would wake him up a bit, and make him take an interest in things.'

Bingo shook his head a bit wistfully.

'Your proposition attracts me,' he said, 'but I'm afraid it can't be done. You see, She would never forgive me. She is devoted to the little brute.'

'Great Scott!' I cried. 'I've got it!' I don't know if you know that feeling when you get an inspiration, and tingle all down your spine from the soft collar as now worn to the very soles of the old Waukeesis? Jeeves, I suppose, feels that way more or less all the time, but it isn't often it comes to me. But now all Nature seemed to be shouting at me 'You've clicked!' and I grabbed young Bingo by the arm in a way that must have made him feel as if a horse had bitten him. His finely-chiselled features were twisted with agony and what not, and he asked me what the dickens I thought I was playing at.

'Bingo,' I said, 'what would Jeeves have done?'

'How do you mean, what would Jeeves have done?'

'I mean what would he have advised in a case like yours? I mean you wanting to make a hit with Honoria Glossop and all that. Why, take it from me, laddie, he would have shoved you behind that clump of bushes over there; he would have got me to lure Honoria on to the bridge somehow; then, at the proper time, he would have told me to give the kid a pretty hefty jab in the small of the back, so as to shoot him into the water; and then you would have dived in and hauled him out. How about it?'

'You didn't think that out by yourself, Bertie?' said young Bingo, in a hushed sort of voice.

'Yes, I did. Jeeves isn't the only fellow with ideas.'

'But it's absolutely wonderful.'

'Just a suggestion.'

'The only objection I can see is that it would be so dashed awkward for you. I mean to say, suppose the kid turned round and said you had shoved him in, that would make you frightfully unpopular with Her.'

'I don't mind risking that.'

The man was deeply moved.

'Bertie, this is noble.'

'No, no.'

He clasped my hand silently, then chuckled like the last drop of water going down the waste-pipe in a bath.

'Now what?' I said.

'I was only thinking,' said young Bingo, 'how fearfully wet Oswald will get. Oh, happy day!'

●

*Part Two*

# SOMEBODY HAS TO DO IT

A banker is a man who lends you an umbrella when the weather is fair, and takes it away from you when it rains.

**Anon.**

# *The Great Pursuit*

## Tom Sharpe

When anyone asked Frensic why he took snuff he replied that it was because by rights he should have lived in the eighteenth century. It was, he said, the century best suited to his temperament and way of life, the age of reason, of style, of improvement and expansion and those other characteristics he so manifestly possessed. That he didn't, and happened to know that the eighteenth century hadn't either, only heightened his pleasure at his own affectation and the amazement of his audience and, by way of paradox, justified his claim to be spiritually at home with Sterne, Swift, Smollett, Richardson, Fielding and other giants of the rudimentary novel whose craft Frensic so much admired. Since he was a literary agent who despised nearly all the novels he handled so successfully, Frensic's private eighteenth century was that of Grub Street and Gin Lane and he paid homage to it by affecting an eccentricity and cynicism which earned him a useful reputation and armoured him against the literary pretensions of unsaleable authors. In short he bathed only occasionally, wore woollen vests throughout the summer, ate a great deal more than was good for him, drank port before lunch and took snuff in large quantities so that anyone wishing to deal with him had to prove their hardiness by running the gauntlet of these deplorable habits. He also arrived early for work, read every manuscript that was submitted to him, promptly returned those he couldn't sell and just as promptly sold the others and in general conducted his business with surprising efficiency. Publishers took Frensic's opinions seriously. When Frensic said a book would sell, it sold. He had a nose for a bestseller, an infallible nose.

It was, he liked to think, something he had inherited from his father, a successful wine-merchant whose own nose for a palatable claret at a popular price had paid for that expensive education which, together with Frensic's more metaphysical nose, gave him the edge over his competitors. Not that the connection between a good education and his success as a connoisseur of commercially rewarding literature was direct. He had arrived at his talent circuitously and if his admiration for the eighteenth century, while real, nevertheless concealed an inversion, it was by exactly the same process that he had arrived at his success as a literary agent.

At twenty-one he had come down from Oxford with a second-class degree in English and the ambition to write a great novel. After a year behind the counter of his father's wine shop in Greenwich and at his desk in a room in Blackheath the 'great' had been abandoned. Three more years as an advertising copy-writer and the author of a rejected novel about life behind the counter of a wine shop in Greenwich had completed the demolition of his literary ambitions. At twenty-four Frensic hadn't needed his nose to tell him he would never be a novelist. The two dozen literary agents who had refused to handle his work had said so already. On the other hand his experience of them had revealed a profession entirely to his taste. Literary agents, it was obvious, lived interesting, comfortable and thoroughly civilised lives. If they didn't write novels, they met novelists, and Frensic was still idealistic enough to imagine that this was a privilege; they spent their days reading books; they were their own masters, and if his own experience was anything to go by they showed an encouraging lack of literary perspicacity. In addition they seemed to spend a great deal of time eating and drinking and going to parties, and Frensic, whose appearance tended to limit his sensual pleasures to putting things into himself rather than into other people, was something of a gourmet. He had found his vocation.

At twenty-five he opened an office in King Street next to Covent Garden and sufficiently close to Curtis Brown, the largest literary agency in London, to occasion some profitable postal confusion, and advertised his services in the *New*

*Statesman*, whose readers seemed more prone to pursue those literary ambitions he had so recently relinquished. Having done that he sat down and waited for the manuscripts to arrive. He had to wait a long time and he was beginning to wonder just how long his father could be persuaded to pay the rent when the postman delivered two parcels. The first contained a novel by Miss Celia Thwaite of The Old Pumping Station, Bishop's Stortford and a letter explaining that *Love's Lustre* was Miss Thwaite's first book. Reading it with increasing nausea, Frensic had no reason to doubt her word. The thing was a hodgepodge of romantic drivel and historical inaccuracy and dealt at length with the unconsummated love of a young squire for the wife of an absent-bodied crusader whose obsession with his wife's chastity seemed to reflect an almost pathological fetishism on the part of Miss Thwaite herself. Frensic wrote a polite note explaining that *Love's Lustre* was not a commercial proposition and posted the manuscript back to Bishop's Stortford.

The contents of the second package seemed at first sight to be more promising. Again it was a first novel, this time called *Search for a Lost Childhood* by a Mr P. Piper who gave as his address the Seaview Boarding House, Folkestone. Frensic read the novel and found it perceptive and deeply moving. Mr Piper's childhood had not been a happy one but he wrote discerningly about his unsympathetic parents and his own troubled adolescence in East Finchley. Frensic promptly sent the book to Jonathan Cape and informed Mr Piper that he foresaw an immediate sale followed by critical acclaim. He was wrong. Cape rejected the book. Bodley Head rejected it. Collins rejected it. Every publisher in London rejected it with comments that ranged from the polite to the derisory. Frensic conveyed their opinions in diluted form to Piper and entered into a correspondence with him about ways of improving it to meet the publishers' requirements.

He was just recovering from this blow to his acumen when he received another. A paragraph in *The Bookseller* announced that Miss Celia Thwaite's first novel, *Love's Lustre,* had been sold to Collins for fifty thousand pounds, to an American publisher for a quarter of a million dollars, and that she stood a good chance of winning the Georgette Heyer Memorial Prize for Romantic Fiction. Frensic read the paragraph incredulously and underwent a literary conversion. If publishers were prepared to pay such enormous sums for a book which Frensic's educated taste had told him was romantic trash, then everything he had learnt from F. R. Leavis and more directly from his own supervisor at Oxford, Dr Sydney Louth, about the modern novel was entirely false in the world of commercial publishing; worse still it constituted a deadly threat to his own career as a literary agent. From that moment of revelation Frensic's outlook changed. He did not discard his educated standards. He stood them on their head. Any novel that so much as approximated to the criteria laid down by Leavis in *The Great Tradition* and more vehemently by Miss Sydney Louth in her work, *The Moral Novel,* he rejected out of hand as totally unsuitable for publication while those books they would have dismissed as beneath contempt he pushed for all he was worth. By virtue of this remarkable reversal Frensic prospered. By the time he was thirty he had established an enviable reputation among publishers as an agent who recommended only those books that would sell. A novel from Frensic could be relied upon to need no alterations and little editing. It would be exactly eighty thousand words long or, in the case of historical romance where the readers were more voracious, one hundred and fifty thousand. It would start with a bang, continue with more bangs and end happily with an even bigger bang. In short, it would contain all those ingredients that public taste most appreciated.

But if the novels Frensic submitted to publishers needed few changes, those that arrived on his desk from aspiring authors seldom passed his scrutiny without fundamental alteration. Having discovered the ingredients of popular success in *Love's Lustre,* Frensic applied them to every book he handled so that they emerged from the process of rewriting like literary plum puddings or blended wines and incorporated sex, violence, thrills, romance and mystery, with the occasional dollop of significance to give them cultural respectability. Frensic was very keen on cultural respectability. It ensured reviews in the better papers and gave readers the illusion that they were participating in a pilgrimage to a shrine of meaning. What the meaning was remained, necessarily, unclear. It came under the general heading of meaningfulness but without it a section of the public who despised mere escapism would have been lost to Frensic's authors. He therefore always insisted on significance, and while on the whole he lumped it with insight and sensibility as being in any large measure as lethal to a book's chances as a pint of strychnine in a clear soup, in homeopathic doses it had a tonic effect on sales.

So did Sonia Futtle, whom Frensic chose as a partner to handle foreign publishers. She had previously worked for a New York agency and being an American her contacts with US publishers were invaluable. And the American market was extremely profitable. Sales were larger, the percentage from authors' royalties greater, and the incentives offered by Book Clubs enormous. Appropriately for one who was to expand their business in this direction, Sonia Futtle had already expanded personally in most others and was of distinctly unmarriageable proportions. It was this as much as anything that had persuaded Frensic to change the agency's name to Frensic & Futtle and to link his impersonal fortune with hers. Besides, she was an enthusiast for books which dealt with interpersonal relations and Frensic had developed an allergy to interpersonal relationships. He concentrated on less demanding books, thrillers, detective stories, sex when unromantic, historical novels when unsexual, campus novels, science fiction and violence. Sonia Futtle handled romantic sex, historical romance, liberation books whether of women or negroes, adolescent traumas, interpersonal relationships and animals. She was particularly good with animals, and Frensic, who had once almost lost a finger to the heroine of *Otters to Tea,* was happy to leave this side of the business to her. Given the chance he would have relinquished Piper too. But Piper stuck to Frensic as the only agent ever to have offered him the slightest encouragement and Frensic, whose success was in inverse proportion to Piper's failure, reconciled himself to the knowledge that he could never abandon Piper and that Piper would never abandon his confounded *Search for a Lost Childhood*.

Each year he arrived in London with a fresh version of his novel and Frensic took him out to lunch and explained what was wrong with it while Piper argued that a great novel must deal with real people in real situations and could never conform to Frensic's blatantly commercial formula. And each year they would part amicably, Frensic to wonder at the man's incredible perseverance and Piper to start work in a different boarding-house in a different seaside town on a different search for the same lost childhood. And so year after year the novel was partially transformed and the style altered to suit Piper's latest model. For this Frensic had no one to blame but himself. Early in their acquaintance he had rashly recommended Miss Louth's essays in *The Moral Novel* to Piper as something he ought to study and, while Frensic had come to regard her appreciations of the great novelists of the past as pernicious to anyone trying to write a novel today, Piper had adopted her standards as his own. Thanks to Miss Louth he had produced a Lawrence version of *Search for a Lost Childhood*, then a Henry James; James had been superseded by Conrad, then by George Eliot; there had been a Dickens version and even a Thomas Wolfe; and one awful summer a Faulkner. But through them all there stalked the figure of Piper's father, his miserable mother and the self-consciously pubescent Piper himself. Derivation followed derivation but the insights remained implacably trite and the action non-existent. Frensic despaired but remained loyal. To Sonia Futtle his attitude was incomprehensible.

'What do you do it for?' she asked. 'He's never going to make it and those lunches cost a fortune.'

'He is my *memento mori,*' said Frensic cryptically, conscious that the death Piper served to remind him of was his own, the aspiring young novelist he himself had once been and on the betrayal of whose literary ideals the success of Frensic & Futtle depended.

But if Piper occupied one day in his year, a day of atonement, for the rest Frensic purused his career more profitably. Blessed with an excellent appetite, an impervious liver and an inexpensive source of fine wines from his father's cellars, he was able to entertain lavishly. In the world of publishing this was an immense advantage. While other agents wobbled home from those dinners over which books are conceived, publicised or bought, Frensic went portly on eating, drinking and advocating his novels *ad nauseam* and boasting of his 'finds'.

●

Publishers often need to say no thank you.
Telegram to Michael Joseph from an author:

MUST HAVE IMMEDIATE DECISION AS HAVE OTHER IRON IN FIRE.

From Michael Joseph to author:

SUGGEST YOU EXTRACT IRONS AND INSERT TYPESCRIPT.

●

If you were searching for a word to describe the conversations that go on down the mine, boring would spring to your lips. Oh, God! They're very boring. If you ever want to hear things like: 'Hello, I've found a bit of coal.' 'Have you really?' 'Yes, no doubt about it, this black substance is coal all right.' 'Jolly good, the very thing we're looking for.' It's not enough to keep the mind alive, is it?

**Peter Cook**, 'Sitting on a Bench', monologue

# *Yes Minister*

## Jonathan Lynn and Antony Jay

*The Skeleton in the Cupboard*

*November 16th*
An interesting situation emerged today from another meeting to which my old friend Dr Cartwright came.

It was a fairly dull routine meeting to start with, all about local government and administration. As Humphrey predicted, our Department was increasing in size, staffing and budget. He is plainly in his element. So far, however, it hasn't involved much in the way of policy decisions, which is where I come in.

We'd reached item seven on the agenda, and so far it had been pretty uneventful. The only interest had been in Bernard's pedantic linguistic quibbles, about which he is becoming obsessional.

'Item seven,' I asked, 'what's it about?'

'If I may just recapitulate,' began Sir Humphrey.

Bernard made a little sign and caught my eye.

'Yes Bernard?'

'Um – one can't actually recapitulate an item if one hasn't started it yet,' he volunteered.

Sir Humphrey, who doesn't like to be corrected by *anyone*, let alone a mere Private Secretary, thanked him coldly and proceeded to complete his sentence, thus demonstrating to Bernard that the correction was both impertinent and unnecessary.

'Thank you, Bernard, where would we be without you? Minister, may I just, recapitulating *on our last meeting* and on our submissions which you have doubtless received in your boxes . . .'

I was thoroughly amused, and not paying full attention. 'Doubtless,' I interrupted cheerfully, and then realised that I didn't know what he was talking about. After all, they give me mountains of paper to read virtually every day, I can't remember everything.

'Which minutes?' I asked.

'On the proposal to take disciplinary action against the South-West Derbyshire County Council.'

I still had no idea what the proposal was. But I didn't like to admit it, it's always better to make them think that one is completely on top of the job. So I casually asked Bernard to remind me.

The problem was that the council in question had failed to complete their statutory returns and supply us with the statistical information that the DAA required.

I asked what we were going to do about it. Apparently a policy decision was required from me. Sir Humphrey offered me assorted alternatives. 'A rebuke from the Minister, a press statement about their incompetence, withholding various grants and allowances, or, ultimately, as you are no doubt fully aware . . .'

'Yes, yes,' I interrupted helpfully.

'Good,' he said, and fell silent.

Again I was in a bit of a hole. I had no idea what he'd been about to say. But clearly he was waiting for my comments.

'I'm fully aware of . . . what?' I prompted him.

'What?'

'What am I fully aware of?'

'I can't think of anything.' Then he realised what he'd said because he added hastily, 'I mean, I can't think what you are . . .'

'You were saying,' I explained, feeling somewhat embarrassed by now. (After all, seven assorted officials of various ages and ranks were silently watching my display of confusion and ineptitude.)

'You were saying: "ultimately, as I'm fully aware" . . .'

'Ah yes, Minister.' Now he was on the ball again. 'Ultimately, taking the local authority to court.'

I asked if a failure to complete returns is all that serious.

Eight officials looked shocked! I was told categorically that it is not merely serious, but catastrophic!

I wanted to know why. Sir Humphrey was quick to explain.

'If local authorities don't send us the statistics we ask for, then government figures will be nonsense. They'll be incomplete.'

I pointed out that government figures are a nonsense anyway. No one denied it, but Bernard suggested that Sir Humphrey wanted to ensure that they are a complete nonsense.

He was rewarded with another withering look from his boss.

I was worried about making an example of South-West Derbyshire, which I happened to know is controlled by my party. Humphrey realised that this was on my mind, and raised the matter with me. I responded by suggesting that we pick on an opposition council instead.

This went down badly. I can't see why. What does he expect? Anyway, the suggestion was met with pursed lips from Sir Humphrey, and everyone else looked down at their blotters.

So I asked if South-West Derbyshire are really all that bad. And suddenly everyone had plenty to say.

One Under-Sec. told me that they won't return their blue forms (whatever they are, something to do with finance I think). An Assistant-Sec. told me that they replied to the DAA's Ethnic Personnel Breakdown Request in longhand, on the back of a departmental circular. And a delightfully attractive lady Assistant-Sec. was appalled because she still hadn't received their Social Worker Revised Case-Load Analysis for the last two quarters. Or their Distributed Data Processing Appropriation Tables. 'They're unbelievable,' she said. 'Really evil.'

This was a definition of evil? Someone who doesn't return his blue form? 'Yes,' I said with heavy irony, 'I don't see how life still goes on in South Derbyshire.'

Sir Humphrey took my remark at face value. 'Exactly, Minister. They really are in a class of their own for incompetence.'

Still worried about my party problems, I enquired if they had no redeeming features. And my old friend Dr Cartwright piped up cheerfully. 'Well, it is interesting that . . .'

Sir Humphrey cut right across him. 'So if that's all right, Minister, we can take appropriate coercive action?'

Dr Cartwright had another try. 'Except that the Minister might . . .'

Again Sir Humphrey interrupted him. 'So can we take it you approve?' It was all beginning to look distinctly fishy.

I decided not to give an immediate answer. 'It's a difficult one. They're friends of ours.'

'They're no friends of good administration.'

I refused to be pressured. 'Give me twenty-four hours. I'll have to square the party organisation. Get the Chairman invited to a drinkies do at Number Ten or something. Soften the blow.'

And I insisted that we press on to the next item.

As the meeting broke up I noticed Dr Cartwright hovering, as if he wanted a private word with me. But Sir Humphrey took him by the arm and gently guided him away. 'I need your advice, Dick, if you could spare me a moment.' And they were gone.

Having thought about this overnight, I think I'll question Bernard more closely tomorrow.

*November 17th*

A fascinating day.

I raised the matter with Bernard as soon as I got to the office. I told him that my instincts told me that there is a good reason not to discipline South-West Derbyshire.

'Furthermore, Dr Cartwright seemed to be trying to tell me something, I think I'll drop in on him.'

'Oh, I wouldn't do that, Minister,' he said rather too hastily.

'Why not?'

He hesitated. 'Well, it is, er, understood that if Ministers need to know anything it will be brought to their attention. If they go out looking for information, they might, er they might . . .'

'Find it?'

'Yes.' He looked sheepish.

I remarked that it may be 'understood', but it's not understood by me.

Bernard obviously felt he had better explain further. 'Sir Humphrey does not take kindly to the idea of Ministers just dropping in on people. "Going walkabout", he calls it.'

I couldn't see anything wrong with that, I reminded him that the Queen does it.

He disagreed. 'I don't think she drops in on Under-Secretaries. Not in Sir Humphrey's department.'

I took a firm line. I asked Bernard for Dr Cartwright's room number.

He virtually stood to attention. 'I must formally advise you against this, Minister,' he said.

'Advice noted,' I said. 'What's his room number?'

'Room 4017. Down one flight, second corridor on the left.'

I told him that if I wasn't back within forty-eight hours he could send a search party.

*Sir Bernard Woolley Recalls:*[1]

I well recall the day that Hacker went walkabout. This was the kind of situation that highlighted the dilemma of a Minister's Private Secretary. On the one hand I was expected to be loyal to the Minister, and any sign of disloyalty to him would mean that I had blotted my copybook. On the other hand, Sir Humphrey was my Permanent Secretary, my career was to be in the Civil Service for the next thirty years, and I owed a loyalty there also.

This is why high-flyers are usually given a spell as Private Secretary. If one can walk the tightrope with skill and manage to judge what is proper when there is a conflict, then one may go straight to the top, as I did.

*['Walking the tightrope' is Sir Bernard's phrase for*

[1] In conversation with the Editors.

*betraying confidences from each side to the other while remaining undetected – Ed.]*

After the Minister left his office I telephoned Graham Jones, Sir Humphrey Appleby's Private Secretary. I let him know that the Minister had gone walkabout. I had no choice but to do this, as I had received specific instructions from Sir Humphrey that this should be discouraged *[i.e. prevented. – Ed.]*.

I actually counted out ten seconds on my watch, from the moment I replaced the receiver, so well did I know the distance from his office to the Minister's, and Sir Humphrey entered the office on the count of 'ten'.

He asked me what had happened. Carefully playing it down, I told him that the Minister had left his own office. Nothing more.

Sir Humphrey seemed most upset that Hacker was, to use his words, 'loose in the building'. He asked me why I had not stopped him.

As it was my duty to defend my Minister, even against the boss of my own department, I informed Sir Humphrey that (a) I had advised against it, but (b) he was the Minister, and there was no statutory prohibition on Ministers talking to their staff.

He asked me to whom the Minister was talking. I evaded the question, as was my duty – clearly the Minister did not want Sir Humphrey to know. 'Perhaps he was just restless' is what I think I said.

I recall Sir Humphrey's irritable reply: 'If he's restless he can feed the ducks in St James's Park.'

Again he asked who the Minister was talking to, and again I evaded – under more pressure by this time – by seeking confirmation that the Minister could talk to anyone he liked.

Sir Humphrey's reply made it clear to me that he attached the greatest departmental importance to the issue. 'I am in the middle of writing your annual report,' he told me. 'It is not a responsibility that either of us would wish me to discharge while I am in a bad temper.'

Then he asked me *again* to whom the Minister was talking.

I realised that I had gone as far as I safely could in defending the Minister's interests. And yet as his Private Secretary. I had to be seen to be standing up for him.

So I resorted to a well-tried formula. I asked for Sir Humphrey's help. Then I said: 'I can quite see that you should be told if the Minister calls on an outsider. But I can't see that it is necessary to inform you if he just wanted, to take a purely hypothetical example, to check a point with, say, Dr Cartwright . . .'

He interrupted me, thanked me, and left the room. I called '4017' after him – well, why not?

I had passed the test with flying colours. I had managed to see that Sir Humphrey knew what he wanted, without actually telling him myself.

The hypothetical example was, and is, an excellent way of dealing with such problems.

[*Hacker's diary continues – Ed.*]

When I got to Cartwright's office I certainly learned a thing or two. Cartwright was delighted to see me, and told me quite openly that I had been misled at yesterday's meeting. I was intrigued.

'But all those things they told me about South-West Derbyshire – aren't they true?'

'They may be, for all I know.'

I asked him precisely what he was saying. To my surprise I got a completely straight answer. I can see why he's going to rise no higher.

'I'm saying that, nevertheless, South-West Derbyshire is the most efficient local authority in the UK.' And he blinked at me pleasantly from behind his half-moon reading glasses.

I was surprised, to say the least. 'The most efficent? But I'm supposed to be ticking them off for being the *least* efficient.'

Then he showed the figures.

This in itself was a surprise, as I'd been told that they didn't send us the figures. This was true – but no one had told me that they kept their own records perfectly well, which were available for us to see.

And the figures are impressive. They have the lowest truancy record in the Midlands, the lowest administrative costs per council house, the lowest ratio in Britain of council workers to rate income, and a clean bill of public health with the lowest number of environmental health officers.[1]

And that's not all. It seems that virtually all the children can read and write, despite their teachers' efforts to give them a progressive education. 'And,' Cartwright finished up, 'they have the smallest establishment of social workers in the UK.'

From the way he reported this fact I gathered he thought that this was a good thing. I enquired further.

'Oh yes. Very good. Sign of efficiency. Parkinson's Law of Social Work, you see. It's well known that social problems increase to occupy the total number of social workers available to deal with them.'

It was at this critical juncture that Sir Humphrey burst into Cartwright's office. I believe that his arrival in Cartwright's office at that moment was no coincidence.

We had a pretty stilted conversation.

'Oh, Minister! Good Heavens!'

'Oh. Hello, Humphrey!'

'Hello, Minister.'

'Yes. Indeed. What a surprise.'

'Yes.'

'Yes.'

For some reason he was making me feel guilty, and I found myself trying to explain my presence there.

'I was just, er, passing.'

'Passing?'

'Yes. Passing.'

'Passing. I see.' He considered my explanation for a moment. 'Where were you going?'

I was trapped. I had no idea what else was on Cartwright's floor. I decided to be vague.

[1] Rat-catchers

'Oh,' I said airily, 'I was just going . . . past.' I said it as if 'past' were a specific place to go. 'Past the door,' I added. I was aware that I sounded fearfully unconvincing but I blundered on. 'Cartwright's – Richard's door. Dick's door. So I thought "hello"!'

'And then did you think anything further?' He is relentless.

'Yes. I thought, why should I just pass the door? I might as well . . . open it.'

'Good thinking, Minister. That's what doors are for.'

'Quite.' I summoned up my courage and finally got to the point. 'And I'd remembered one or two points I wanted to clear up.'

'Good. What points?'

I couldn't see why I should tell him. Or why I shouldn't be in Cartwright's office. Or why he was successfully making me feel guilty. Or why he should consider that he had the right to approve everything that the DAA staff say to me. He behaves as though they are his staff, not mine. [*They were – Ed.*]

But I also couldn't see how not to answer him.

'Oh, just some odd points,' I replied finally, making a suitably vague gesture.

He waited. Silence. Then he repeated it. 'Just some odd points.'

'Yes,' I said.

'How odd?' he asked.

'Well, it's not all *that* odd,' I said argumentatively, wilfully misunderstanding him. 'We had a meeting yesterday, didn't we?'

Sir Humphrey was now tired of the fencing.

'Minister, may I have a word with you?'

'Certainly,' I said, 'as soon as Richard and I have . . .'

He interrupted. 'I mean now.'

Now it was my turn to embarrass him a little. 'OK. Go ahead.' I knew he wouldn't want to talk in front of one of his juniors.

'Upstairs, Minister, in your office if you please.'

'But I'm sure Richard doesn't mind.'

'Upstairs, Minister. I'm sure Dr Cartwright can spare you for a few moments.'

Cartwright missed the heavy sarcasm completely. 'Oh yes,' he said with an obliging smile.

Sir Humphrey opened the door. Having been made to feel like a naughty schoolboy, I marched out of Cartwright's office.

I wonder how he knew I was in that office. I know Bernard wouldn't have told him, so somebody must have seen me and reported it. I might as well be in the Soviet Union. Somehow I've got to get my freedom – but that involves winning the psychological war against Humphrey. And somehow, he always manages to make me feel guilty and unsure of myself.

If only I could find a chink in his armour. If I ever do, he's *had* it!

Anyway, that tense little sparring match in Cartwright's office wasn't the end of the matter. A few minutes later, back in my office after an icy silent journey up in the lift and along the endless corridors, the row came to a head.

He told me that I cannot just go around talking to people in the Department, and expressed the sincere hope that such a thing would not occur again.

I could scarcely believe my ears. I ordered him to explain himself.

'Minister, how can I advise you properly if I don't know who's saying what to whom? I must know what's going on. You simply cannot have completely private meetings. And what if you're told things that aren't true?'

'If they're not true you can put me right.'

'But they may be true.'

'In *that* case . . .' I began triumphantly. He interrupted me, correcting himself hastily.

'That is, not *entirely* false. But misleading. Open to misinterpretation.'

I faced him with a straight question. 'The fact is, you're just trying to keep things from me, aren't you, Humphrey?'

He was indignant. 'Absolutely not, Minister. Records must be kept. You won't be here forever, nor will we. In years to come it may be vital to know what you were told. If Cartwright were moved tomorrow, how could we check on your information?'

On the face of it, that was a specious argument. 'Cartwright *isn't* being moved tomorrow,' I said.

'Oh, isn't he?' came the insolent response.

Bernard interrupted us. Alex Andrews of *The Mail* wanted to do an interview with me for tomorrow. I agreed of course. I told Bernard to stay with us and minute our conversation. Humphrey had given me *his* views on my private meeting with Cartwright. Now he was going to hear *mine*.

I began by repeating what Cartwright had told me: namely, that in his opinion – and the opinion of everyone who knows anything about local government – the South-West Derbyshire County Council is the most efficient in the country.

'Inefficient, I think he means, Minister.'

'Efficient, Humphrey. Effective. Economical. They're just not particularly interested in sending pieces of blue paper to Whitehall.'

Humphrey then explained something that I hadn't quite grasped yet. Apparently they *have* to return those sodding blue forms, it's a statutory requirement.

And we know why. We know who decreed that it should be so.

Even so, statutory requirements can be overlooked occasionally. Discretion can be exercised. So I asked Humphrey what happens if they don't send in their blue forms. South-West Derbyshire carries on, rather well apparently.

'But,' said Humphrey, not seeing at all what I was getting at, 'if they don't send us the information and plans and requests for permission, well, what are we here for?'

An excellent question, as I told him immediately. I asked it at once. 'What *are* we here for?'

'To collate the information, inspect the plans, and grant or withhold permission.'

'And if we didn't?' I asked.

He gazed at me studiously. I might have been talking Ancient Chinese, for all the sense I was making to him.

'I'm sorry, Minister, I don't understand.'

I persevered, 'If we didn't. If we weren't here and we didn't do it – then what?'

'I'm sorry, Minister, you've lost me.'

Yet again, Humphrey demonstrates that his trouble is that he is concerned with means and not ends.

[*Many civil servants of the time deflected criticisms about ends and means by stating flippantly that the only ends in administration are loose ends. If administration is viewed in a vacuum this is, of course, true. Administration can have no end in itself, and is eternal. For ever and ever, amen – Ed.*]

[*Hacker's diary continues – Ed.*]

The upshot of the whole argument was that I refused to discipline the most efficient local authority in Britain, on the grounds that I would look like an idiot if I did.

Sir Humphrey told me that was my job. I *think* he meant to discipline South-West Derbyshire, rather than to look like an idiot, but I'm not certain. He said that I had no alternative to consider, no discretion to exercise, and that the Treasury and the Cabinet Office insist.

[*By Cabinet Office Sir Humphrey clearly meant the Cabinet Secretary rather than the PM. But he could never have said so – the fiction had to be preserved that Britain was governed by Ministers who told civil servants what to do, not vice versa – Ed.*]

I still refused to co-operate.

'Minister. You don't seem to understand. It's not up to you or me. It's the law.'

And there we left it. I felt a bit like a dog refusing to go for a walk – sitting down and digging in my paws while being dragged along the pavement on my bottom.

But there must be some way out. The more I think of it, the less willing I am to discipline that council until there is *really* no alternative.

And the more I think of it, the more I conclude that Bernard must have told Humphrey that I'd gone to talk to Cartwright.

*November 18th*

I had no free time to talk to Bernard on his own yesterday.

But first thing this morning, while I was doing my letters, I had a serious word with Bernard. I asked him how Humphrey had found out yesterday that I was with Cartwright.

'God moves in a mysterious way,' he said earnestly.

'Let me make one thing quite clear,' I said, 'Sir Humphrey is not God. OK?'

Bernard nodded. 'Will you tell him, or shall I?' he replied.

Very droll. But again I asked him how Humphrey knew where to find me.

I am fortunate that my dictaphone had been left running. I noticed it some minutes later. As a result I am able to record his reply for posterity in this diary.

'Confidentially, Minister, everything you tell me is in complete confidence. So, equally, and I'm sure you appreciate this, and by appreciate I don't actually mean appreciate, I mean understand, that everything that Sir Humphrey tells me is in complete confidence. As indeed everything I tell you is in complete confidence. And for that matter, everything I tell Sir Humphrey is in complete confidence.'

'So?' I said.

'So, in complete confidence, I am confident you will understand that for me to keep Sir Humphrey's confidence and your confidence means that my conversations must be completely confidential. As confidential as conversations between you and me are confidential, and I'll just get Alex Andrews as he's been waiting to see you, Minister.'

There it is. Word for word. What was I supposed to make of that? Nothing, of course.

My meeting with Alex Andrews of *The Mail* was today. I'd been very keen to fit him in at the earliest opportunity. I'd been hoping for a Profile, or something of that sort, but no such luck. Still, I've done him a good turn today, it's no skin off my nose, and perhaps he'll do the same for me one day.

He asked for my help in a fascinating story that he had just come across. 'Did you know that your government is about to give away forty million pounds' worth of buildings, harbour installations, a landing-strip, to a private developer? For nothing?'

I thought he was having me on. 'Forty million pounds?'

'Scout's Honour.'

'Why ask me?' I said. Suddenly I had a dreadful moment of panic. 'I didn't do it, did I?'

[*You may think that Hacker should have known if he had done it. But a great many things are done in a Minister's name, of which he may have little or no awareness – Ed.*]

Alex smiled, and told me to relax. Thank God!

Then he told me the story. It goes back a long way. Almost thirty years ago the Ministry of Defence took a lease on a Scottish island. They put up barracks, married quarters, an HQ block, and the harbour and airstrip. Now the lease has expired and they all become the property of the original landowner. And he is turning it into an instant holiday camp. Chalets, yachting marina, staff quarters – it's all there. He is going to make a fortune.

I listened, open-mouthed. 'But he can't do that!' I began. 'The law says that . . .'

Andrews interrupted me. 'You're talking about English law. This contract was under Scottish law and some idiot didn't realise the difference.'

I was relieved that at least I am in the clear. Even *The Mail* can't blame me for a cock-up in the early fifties. Though I'm sure they would if they could. And I couldn't at first see what he wanted from me. He already had the story. Thirty years late, as quick with the news as ever – still, not bad for Fleet Street!

They are running the story tomorrow. But apparently they don't want to leave it at that. The Editor wants Alex to follow up with an investigative feature, he wants him to go through the files, and find out exactly how it happened.

I couldn't see the point, not now.

'Well,' he explained, 'there may be lessons for today. And we might find who was responsible.'

I asked why it would matter? It would, in any case, have been handled by quite a junior official.

He nodded. 'OK, but that was thirty years ago. He could be in a very senior position now, even a Permanent Secretary, running a great department, responsible for spending billions of pounds of public money.'

A very unlikely eventuality, in my opinion. These hacks will do anything to try and find a story where there isn't one.

He agreed it was pretty unlikely. But he asked to see the papers.

Naturally I had to be a bit cautious about that. I can't just hand files over, as he well knows. But I advised him that, as it was a thirty-year lease that was in question, he would be able to get the papers from the Public Record Office under the Thirty-Year Rule.

He was unimpressed. 'I thought you'd say that. I've asked for them already. But I want a guarantee that I *will* get them. All of them.'

I hate being asked to guarantee anything. I don't really think it's fair. And anyway, was I in a position to? 'Well,' I said, carefully feeling my way, 'Defence papers are sometimes . . .'

He interrupted me. 'Don't come that one. It's not top security. Look, you made a manifesto commitment about telling voters the facts. This is a test case. Will you guarantee that no papers are removed before the files are opened?'

I could see no reason not to give him that guarantee. 'Fine,' I said throwing caution to the winds. 'No problem.'

'Is that a promise?' Journalists are suspicious bastards.

'Sure,' I said with a big reassuring smile.

'A real promise? Not a manifesto promise?'

Some of these young Fleet Street fellows can be really rather insulting.

'Your trouble, Alex,' I said, 'is that you can't take yes for an answer.'

'Because otherwise,' he continued as if I hadn't even spoken, 'we do the feature on Ministers ratting on manifestos.'

Clearly I shall now have to stand by that promise. It's fortunate that I have every intention of doing so.

[*The following day* The Mail *ran the story, exactly as predicted in Hacker's diary. That night Sir Humphrey's diary contains the following entry – Ed.*]

Horrible shock.

A story in today's *Mail* about the Glenlock Island base.

I read it on the 8.32 from Haslemere to Waterloo. Was seized instantly by what Dr Hindley calls a panic attack. A sort of tight feeling in the chest, I felt I couldn't breathe, and I had to get up and walk up and down the compartment which struck one or two of the regulars on the 8.32 as a bit strange. Or perhaps I just *think* that because of the panic attack.

Fortunately Valium did the trick as the day wore on, and I'll take a few Mogadon[1] tonight.

I tell myself that no one will ever connect that incident with me, and that it's all ancient history anyway, and that that's the last that anyone will want to know about it.

I tell myself that – but somehow it's not helping!

Why has this come up now, so many years later, when I thought it was all forgotten?

If only there was someone I could talk to about this.

Oh my God . . .

[*Hacker's diary continues – Ed.*]

*November 21st*

They ran that story in *The Mail* today. Quite amusing.

*November 22nd*

Today was the happiest day of my ministerial life.

All my prayers were answered.

As Humphrey and I were finishing up our weekly departmental meeting I asked him if he'd seen the story in yesterday's *Mail.*

'I'm not sure,' he said.

I reminded him. I knew he must have seen it, someone must have drawn his attention to it. 'You know,' I added, 'about that frightful cock-up thirty years ago over the terms of the Scottish island base.'

[1] Brand of sleeping pills in common use in the 1980s.

Now, as I think back, he seemed to flinch a little as I said 'that frightful cock-up'. Though I must say, I wasn't really aware of it at the time.

Anyway, he did remember the article, and he said that he believed that he *had* glanced at it, yes.

'I must say,' I said, chuckling, 'I think it's pretty funny – forty million quid down the tube. Someone really boobed there, didn't they?'

He nodded and smiled, a little wanly.

'Still, it couldn't happen in your Department, could it?'

'No,' he said with absolute firmness. 'Oh no. Absolutely.'

I said that I'd been wondering who it was.

'That, Minister, is something that we shall never know.'

I pointed out that it must be on the files. Everything is always put in writing, as he so constantly reminds me.

Humphrey agreed that it would be on the record somewhere, but it would take ages to find out and it's obviously not worth anyone's time.

'Actually, you're wrong there,' I said. '*The Mail* are doing a big feature on it when the papers are released under the Thirty-Year Rule. I've promised them a free run of all the files.'

Humphrey literally rocked backwards on his feet.

'Minister!'

I was slightly shaken by his anger. Or was it anger? I couldn't tell.

'It's all right, isn't it?' I asked anxiously.

Yes, it *was* anger! 'All right? *All right*? No, it is certainly not all right.'

I asked why not. He told me it was 'impossible and unthinkable'. That didn't sound like much of an explanation to me, and I said as much.

'It . . . it's . . . top security, Minister.'

'A few barracks?'

'But there were secret naval installations, anti-submarine systems, low-level-radar towers.'

I pointed out that he couldn't possibly know what had been there. He agreed at once, but added – rather lamely, I thought – that that's the sort of thing those island bases always had.

'They'll have been dismantled,' I said. His objection was clearly quite irrelevant.

'But the papers will have references.'

'It's ancient history.'

'Anyway,' he said with evident relief, 'we'd have to consult. Get clearances.'

A few months ago I would have accepted that sort of remark from Humphrey. Now, I'm just a little older and wiser.

'Who from?' I asked.

He looked wildly about, and spoke completely incoherently. 'Security implications . . . M15, M16 . . . the national interest . . . foreign powers . . . consult our allies . . . top brass . . . CIA . . . NATO, SEATO, Moscow!'

'Humphrey,' I asked carefully, 'are you all right?'

'*Not* Moscow, no, I don't mean Moscow,' he corrected himself hastily. I got the impression that he was just saying the first words that came into his head, and that the word Moscow had been uttered simply because it rhymed.

He could see I wasn't convinced, and added: 'There could be information that would damage people still alive.'

This seemed to matter to him greatly. But it cut no ice with me.

'Whoever drafted that contract,' I insisted, '*ought* to be damaged if he's still alive.'

'Oh, quite, absolutely, no question of protecting officials. Of course not. But responsible Ministers . . .'

I interrupted him. I wasn't the least concerned about some Minister who'd been responsible thirty years ago. It couldn't matter less. Anyway, the other lot were in office then, so it's fairly amusing.

I simply couldn't figure out the reason for his intense opposition to release these papers. I asked him why he was *so* concerned.

He sat back in his chair and crossed his legs casually. 'I'm not. Not at all. I mean, not personally. But it's the principle, the precedent . . . the . . . the . . .' he was lost for words '. . . the policy.'

Trapped. I'd got him. 'Policy's up to me, Humphrey,

remember?' I said with a smile. And before he could continue the argument I added, 'And I've promised, so it's done now, OK?'

He just sat there, sagging slightly, looking at me. Evidently he was trying to decide whether or not to say something. Finally he gave up. He stood wearily and, without looking at me, walked silently out of the room and shut the door behind him.

He seemed tired, listless, and quite without his usual energy.

Bernard had been present throughout the meeting. He waited, patiently, as usual, to be either used or dismissed.

I gazed at the door which Humphrey had closed quietly behind him.

'What's the matter with Humphrey?' I asked. There was no reply from Bernard. 'Have I done something wrong?' Again there was no reply. 'There *aren't* any security aspects, are there?' This time I waited a while, but answer came there none. 'So what is the problem?' I turned to look at Bernard, who appeared to be staring vacantly into space like a contented heifer chewing the cud.

'Am I talking to myself?'

He turned his gaze in my direction.

'No Minister, I am listening.'

'Then why don't you reply?'

'I'm sorry,' he said. 'I thought your questions were purely rhetorical. I can see no reason for Sir Humphrey to be so anxious.'

And then the penny dropped.

Suddenly I saw it.

I didn't know how I could have been so blind. So dumb. And yet, the answer – obvious though it was – seemed scarcely credible.

'Unless . . .' I began, and then looked at Bernard. 'Are you thinking what I'm thinking?'

He looked puzzled. 'I don't think so, Minister,' he replied cautiously, and then added with a flash of cheerful honesty, 'I'm not thinking anything really.'

'I *think,*' I said, uncertain how to broach it, 'that I smell a rat.'

'Oh. Shall I fetch the Environmental Health Officer?'

I didn't like actually to put my suspicions into words. Not yet. I thought I'd go carefully. So I asked Bernard how long Sir Humphrey had been here at the Department of Administrative Affairs.

'Oh, all his career, hasn't he? Ever since it was founded.'

'When was that?' I asked.

'1964. Same time that they started the Department of Economic Affairs . . .' he stopped dead, and stared at me, wide-eyed. 'Oh,' he said. 'Now I think I'm thinking what you're thinking.'

'Well?' I asked.

He wanted to be cautious too. 'You're thinking: where was he before 1964?'

I nodded slowly.

'It'll be in *Who's Who*.' He stood, then hurried to the glass-fronted mahogany bookcase near the marble fireplace. He fished out *Who's Who*, talking as he leafed through the pages. 'He must have been in some other Department, and been trawled when the DAA started.' [*'Trawled', i.e. caught in a net, is the standard Civil Service word for 'head-hunting' through other departments – Ed.*]

He ran his forefinger down a page, and said in one sentence: 'Ah here we are oh my God!'

I waited.

Bernard turned to me. 'From 1950 to 1956 he was an Assistant Principal at the Scottish Office. Not only that. He was on secondment from the War Office. His job was Regional Contracts Officer. Thirty years ago.'

There could be no doubt who the culprit was. The official who had chucked away that forty million pounds of the taxpayers' money was the current Permanent Under-Secretary of the Department of Administrative Affairs, Sir Humphrey Appleby, KCB, MVO, MA (Oxon).

Bernard said, 'This is awful,' but his eyes were twinkling.

'Terrible,' I agreed, and found myself equally unable to prevent a smile creeping across my face. 'And the papers are all due for release in a few weeks' time.'

I suddenly felt awfully happy. And I told Bernard to get Humphrey back into my office at once.

He picked up the phone and dialled. 'Hello Graham, it's Bernard. The Minister wondered if Sir Humphrey could spare some time for a meeting some time in the next couple of days.'

'At once,' I said.

'In fact, some time during the course of today is really what the Minister has in mind.'

'At once,' I repeated.

'Or to be precise, any time within the next sixty seconds really.'

He listened for a moment, then replaced the receiver. 'He's coming round now.'

'Why?' I was feeling malicious. 'Did he faint?'

We looked at each other in silence. And we both tried very hard not to laugh.

Bernard's mouth was twitching from the strain.

'This is very serious, Bernard.'

'Yes Minister,' he squeaked.

I was, by now, crying from the effort not to laugh. I covered my eyes and my face with my handkerchief.

'No laughing matter,' I said, in a strangled muffled gasp, and the tears rolled down my cheeks.

'Absolutely not,' he wheezed.

We recovered as best we could, shaking silently, but didn't dare look at each other for a little while. I sat back in my chair and gazed reflectively at the ceiling.

'The point is,' I said, 'how do I best handle this?'

'Well, in my opinion . . .'

'The question was purely rhetorical, Bernard.'

Then the door opened, and a desperately worried little face peeped around it.

It was Sir Humphrey Appleby. But not the Humphrey Appleby I knew. This was not a God bestriding the Department of Administrative Affairs like a colossus, this was a guilty ferret with shifty beady eyes.

'You wanted a word, Minister?' he said, still half-hidden behind the door.

I greeted him jovially. I invited him in, asked him to sit down and – rather regretfully – dismissed Bernard. Bernard made a hurried and undignified exit, his handkerchief to his mouth, and curious choking noises emanating from it.

Humphrey sat in front of me. I told him that I'd been thinking about this Scottish island scandal, which I found very worrying.

He made some dismissive remark, but I persisted. 'You see, it probably hasn't occurred to you but that official could still be in the Civil Service.'

'Most unlikely,' said Sir Humphrey, presumably in the hope that this would discourage me from trying to find out.

'Why? He could have been in his mid-twenties then. He'd be in his mid-fifties now,' I was enjoying myself thoroughly. 'Might even be a Permanent Secretary.'

He didn't know how to reply to that. 'I, er, I hardly think so,' he said, damning himself further.

I agreed, and said that I sincerely hoped that anyone who made a howler like that could *never* go on to be a Permanent Secretary. He nodded, but the expression on his face looked as though his teeth were being pulled out without an anaesthetic.

'But it was so long ago,' he said. 'We can't find out that sort of thing now.'

And then I went for the jugular. This was the moment I'd been waiting for. Little did I dream, after he had humiliated me in front of Richard Cartwright, that I would be able to return the compliment so soon.

And with the special pleasure of using his own arguments on him.

'Of course we can find out,' I said. 'You were telling me that everything is minuted and full records are always kept in the Civil Service. And you were quite right. Well, legal documents concerning a current lease could not possibly have been thrown away.'

He stood. Panic was overcoming him. He made an emotional plea, the first time I can remember him doing such a thing. 'Minister, aren't we making too much of this? Possibly blighting a brilliant career because of a tiny slip thirty years ago. It's not such a lot of money wasted.'

I was incredulous. 'Forty million?'

'Well,' he argued passionately, 'that's not such a lot compared with Blue Streak, the TSR2, Trident, Concorde, high-rise council flats, British Steel, British Rail, British Leyland, Upper Clyde Ship Builders, the atomic power station programme, comprehensive schools, or the University of Essex.'

[*In those terms, his argument was of course perfectly reasonable – Ed.*]

'I take your point,' I replied calmly. 'But it's still over a hundred times more than the official in question can have earned in his entire career.'

And then I had this wonderful idea. And I added: 'I want you to look into it and find out who it was, OK?'

Checkmate. He realised that there was no way out. Heavily, he sat down again, paused, and then told me that there was something that he thought I ought to know.

Surreptitiously I reached into my desk drawer and turned on my little pocket dictaphone. I wanted his confession to be minuted. Why not? All conversations have to be minuted. Records must be kept, mustn't they?

This is what he said. 'The identity of this official whose alleged responsibility for this hypothetical oversight has been the subject of recent speculation is not shrouded in quite such impenetrable obscurity as certain previous disclosures may have led you to assume, and, in fact, not to put too fine a point on it, the individual in question was, it may surprise you to learn, the one to whom your present interlocutor is in the habit of identifying by means of the perpendicular pronoun.'

'I beg your pardon?' I said.

There was an anguished pause.

'It was I,' he said.

I assumed a facial expression of deep shock. 'Humphrey! No!'

He looked as though he was about to burst into tears. His fists clenched, knuckles whitened. Then he burst out. 'I was under pressure! We were overworked! There was a panic! Parliamentary questions tabled.' He looked up at me for support. 'Obviously I'm not a trained lawyer, or I wouldn't

have been in charge of the legal unit.'
[*True enough. This was the era of the generalist, in which it would have seemed sensible and proper to put a classicist in charge of a legal unit or a historian in charge of statistics – Ed.*]
'Anyway – it just happened. But it was thirty years ago, Minister. Everyone makes mistakes.'

I was not cruel enough to make him suffer any longer. 'Very well Humphrey,' I said in my most papal voice. 'I forgive you.'

He was almost embarrassingly grateful and thanked me profusely.

I expressed surprise that he hadn't told me. 'We don't have any secrets from each other, do we?' I asked him.

He didn't seem to realise that I had my tongue in my cheek. Nor did he give me an honest answer.

'That's for you to say, Minister.'

'Not entirely,' I replied.

Nonetheles, he was clearly in a state of humble gratitude and genuinely ready to creep. And now that he was so thoroughly softened up, I decided that this was the moment to offer my *quid pro quo*.

'So what do I do about this?' I asked. 'I've promised to let *The Mail* see all the papers. If I go back on my word I'll be roasted.' I looked him straight in the eye. 'On the other hand, I might be able to do something if I didn't have this other problem on my plate.'

He knew only too well what I was saying. He's done this to me often enough.

So, immediately alert, he asked me what the other problem was.

'Being roasted by the press for disciplining the most efficient council in Britain.'

He saw the point at once, and adjusted his position with commendable speed.

After only a momentary hesitation he told me that he'd been thinking about South-West Derbyshire, that obviously we can't change the law as such, but that it might be possible to show a little leniency.

We agreed that a private word to the Chief Executive would

suffice for the moment, giving them a chance to mend their ways.

I agreed that this would be the right way to handle the council. But it still left one outstanding problem: how would I explain the missing papers to *The Mail*?

We left it there. Humphrey assured me that he would give the question his most urgent and immediate attention.

I'm sure he will. I look forward to seeing what he comes up with tomorrow.

*November 23rd*

When I arrived at the office this morning Bernard informed me that Sir Humphrey wished to see me right away.

He hurried in clutching a thin file, and looking distinctly more cheerful.

I asked him what the answer was to be.

'Minister,' he said, 'I've been on to the Lord Chancellor's Office, and this is what we normally say in circumstances like this.'

He handed me the file. Inside was a sheet of paper which read as follows:

> This file contains the complete set of available papers except for:
> (a) a small number of secret documents
> (b) a few documents which are part of still active files
> (c) some correspondence lost in the floods of 1967
> (d) some records which went astray in the move to London
> (e) other records which went astray when the War Office was incorporated into the Ministry of Defence
> (f) the normal withdrawal of papers whose publication could give grounds for an action for libel or breach of confidence or cause embarrassment to friendly governments.

[*1967 was, in one sense, a very bad winter. From the Civil Service point of view it was a very good one. All sorts of embarrassing records were lost – Ed.*]

I read this excellent list. Then I looked in the file. There were no papers there at all! Completely empty.

'Is *this* how many are left? None?'

'Yes Minister.'

*'Basically I like it but take out the carrot'*

# *It's a Funny Business*

## Terry Wogan

Since you didn't ask, I was born in Limerick, with catarrh. This is no slur on that somewhat moist gem set in the verdant delta of the Shannon. There are worse things than catarrh, though not in the early morning, if you happen to be married to a sufferer. Look at Jimmy Young, if you can bear it, and he was born in Gloucestershire! I live in the Thames Valley now, and that makes my catarrh worse, so you can't entirely blame Limerick. I blame my nose, it seems to have an unerring instinct for humidity. The unfortunate proboscis is probably only getting its own back, anyway, for the appalling treatment it received during my youth. I know what you're thinking, and it's not *that* – I was a delicately nurtured youth, with short-finger-nails and impeccably starched handkerchiefs. But, I was a rugby player in my youth and early manhood – ah the manly camaraderie of the showers – and on the field the old hooter, although Heaven knows, hardly in the Cyrano de Bergerac class, was ever the brunt of some hairy agricultural eejit, who would persist in taking the short cut through me, rather than around, and for some reason the old nose was always the first to go. We used to wear shin-guards and gum-shields, but nothing for the nasal extremity. Something like a Norman soldier's helmet might have been a good idea . . .

Nose apart, the rest of me had a fairly uneventful childhood in Limerick, apart from the rain. The few sepia prints extant show me as a somewhat chubby (hard to believe, isn't it?) little fellow, with short trousers just a shade too long, but generously masking an unwholesome pair of knees.

Most of my memories of childhood are of the resonant

baritone of my father reverberating from the bathroom. He used to sing while he was shaving, and a bloody business it was, too. Sometimes our bathroom resembled nothing so much as Sweeney Todd's on a Saturday night. My father's well-worn favourites were Victorian crowd-pleasers such as 'Many Brave Hearts Lie Asleep In The Deep', or 'Dead for Bread'. He favoured the more bravura baritone arias from opera, such as 'Valentine's Goodbye' from 'Faust', and it can only have been a merciful providence that spared us *Lieder*.

I remember, too, the Sundays we would go fishing together – or, rather, we would arrive at river or shore, and get *ready* to fish. A meticulous man, he would spend hours tying flies, and talking of days spent tickling trout in Wicklow mountain streams, and then, with the sun going down and the last of the sandwiches an indigestible memory, we would head for home . . . Ever since, I've been unable to prepare properly for anything (as any regular listener, etc).

At school, although I occasionally took part in debates, and trod the boards in the statutory D'Oyly Carte extravaganzas, I was far from being the life and soul of the classroom. 'Shy and introverted' would describe me better, and I find it extraordinary how many people in the theatre, television and radio also fit that description. Here we have a medium that is tailor-made for the extrovert, the gregarious show-off, and it's chockfull of people who are struck mumchance if they can't hide behind a role, a microphone or a camera. Introverted egotists, that's what we are, and yes, we like to be thought of as 'shy'. Shy's nice – it bespeaks an engaging modesty, a lack of bombast and self-importance. Now that I think of it, you won't hear too many people in show-business admitting to being show-offs.

When I was 15, Limerick having had its fill of Wogans, we left in a masked manner for the teeming metropolis of Dublin, a city whose claim to fame at the time was the length of its cinema queues and the splendour of its ice-cream parlours; at least, as far as one 'culchie' was concerned. (A native of Dublin is a 'gurrier'; anyone unfortunate enough to be born on the wrong side of the Dublin mountains is a 'bogman', a 'culchie', probably lured from his hovel by the promise of raw meat.)

Heaven, in the Dublin of those days, was a seat in the stalls and a Knickerbocker Glory afterwards.

I suppose the reason I'm not really 'show-biz' is because I missed the great days of variety and the clamour of the music-hall. I'm a child of the radio-cinema generation. My sense of humour, my view of life were coloured, enhanced and ultimately influenced by the great radio shows of the '50s: 'Hancock's Half-Hour', 'Take It From Here', 'The Goon Show'. The Light Programme was my life-line and I listened with an avidity unmatched by any of my school-mates. So, I can't really be too hard on my children when they seem transfixed by the old goggle-box; all I can hope is that it has the same benign influence on them that radio had on me.

Like all my contemporaries, I loved the cinema, particularly musicals. Probably, I was a little young for the sophisticated Astaire and Rogers, for my affections lay more with Doris Day and Donald O'Connor. One of Dublin's features, apart from the aforementioned queues, was 'Cine-Variety'. At least three large cinema-theatres in the city would stage marathon combinations of variety and film shows, the largest and the best being the Theatre Royal. Their show included an organist, pit orchestra, dancing girls, speciality act, comedian followed by 'B' feature, cartoon, and the 'big' film.

The organist would come rising from the pit, his mighty Wurlitzer ablaze, the words of 'Keep Your Sunny Side Up' flashed on to the screen, complete with bouncing ball, inviting the audience to join in and sing lustily. In all the years I went to the Theatre Royal, Dublin I never heard a peep out of them. That poor organist must have had feelings of tempered steel . . . That selfsame audience had a short way with comedians as well, which probably explains my own reluctance to 'get out there and kill 'em!' My impressionable youth was masked by the sight of fresh-faced young types trying to do just that, only to be left for dead themselves by waves of indifference from an audience that was only waiting for the movie anyway.

After a course in general philosophy – which seemed to consist mainly in trying to prove my own existence by reason alone – the consensus was that Descartes' reputation had little to fear from my lumbering logic, and that I might be as well off eschewing the intellectual life, and settling for a bit of the old mammon. So I joined the Royal Bank of Ireland. I didn't know what to expect, since I had only been inside a bank a couple of times in my young life, and certainly I'd never thought of it as a career. Looking back, the five years I spent toiling in the service of other people's money seem like a dream. At the time, being a bank clerk was no small thing for a decent Irish lad. You didn't get paid, of course, but you could guarantee other people's passport photographs, and you met a very nice class of girl at the bank socials.

The memories of my years in the financial field are all happy ones. Nay, hysterical. I was fortunate enough to be posted to the Cattle Market branch ('an enviable billet', as the man who taught me how to count notes with my left hand, in the Training School, put it). On all sides, merry cattle jobbers and farmers hurled invective, which mingled easily with the flying sponges of the tellers and the girlish giggles of typists being groped in the safe.

The whole place resembled nothing so much as the Dreamland Ballroom, Muff, on St Patrick's Night, with a bar extension. The manager of the Cattle Market branch of the Royal Bank of Ireland fancied himself a bit of a martinet, and at his worst he did have some of the elusive charm one associates with Attila the Hun. The effect, as Perelman might have put it, was somewhat vitiated by his clothes, which were apparently carved from some left-over gunny sacking, and his footwear, which was invariably children's open-toed sandals.

Still, he was no fool, and I was quickly put to the work best-suited to my talents: sorting two-bob bits from half-crowns, sealing up used notes and carrying them to Head Office. 'Good man, Wogan,' the manager would croak at a particularly shrewdly-placed seal. 'There's a future for you in the bank! Neat work. A job well done. The only difference between the difficult and the impossible is that the latter takes a little longer to do, ha-ha! There's no business like show-business, and there's no people like show-people. They laugh when other people cry.'

This view of hard-nosed show-people chuckling away at other people's grief is one I shall carry to the grave. Notes sealed and placed in sturdy leather holdall, I'd set off for Head Office, with the porter as an unwilling bodyguard. We had no means of self-defence, even if we had *wanted* to fight for £5,000 in old notes that smelt strongly of manure, and we took public transport. I like to think the reason we were never attacked was that *nobody* would credit such foolishness – they probably took us for decoys. Sitting ducks we certainly were.

Then, the Bank's Note Department having exchanged our grubby old notes for crisp new ones, the porter and myself would carry the £5,000 round the corner to Bewley's Oriental Café to fortify ourselves with bowls of coffee so strong that you felt as if everyone of your nerve-ends was waving away in the breeze . . .

A job as desirable as that of a bank clerk naturally carried with its heavy social obligations: prospective wives had to be vetted by one's manager, to see if they were acceptable to the bank. The manager was at all times to be addressed as 'Manager' except, of course, in the unlikely event of a social meeting, when he was to be known as 'Mr —'. Honesty, decency and clean-living were prerequisites as was wearing a tie – but not a blazer, except on Saturday, when it was Liberty Hall. Other members of the staff were to be addressed as 'Mr —' or 'Miss —' at all times during office hours, loud laughter was out, singing was a non-starter, and whistling, particularly with your hands in your pockets, was out of the question. All cash shortages had to be made up before the bank closed.

Despite all this, the general ambience of the place was, as I've said, reminiscent of the Moulin Rouge in the paling days of Toulouse-Lautrec: you could not engage in airy badinage with a female customer without being goosed with a broom-handle by a cheery fellow-teller or hit in the eye with a wet sponge. At regular intervals, tellers would sneak into each other's cubicles and tear bank-notes to shreds. Work was to be avoided at all costs, and some unfortunate customer entering the bank with a large lodgment would, like as not, find the place deserted as the tellers, cashiers, accountant and clerk ducked beneath the counter. Some people stood around looking bemused for ten minutes before the manager, alerted by the unearthly hush, restored normal banking services. He himself could often be found locked in the lavatory, which he used as a safe haven, or bunker, to avoid the more aggressive or drunken of his customers.

One fine day, when I'd been slaving away in the service of mammon for about five years, I answered an ad in an Irish national daily newspaper for an 'announcer/newsreader' required by RTE, the Irish radio and television service, and within three months my whole life had changed.

I spent eight years with RTE, five of them as a staff announcer; newsreader and presenter, and the rest as a freelance broadcaster. They were happy, exciting years, and whatever success I've achieved in Britain on television and radio is owed, in large part, to the experience I gained in Ireland. I was there for the opening night of Irish television, when, on a wing and a prayer, the new service was launched with an ambitious live outside broadcast. It was snowing, and as a tenor sang with the Army Band for our delight, the passing pedestrians, with that total lack of a sense of occasion that characterises the Irish, hurled snowballs at the unfortunate singer. It isn't easy to intone 'Galway Bay' with the precise degree of reverence required when you're ducking, bobbing and weaving in a blizzard.

I behaved with all the usual coltishness of the boy broadcaster in those days: unbuttoning lady-announcers' blouses as they read the news, setting fire to other announcers' scripts, pouring water over people's heads as they broadcast long announcements. One afternoon as I started the half-hour one o'clock news bulletin, my nose began to bleed. Have you any idea how difficult it is to be fair, balanced and well modulated when you're in a blind panic, bleeding to death? Have you any idea how difficult it is to read at all, when the words of the script are being blotted out by huge blobs of your own blood! Let's just say that the Great British Listening Public might have been spared a great deal of heartbreak every morning, if I wasn't such a quick little coagulator . . .

I remember introducing guitarists 'live' for television, who promptly fell off their own stools; inviting a quiz-show winner to take a prize, only for her to point out that there weren't any – the production assistant had forgotten them; heart-stopping moments, moments when you stare at the camera with a rictus smile of death, while your brain does handsprings in a desperate search for the exit. When people are kind enough to compliment me on my spontaneity or quick wit, I smile a quiet smile. It isn't complacency or engaging modesty; I'm remembering the stark terror of 'live' Irish television in its early days. Anybody who survived that, can survive *anything*!

●

# *Hollywood*

## Peter Ustinov

I had been contracted to play in the film *The Egyptian*, and I was looking forward to acting with Marlon Brando, who was one of its stars along with Victor Mature, Jean Simmons, Michael Wilding, and other famous names. I had already appeared in a view of ancient Rome seen through Polish eyes in *Quo Vadis*, by Sienkiewicz, and now I was about to indulge in a view of ancient Egypt as conceived by a Finn, Waltari. In a sense, Rome is already a part of the modern world, whereas the spirit of ancient Egypt is still wrapped in the secrecy of sphinxes and the smiles of cats which make the enigma of the Mona Lisa seen commonplace.

Unfortunately this relative difficulty of discerning a palpable artistic personality for Egypt outside the stilted murals and the pyramids compels designers to go to *Aïda* for inspiration. And this film was no exception. The sheer size of the décor dwarfed everything that stood before it, men, ideas, intelligence itself.

The only element in this elaborate cocktail half as mysterious as ancient Egypt was the director, Michael Curtiz, a tall and upright Hungarian who had come to Hollywood so long ago that he gazed over the palm trees and stucco castellations of its civilisation with the eye of a blind, all-seeing prophet of its faith. He had never learned American, let alone English, and he had forgotten his Hungarian, which left him in a limbo of his own, both entertaining and wild. His eyes had no visible pupils; they must have been the size of pin-points, and the irises were of the brightest blue, the blue of innocence.

I was presented to him on arrival, and he greeted me with the complicated grace of an Imperial corps-commander welcoming a new lieutenant hot from Budapest. The next day I was presented to him again, with precisely the same result. He had evidently forgotten me in the interim. I reckoned I was introduced to him at least ten times during the first week, each time for the first time. After that a kind of a shadow passed across his face, as though he was trying to place me.

I came down on to the floor for my début to find him filming a tavern scene. Jean Simmons was sweeping the floor with a large besom broom. Victor Mature was very angry about something or other in Ancient Thebes, and he dashed a papier mâché goblet to the ground.

'No lips of mine shall ever touch this chalice!' he cried out.

In the centre of the stage sat my stand-in, dressed identically to me, chewing gum and looking round with a very contemporary kind of detachment. I touched Mike Curtiz's arm. He bridled in irritation, then stared at me, trying to place me.

'Cut,' he cried. 'Vie you not on set?'

'Nobody called me,' I said.

'God damn, dat no excuse.'

Angrily, I took the place of my stand-in.

'Vie you not bring my attention?' he shouted at the stand-in.

'I tried to, sir,' shrugged the stand-in.

'We all did!' cried Jean Simmons.

'That's right,' confirmed Victor Mature.

'Ven nobody have interest film in heart, vil suffer only von ting, film,' grumbled Curtiz.

Of course, by now, Marlon Brando was no longer part of the cast. He had taken one look at the final script, and become victim of a rare illness, from which he made a miraculous recovery once shooting had begun on his replacement.

Communications with Mike Curtiz were extraordinarily difficult. He seemed to understand absolutely nothing I said, while agreeing with it all and doing just the opposite. There was only one slender ray of hope. In a moment of rare repose, he suddenly spoke, apropos of nothing.

'Vienna,' he said, with a fatalistic chuckle, 'I remember ven I vas barefoot boy in Vienna mit my broder, selling in the teatre sveets and magazine-programmes. Life!' His eyes looked heavenward a moment in smiling recognition of his fortune, and he retired once again into his more impenetrable abstractions.

It so happened that I had just received a letter from the Theatre in der Josefstadt in Vienna, on appropriately heraldic and evocative notepaper. They were about to perform *The Love of Four Colonels* and asked for certain precisions. It was a letter so technical it could mean nothing to anybody but myself, but I thought the letterhead itself might lure the nostalgic Curtiz further out of his lair, and expose him to human contact by way of his reminiscences.

The next day, after briefly reminding him who I was, I said.

'Mike, you remember yesterday—'

'Of course I remember yesterday,' he interrupted as though I had insulted his powers of retention. I refused to be side-tracked.

'You told us of your boyhood in Vienna.'

'Dat vos not yesterday,' he cried, 'a long time ago!'

His expression became suddenly serene.

'Vienna,' he said, with a fatalistic chuckle. 'I remember ven I vos barefoot boy in Vienna mit my broder, selling in the teatre sveets and magazine-programmes. Life!' His eyes looked heavenward a moment in smiling recognition of his fortune, and before he could retire once again into his more impenetrable abstractions, I nipped in with my letter.

He took it, and to my dismay did not so much as glance at the letterhead but, went straight on to the letter as though it were intended for him.

'We're ready, Mike,' said the cameraman.

'Mein God, vot manners,' cried Curtiz, 'to interrupt van man ven his is reading vun letter!'

The cameraman went away in disgust, and Mike Curtiz returned to his incomprehensible reading matter. Then, to my horror, he stuffed it into his pocket, and prepared to direct.

My chief concern was how to recuperate it, and I waited till the end of the day. I cornered him as he was about to leave the set.

'Mike,' I said, 'could I have my letter, please?'

'No,' he replied gently, on a tone of high morality. 'I am not de kind director write letter actors. I know it exist director too scared actors, so dey write letter instead to say vot tink. I not such. If I tink stink, I say. If I tink voonderful, I say. Always I say. No letter. Always say.'

I gritted my teeth.

'Mike,' I said, 'you have a letter *belonging to me*.'

'I no mail-man,' he retorted heatedly. 'Ven is letter for you, it vil be post-office, mit your name on, not mine name on.'

'Mike,' I screamed, 'you have a letter belonging to me from *Vienna*!'

'Vienna,' he said, with a fatalistic chuckle, 'I remember ven I vos barefoot boy in Vienna mit my broder—'

Before he had finished the sentence, I dug into his pocket and removed my letter. He noticed nothing. I made no further attempt to reach a more accessible unity. We were both better off this way.

Curiously enough, he was much more perceptive than he seemed to be, even though extremely absent-minded. Rumour had it that he had injured himself badly not long ago by stepping out of his Cadillac while it was in motion to commit a new idea to paper. Needless to say, he was driving himself.

●

*'Apparently it's a free sample of toothpaste.'*

# *Occasional Licenses*

## *Some experiences of an Irish R.M.*

**E.Œ. Somerville and M. Ross**

'It's out of the question,' I said, looking forbiddingly at Mrs Moloney through the spokes of the bicycle that I was pumping up outside the grocer's shop in Skebawn.

'Well, indeed, Major Yeates,' said Mrs Moloney, advancing excitedly, and placing on the nickel plating a hand that I had good and recent cause to know was warm, 'sure I know well that if th' angel Gabriel came down from heaven looking for a license for the races, your honour wouldn't give it to him without a charackther, but as for Michael! Sure, the world knows what Michael is!'

I had been waiting for Philippa for already nearly half an hour, and my temper was not at its best.

'Character or no character, Mrs Moloney,' said I with asperity, 'the magistrates have settled to give no occasional licenses, and if Michael were as sober as—'

'Is it sober! God help us!' exclaimed Mrs Moloney with an upward rolling of her eye to the Recording Angel; 'I'll tell your honour the truth. I'm his wife, now, fifteen years and I never seen the sign of dhrink on Michael only once, and that was when he went out o' good-nature helping Timsy Ryan to whitewash his house, and Timsy and himself had a couple o' pots o' porther, and look, he was as little used to it that his head got light, and he walked away out to dhrive in the cows and it no more than eleven o'clock in the day! And the cows, the craytures, as much surprised, goin' hither and over the four corners of the road from him! Faith, ye'd have to laugh.

"Michael," says I to him, "ye're dhrunk!" "I am," says he, and the tears rained from his eyes. I turned the cows from him. "Go home," I says, "and lie down on Willy Tom's bed—"'

At this affecting point my wife came out of the grocer's with a large parcel to be strapped to my handlebar, and the history of Mr Moloney's solitary lapse from sobriety got no further than Willy Tom's bed.

'You see,' I said to Philippa, as we bicycled quietly home through the hot June afternoon, 'we've settled we'll give no licenses for the sports. Why even young Sheehy, who owns three pubs in Skebawn, came to me and said he hoped the magistrates would be firm about it, as these one-day licenses were quite unnecessary, and only led to drunkenness and fighting, and every man on the Bench has joined in promising not to grant any.'

'How nice, dear!' said Philippa absently. 'Do you know Mrs McDonnell can only let me have three dozen cups and saucers; I wonder if that will be enough?'

'Do you mean to say you expect three dozen people?' said I.

'Oh, it's always well to be prepared,' replied my wife evasively.

During the next few days I realised the true inwardness of what it was to be prepared for an entertainment of this kind. Games were not at a high level in my district. Football, of a wild, guerilla species, was waged intermittently, blended in some inextricable way with Home Rule and a brass band, and on Sundays gatherings of young men rolled a heavy round stone along the roads, a rudimentary form of sport, whose fascination lay primarily in the fact that it was illegal, and, in lesser degree, in betting on the length of each roll. I had had a period of enthusiasm, during which I thought I was going to be the apostle of cricket in the neighbourhood, but my mission dwindled to single wicket with Peter Cadogan, who was indulgent but bored, and I swiped the ball through the dining-room window, and someone took one of the stumps to poke the laundry fire. Once a year, however, on that festival of the Roman Catholic Church which is familiarly known as 'Pether and Paul's day,' the district was wont to make a spasmodic effort at athletic sports, which were duly patronised by the gentry and promoted by the publicans, and this year the honour of a steward's green rosette was conferred upon me. Philippa's genius for hospitality here saw its chance, and broke forth into unbridled tea-party in connection with the sports, even involving me in the hire of a tent, the conveyance of chairs and tables, and other large operations.

It chanced that Flurry Knox had on this occasion lent the fields for the sports, with the proviso that horse-races and a tug-of-war were to be added to the usual programme; Flurry's participation in events of this kind seldom failed to be of an inflaming character. As he and I planted larch spars for the high jump, and stuck furze-bushes into hurdles (locally known as 'hurrls'), and skirmished hourly with people who wanted to sell drink on the course, I thought that my next summer leave would singularly coincide with the festival consecrated to St. Peter and St. Paul. We made a grand stand of quite four feet high, out of old fish-boxes, which smelt worse and worse as the day wore on, but was, none the less, as sought after by those for whom it was not intended, as is the Royal enclosure at Ascot; we broke gaps in all the fences to allow carriages on to the ground, we armed a gang of the worst blackguards in Skebawn with cart-whips, to keep the course, and felt that organisation could go no further.

The momentous day of Pether and Paul opened badly, with heavy clouds and every indication of rain, but after a few thunder showers things brightened, and it seemed within the bounds of possibility that the weather might hold up. When I got down to the course on the day of the sports the first thing I saw was a tent of that peculiar filthy grey that usually enshrines the sale of porter, with an array of barrels in a crate beside it; I bore down upon it in all the indignant majesty of the law, and in so doing came upon Flurry Knox, who was engaged in flogging boys off the Grand Stand.

'Sheehy's gone one better than you!' he said, without taking any trouble to conceal the fact that he was amused.

'Sheehy!' I said; 'why, Sheehy was the man who went to every magistrate in the country to ask them to refuse a license for the sports.'

'Yes, he took some trouble to prevent any one else having a look in,' replied Flurry; 'he asked every magistrate but one, and that was the one that gave him the license.'

'You don't mean to say that it was you?' I demanded in high wrath and suspicion, remembering that Sheehy bred horses, and that my friend Mr Knox was a person of infinite resource in the matter of a deal.

'Well, well,' said Flurry, rearranging a disordered fish-box, 'and me that's a churchwarden, and sprained my ankle a month ago with running downstairs at my grandmother's to be in time for prayers! Where's the use of a good character in this country?'

'Not much when you keep it eating its head off for want of exercise,' I retorted; 'but if it wasn't you, who was it?'

'Do you remember old Moriarty out at Castle Ire?'

I remembered him extremely well as one of those representatives of the people with whom a paternal Government had leavened the effete ranks of the Irish magistracy.

'Well,' resumed Flurry, 'that license was as good as a five-pound note in his pocket.'

I permitted myself a comment on Mr Moriarty suitable to the occasion.

'Oh, that's nothing,' said Flurry easily; 'he told me one day when he was half screwed that his Commission of the Peace was worth a hundred and a fifty a year to him in turkeys and whisky, and he was telling the truth for once.'

At this point Flurry's eye wandered, and following its direction I saw Lady Knox's smart 'bus cleaving its way through the throng of country people, lurching over the ups and downs of the field like a ship in a sea. I was too blind to make out the component parts of the white froth that crowned it on top, and seethed forth from it when it had taken up a position near the tent in which Philippa was even now propping the legs of the tea-table, but from the fact that Flurry addressed himself to the door, I argued that Miss Sally had gone inside.

Lady Knox's manner had something more than its usual bleakness. She had brought, as she promised, a large contingent, but from the way that the strangers within her gates melted impalpably and left me to deal with her single-handed, I drew further deduction that all was not well.

'Did you ever in your life see such a gang of women as I have brought with me?' she began with her wonted directness, as I piloted her to the Grand Stand, and placed her on the stoutest looking of the fish-boxes. 'I have no patience with men who yacht! Bernard Shute has gone off to the Clyde, and I had counted on his being a man at my dance next week. I suppose you'll tell me you're going away too.'

I assured Lady Knox that I would be a man to the best of my ability.

'This is the last dance I shall give,' went on her ladyship, unappeased; 'the men in this country consist of children and cads.'

I admitted that we were but a poor lot, 'but,' I said, 'Miss Sally told me—'

'Sally's a fool!' said Lady Knox, with a falcon eye at her daughter, who happened to be talking to her distant kinsman, Mr Flurry of that ilk.

The races had by this time begun with a competition known as the 'Hop, Step, and Lep'; this, judging by the yells, was a highly interesting display, but as it was conducted between two impervious rows of onlookers, the aristocracy on the fish-boxes saw nothing save the occasionally purple face of a competitor, starting into view above the wall of blacks like a jack-in-the-box. For me, however, the odorous sanctuary of the fish-boxes was not to be. I left it guarded by Slipper with a cart-whip of flail-like dimensions, as disreputable an object as could be seen out of low comedy, with someone's old white cords on his bandy legs, butcher-boots three sizes too big for him, and a black eye. The small boys fled before him; in the glory of his office he would have flailed his own mother off the fish-boxes had occasion served.

I had an afternoon of decidedly mixed enjoyment. My stewardship blossomed forth like Aaron's rod, and added to itself the duties of starter, handicapper, general referee, and chuckerout, besides which I from time to time strove with emissaries who came from Philippa with messages about water and kettles. Flurry and I had to deal single-handed with the foot-races (our brothers in office being otherwise engaged at Mr Sheehy's), a task of many difficulties, chiefest being that the spectators all swept forward at the word 'Go!' and ran the race with the competitors, yelling curses, blessings, and advice upon them taking short cuts over anything and everybody, and mingling inextricably with the finish. By fervent applications of the whips, the course was to some extent purged for the quarter-mile, and it would, I believe, have been a triumph of handicapping had not an unforeseen disaster overtaken the favourite – old Mrs Knox's bath-chair boy. Whether, as was alleged, his braces had or had not been tampered with by a rival was a matter that the referee had subsequently to deal with in the thick of a free fight; but the painful fact remained that in the course of the first lap what were described as 'his galluses' abruptly severed their connection with the garments for whose safety they were responsible, and the favourite was obliged to seek seclusion in the crowd.

The tug-of-war followed close on this *contretemps*, and had the excellent effect of drawing away, like a blister, the inflammation set up by the grievances of the bath-chair boy. I cannot at this moment remember of how many men each team consisted; my sole aim was to keep the numbers even, and to baffle the volunteers who, in an ecstasy of sympathy, attached themselves to the tail of the rope at moments when their champions weakened. The rival forces dug their heels in and tugged, in an uproar that drew forth the innermost line of customers from Mr Sheehy's porter tent, and even attracted 'the quality' from the haven of the fish-boxes, Slipper, in the capacity of Squire of Dames, pioneering Lady Knox through the crowd with the cart-whip, and with language whose nature was providentially veiled, for the most part, by the din. The tug-of-war continued unabated. One team was getting the worst of it, but hung doggedly on, sinking lower and lower till they gradually sat down; nothing short of the trump of judgement could have conveyed to them that they were breaking the rules, and both teams settled down by slow degrees on to their sides, with the rope under them, and their heels still planted in the ground, bringing about complete deadlock. I do not know the record duration for a tug-of-war, but I can certify that the Cullinagh and Knockranny teams lay down on the ground at full tension for half an hour, like men in apoplectic fits, each man with his respective adherents howling over him, blessing him and adjuring him to continue.

With my own nauseated eyes I saw a bearded countryman, obviously one of Mr Sheehy's best customers, fling himself on his knees beside one of his combatants, and kiss his crimson and streaming face in a rapture of encouragement. As he shoved unsteadily past me on his return journey to Mr Sheehy's, I heard him informing a friend that 'he cried a handful over Danny Mulloy, when he seen the poor brave boy so shtubborn, and, indeed, he couldn't say why he cried.'

'For good nature ye'd cry,' suggested the friend.

'Well, just that, I suppose,' returned Danny Mulloy's admirer resignedly; 'indeed, if it was only two cocks ye seen fightin' on the road, yer heart'd take part with one o' them!'

I had begun to realise that I might as well abandon the tug-of-war and occupy myself elsewhere, when my wife's much harassed messenger brought me the portentous tidings that Mrs Yeates wanted me at the tent at once. When I arrived I found the tent literally bulging with Philippa's guests; Lady Knox, seated on a hamper, was taking off her gloves, and loudly announcing her desire for tea, and Philippa, with a flushed face and a crooked hat, breathed into my ear the awful news that both the cream and the milk had been forgotten.

'But Flurry Knox says he can get me some,' she went on; 'he's gone to send people to milk a cow that lives near here. Go out and see if he's coming.'

I went out and found, in the first instance, Mrs Cadogan, who greeted me with the prayer that the divil might roast Julia McCarthy, that legged it away to the races like a wild goose, and left the cream afther her on the servants' hall table. 'Sure, Misther Flurry's gone looking for a cow, and what cow would there be in a backwards place like this? And look at me striving to keep the kettle simmering on the fire, and not as much coals undher it as'd redden a pipe!'

'Where's Mr Knox?' I asked.

'Himself and Slipper's galloping the counthry like the deer. I believe it's to the house above they went, sir.'

I followed up a rocky hill to the house above, and there found Flurry and Slipper engaged in the patriarchal task of driving two brace of coupled and spancelled goats into a shed.

'It's the best we can do,' said Flurry briefly; 'there isn't a cow to be found, and the people are all down at the sports. Be d– –d to you, Slipper, don't let them go from you!' as the goats charged and doubled like football players.

'But goat's milk!' I said, paralysed by horrible memories of what tea used to taste like at Gib.

'They'll never know it!' said Flurry, cornering a venerable nanny; 'here, hold this divil, and hold her tight!'

I have no time to dwell upon the pastoral scene that followed. Suffice it to say, that at the end of ten minutes of scorching profanity from Slipper, and incessant warfare with the goats, the latter had reluctantly yielded two small jugfuls, and the dairymaids had exhibited a nerve and skill in their trade that won my lasting respect.

'I knew I could trust *you*, Mr Knox!' said Philippa, with shining eyes, as we presented her with the two foaming beakers. I suppose a man is never a hero to his wife, but if she could have realised the bruises on my legs, I think she would have reserved a blessing for me also.

What was thought of the goats' milk I gathered symptomatically from a certain fixity of expression that accompanied the first sip of tea, and from observing that comparatively few ventured on second cups. I also noted that after a brief conversation with Flurry, Miss Sally poured hers secretly on to the grass. Lady Knox had throughout the day preserved an aspect so threatening that no change was perceptible in her demeanour. In the throng of hungry guests I did not for some time notice that Mr Knox had withdrawn until something in Miss Sally's eye summoned me to her, and she told me she had a message from him for me.

'Couldn't we come outside?' she said.

Outside the tent, within less than six yards of her mother,

Miss Sally confided to me a scheme that made my hair stand on end. Summarised, it amounted to this: That, first, she was in the primary stage of a deal with Sheehy for a four-year-old chestnut colt, for which Sheehy was asking double its value on the assumption that it had no rival in the country; that, secondly, they had just heard it was going to run in the first race; and, thirdly and lastly, that as there was no other horse available, Flurry was going to take old Sultan out of the 'bus and ride him in the race; and that Mrs Yeates had promised to keep mamma safe in the tent, while the race was going on, and 'you know, Major Yeates, it would be delightful to beat Sheehy after his getting the better of you all about the license!'

With this base appeal to my professional feelings, Miss Knox paused and looked at me insinuatingly. Her eyes were greeny-grey, and very beguiling.

'Come on,' she said; 'they want you to start them!'

Pursued by visions of the just wrath of Lady Knox, I weakly followed Miss Sally to the farther end of the second field, from which point the race was to start. The course was not a serious one: two or three natural banks, a stone wall, and a couple of 'hurrls.' There were but four riders, including Flurry, who was seated composedly on Sultan, smoking a cigarette and talking confidentially to Slipper. Sultan, although something stricken in years and touched in the wind, was a brown horse who in his day had been a hunter of no mean repute; even now he occasionally carried Lady Knox in a sedate and gentlemanly manner, but it struck me that it was trying rather high to take him from the pole of the 'bus after twelve miles on a hilly road, and hustle him over a country against a four-year-old. My acutest anxiety, however, was to start the race as quickly as possible, and to get back to the tent in time to establish an *alibi*; therefore I repressed my private sentiments, and, tying my handkerchief to a stick, determined that no time should be fashionably frittered away in false starts.

They got away somehow; I believe Sheehy's colt was facing the wrong way at the moment when I dropped the flag, but a friend turned him with a stick, and, with a cordial and timely whack, speeded him on his way on sufficiently level terms, and then somehow, instead of returning to the tent, I found myself with Miss Sally on the top of a tall narrow bank, in a precarious line of other spectators, with whom we toppled and swayed, and, in moments of acuter emotion, held on to each other in unaffected comradeship.

Flurry started well, and from our commanding position we could see him methodically riding at the first fence at a smart hunting canter, closely attended by James Canty's brother on a young black mare, and by an unknown youth on a big white horse. The hope of Sheehy's stable, a leggy chestnut, ridden by a cadet of the house of Sheehy, went away from the friend's stick like a rocket, and had already refused the first bank twice before old Sultan decorously changed feet on it and dropped down into the next field with tranquil precision. The white horse scrambled over it on his stomach, but landed safely, despite the fact that his rider clasped him round the neck during the process; the black mare and the chestnut shouldered one another over at the hole the white horse had left, and the whole party went away in a bunch and jumped the ensuing hurdle without disaster. Flurry continued to ride at the same steady hunting pace, accompanied respectfully by the white horse and by Jerry Canty on the black mare. Sheehy's colt had clearly the legs of the party, and did some showy galloping between the jumps, but as he refused to face the banks without a lead, the end of the first round found the field still a sociable party personally conducted by Mr Knox.

'That's a dam nice horse,' said one of my hangers-on, looking approvingly at Sultan as he passed us at the beginning of the second round, making a good deal of noise but apparently going at his ease; 'you might depind your life on him, and he have the crabbedest jock in the globe of Ireland on him this minute.'

'Canty's mare's very sour,' said another; 'look at her now, baulking the bank! She's as cross as a bag of weasels.'

'Begob, I wouldn't say but she's a little sign lame,' resumed the first; 'she was going light on one leg on the road a while ago.'

'I tell you what it is,' said Miss Sally, very seriously, in my ear, 'that chestnut of Sheehy's is settling down. I'm afraid he'll gallop away from Sultan at the finish, and the wall won't stop him. Flurry can't get another inch out of Sultan. He's riding him well,' she ended in a critical voice, which yet was not quite like her own. Perhaps I should not have noticed it but for the fact that the hand that held my arm was trembling. As for me, I thought of Lady Knox, and trembled too.

There now remained but one bank, the trampled remnant of the furze hurdle, and the stone wall. The pace was beginning to improve, and the other horses drew away from Sultan; they charged the bank at full gallop, the black mare and the chestnut flying it perilously, with a windmill flourish of legs and arms from their riders, the whie horse racing up to it with a gallantry that deserted him at the critical moment, with the result that his rider turned a somersault over his head and landed, amidst the roars of the onlookers, sitting on the fence facing his horse's nose. With creditable presence of mind he remained on the bank, towed the horse over, scrambled on to his back again and started afresh. Sultan, thirty yards to the bad, pounded doggedly on, and Flurry's cane and heels remained idle; the old horse, obviously blown, slowed cautiously coming in at the jump. Sally's grip tightened on my arm, and the crowd yelled as Sultan, answering to a hint from the spurs and a touch at his mouth, heaved himself on to the bank. Nothing but sheer riding on Flurry's part got him safe off it, and saved him from the consequences of a bad peck on landing; none the less, he pulled himself together and went away down the hill for the stone wall as stoutly as ever. The high road skirted the last two fields, and there was a gate in the roadside fence beside the place where the stone wall met it at right angles. I had noticed this gate, because during the first round Slipper had been sitting on it, demonstrating with his usual fervour. Sheehy's colt was leading, with his nose in the air, his rider's hands going like a circular saw, and his temper, as a bystander remarked, 'up on end'; the black mare, half mad from spurring, was going hard at his heels, completely out of hand; the white horse was steering steadily for the wrong side of the flag, and Flurry, by dint of cutting corners and of saving every yard of ground, was close enough to keep his antagonists' heads over their shoulders, while their right arms rose and fell in unceasing flagellation.

'There'll be a smash when they come to the wall! If one falls they'll all go!' panted Sally. 'Oh! – Now! Flurry! Flurry!—'

What had happened was that the chestnut colt had suddenly perceived that the gate at right angles to the wall was standing wide open, and, swinging away from the jump, he had bolted headlong out on to the road, and along it at top speed for his home. After him fled Canty's black mare, and with her, carried away by the spirit of stampede, went the white horse.

Flurry stood up in his stirrups and gave a view-halloa as he cantered down to the wall. Sultan came at it with the send of the hill behind him, and jumped it with a skill that intensified, if that were possible, the volume of laughter and yells around us. By the time the black mare and the white horse had returned and ignominiously bundled over the wall to finish as best they might, Flurry was leading Sultan towards us.

'That blackguard, Slipper!' he said, grinning; 'everyone'll say I told him to open the gate! But look here, I'm afraid we're in for trouble. Sultan's given himself a bad over-reach; you could never drive him home tonight. And I've just seen Norris lying blind drunk under a wall!'

Now Norris was Lady Knox's coachman. We stood aghast at this 'horror on horror's head,' the blood trickled down Sultan's heel, and the lather lay in flecks on his dripping, heaving sides, in irrefutable witness to the iniquity of Lady Knox's only daughter. Then Flurry said:

'Thank the Lord, here's the rain?'

At the moment I admit that I failed to see any cause for gratitude in this occurrence, but later on I appreciated Flurry's grasp of circumstances.

That appreciation was, I think, at its highest development about half an hour afterwards, when I, an unwilling conspirator (a part with which my acquaintance with Mr Knox had rendered me but too familiar) unfurled Mrs Cadogan's umbrella over Lady Knox's head, and hurried her through the rain from the tent to the 'bus, keeping it and my own person well between her and the horses. I got her in, with the rest of her bedraggled and exhausted party, and slammed the door.

'Remember, Major Yeates,' she said through the window, 'you are the *only* person here in whom I have any confidence. I don't wish *any* one else to touch the reins!' this with a glance towards Flurry, who was standing near.

'I'm afraid I'm only a moderate whip,' I said.

'My dear man,' replied Lady Knox testily, 'those horses could drive themselves!'

I slunk round to the front of the 'bus. Two horses, carefully rugged, were in it, with the inevitable Slipper at their heads.

'Slipper's going with you,' whispered Flurry, stepping up to me; 'she woin't have me at any price. He'll throw the rugs over them when you get to the house, and if you hold the umbrella well over her she'll never see. I'll manage to get Sultan over somehow, when Norris is sober. That will be all right.'

I climbed to the box without answering, my soul being bitter within me, as is the soul of a man who has been persuaded by womankind against his judgement.

'Never again!' I said to myself, picking up the reins; 'let her marry him or Bernard Shute, or both of them if she likes, but I won't be roped into this kind of business again!'

Slipper drew the rugs from the horses, revealing on the near side Lady Knox's majestic carriage horse, and on the off, a thickset brown mare of about fifteen hands.

'What brute is this?' said I to Slipper, as he swarmed up beside me.

'I don't rightly know where Misther Flurry got her,' said Slipper, with one of his hiccoughing crows of laughter; 'give her the whip, Major, and' – here he broke into song:

'*Howld to the shteel,*

*Honamaundhiaoul; she'll run like an eel!*'

'If you don't shut your mouth,' said I, with pent-up ferocity, 'I'll chuck you off the 'bus.'

Slipper was but slightly drunk, and, taking this delicate rebuke in good part, he relapsed into silence.

Wherever the brown mare came from, I can certify that it was not out of double harness. Though humble and anxious to oblige, she pulled away from the pole as if it were red hot, and at critical moments had a tendency to sit down. However, we squeezed without misadventure among the donkey carts and between the groups of people, and bumped at length in safety out on to the high road.

Here I thought it no harm to take Slipper's advice, and I applied the whip to the brown mare, who seemed inclined to turn round. She immediately fell into an uncertain canter that no effort of mine could frustrate; I could only hope that Miss Sally would foster conversation inside the 'bus and create a distraction; but judging from my last view of the party, and of Lady Knox in particular, I thought she was not likely to be successful. Fortunately the rain was heavy and thick, and a rising west wind gave every promise of its continuance. I had little doubt but that I should catch cold, but I took it to my bosom with gratitude as I reflected how it was drumming on the roof of the 'bus and blurring the windows.

We had reached the foot of a hill, about a quarter of a mile from the racecourse; the Castle Knox horse addressed himself to it with dignified determination, but the mare showed a sudden and alarming tendency to jib.

'Belt her, Major!' vociferated Slipper, as she hung back from the pole chain, with the collar half-way up her ewe neck, 'and give it to the horse, too! He'll dhrag her!'

I was in the act of 'belting' when a squealing whinny struck upon my ear, accompanied by a light pattering gallop on the road behind us; there was an answering roar from the brown mare, a roar, as I realised with a sudden drop of the heart, of outraged maternal feeling, and in another instant a pale, yellow foal sprinted up beside us, with shrill whickerings of joy. Had there at this moment been a boghole handy, I should have turned the bus into it without hesitation; as there was no accommodation of that kind, I laid the whip severely into everything I could reach, including the foal. The result was that we topped the hill at a gallop, three abreast, like a Russian troitska; it was like my usual luck that at this identical moment we should meet the police patrol, who saluted respectfully.

'That the divil may blisther Michael Moloney!' ejaculated Slipper, holding on to the rail; 'didn't I give him the foaleen and a halter on him to keep him! I'll howld you a pint 'twas the wife let him go, for she being vexed about the license! Sure that one's a March foal, an' he'd run from here to Cork!'

There was no sign from my inside passengers, and I held on at a round pace, the mother and child galloping absurdly, the carriage horse pulling hard, but behaving like a gentleman. I wildly resolved plans of how I would make Slipper turn the foal in at the first gate we came to, of what I should say to Lady Knox supposing the worst happened and the foal accompanied us to her hall door, and of how I would have Flurry's blood at the earliest possible opportunity, and here the fateful sound of galloping behind us was again heard.

'It's impossible!' I said to myself; 'she can't have twins!'

The galloping came nearer, and Slipper looked back.

'Murder alive!' he said in a stage whisper, 'Tom Sheehy's afther us on the butcher's pony!'

'What's that to me?' I said, dragging my team aside to let him pass; 'I suppose he's drunk, like everyone else!'

Then the voice of Tom Sheehy made itself heard.

'Shtop! Shtop thief!' he was bawling; 'give up my mare! How will I get my porther home!'

That was the closest shave I have ever had, and nothing could have saved the position but the torrential nature of the rain and the fact that Lady Knox had on a new bonnet. I explained to her at the door of the 'bus that Sheehy was drunk (which was the one unassailable feature of the case), and had come after his foal, which, with the fatuity of its kind, had escaped from a field and followed us. I did not mention to Lady Knox that when Mr Sheehy retreated, apologetically, dragging the foal after him in a halter belonging to one of her own carriage horses, he had a sovereign of mine in his pocket, and during the narration I avoided Miss Sally's eyes as carefully as she avoided mine.

The only comments on the day's events that are worthy of record were that Philippa said to me that she had not been able to understand what the curious taste in the tea had been till Sally told her it was turf-smoke, and that Mrs Cadogan said to Philippa that night 'the Major was that drenched that if he had a shirt between his skin and himself he could have wrung it,' and that Lady Knox said to a mutual friend that though Major Yeates had been extremely kind and obliging, he was an uncommonly bad whip.

●

# *Part Three*

# PERFECT BEASTS

## *The Horse*

I know two things about the horse
And one of them is rather coarse.

**Naomi Royde-Smith**

# *A Wilderness of Monkeys*
# Gerald Durrell

Perhaps the most noisy, the most irritating and the most lovable creatures that shared our marquee were the monkeys. There were forty of them altogether, and life under the same roof with forty monkeys is anything but quiet. The adult animals were not so bad; it was the baby monkeys that caused so much trouble and extra work for us: they would scream loudly if left alone, demand bottles full of warm milk at the most ungodly hours of the night and morning; they would get stricken with all sorts of baby complaints and frighten us to death; they would escape from the nursery and get near the Golden Cat's cage, or fall into kerosene tins full of water, and generally drive us to the edge of a nervous breakdown. We were forced to think up the most Machiavellian schemes for dealing with these babies, and some of them were quite extraordinary. Take the case of the baby Drills: these baboons are extremely common in the forests of the Cameroons, and we were always being brought babies of all ages. The Drill is that rather ugly-looking creature you can see in most zoos, who has a bright pink behind and does not hesitate to share its glory with you. Very young Drills are among the most pathetic and ridiculous-looking creatures in the world: they are covered with a very fine silvery grey fur, and their heads, hands and feet look at least three times too big for their bodies. The hands, feet and face are a shade that we used to describe as boiled baby pink, and their minute bottoms were the same colour. The skin on their bodies was white, spotted in places with large areas, exactly like big birthmarks, of bright china blue. Like all baby monkeys, they have staring eyes, and their arms and legs are long and attenuated and tremble like the limbs of a very old person. This should give you some idea of a baby Drill.

The early days of a Drill's life are spent clinging with its muscular hands and feet to the thick fur of its mother. So our baby Drills, when they had transferred their affections to us and decided that we were their parents, demanded loudly and vociferously that they should be allowed to cling to us. Next to vast quantities of food, the most important thing in a young Drill's life is to feel that it has a good grip on the provider of the food. As it is almost impossible to work when you have four or five baby Drills clinging to you like miniature, cackling Old Men of the Sea, we had to devise some plan to keep them happy. We found two old coats and slung these over the backs of chairs in the centre of the marquee; then we introduced the babies to them. They were used to seeing us in coats, and I expect the garments retained a certain characteristic odour, so they apparently decided that the coats were a sort of skin that we had discarded. They clung to the empty sleeves, the lapels and the tails of these two coats as though they had been glued on, and while we went on with our work around the camp they would hang there, half asleep, occasionally waking up to carry on a cackling conversation with us.

The great numbers of people who used to visit our camp-site and look round the collection always seemed most affected by our group of baby monkeys. A baby monkey, in all its ways, is very like a human baby, only infinitely more pathetic. The women in these parties would gaze at our young monkeys with melting eyes, making inarticulate crooning noises and generally brimming over with mother love. There was one young lady who visited us several times and was so affected by the pathetic expression of the young monkeys that she unwisely took it upon herself to deliver a lecture to me about the extreme cruelty of taking these poor little creatures from their mothers and incarcerating them in cages. She waxed quite poetical on the joys of freedom, and contrasted the carefree, happy existence these babies would have in the tree-tops with the ghastly imprisonment for which I was responsible. That morning a baby monkey had been brought in by a native hunter, and since the young lady seemed to be such an expert on monkey life in the tree-tops, I suggested that she might like to help me perform a little task that had to be gone through with each new monkey that arrived. She agreed eagerly, seeing herself in the role of a sort of simian Florence Nightingale.

The little task consisted, quite simply, in searching the new baby for internal and external parasites. I explained this, and the young lady looked surprised: she said that she did not know that monkeys had parasites – beyond fleas, of course. I produced the little basket that the monkey was brought in, and removing some of its excreta I spread it out on a clean piece of paper and showed her the numbers of threadlike worms it contained. My helper remained strangely silent. Then I brought out the baby: he was a Putty-nose Guenon, an adorable little fellow clad in black fur, with a white shirtfront and a gleaming, heart-shaped patch of white fur on his nose. I examined his tiny hands and feet and his long slender fingers and toes and found no fewer than six jiggers comfortably ensconced. These minute creatures burrow their way into the skin of the feet and hands, particularly under the nails, where the skin is soft, and there they eat and swell and grow, until they reach the size of a match-head. Then they lay their eggs and die; in due course the eggs hatch and the baby jiggers continue the good work that their parent had begun. If a jigger infection is not dealt with in the early stages it can lead to the loss of the joint of a toe or finger, and in extreme cases it can destroy all the toes or fingers, for the jiggers go on burrowing and breeding until they have hollowed the part out to a bag of skin filled with pus. I have had jiggers in my foot on several occasions, and can vouch for the fact that they can be extremely painful. All this I explained to my helper in graphic detail. Then I got the tube of local anaesthetic, froze the fingers and toes of the little Guenon, and with a sterilised needle proceeded to remove the jiggers and disinfect the wounds they left. I found this local anaesthetic a boon, for the operation is painful and the baby monkeys would not sit still otherwise.

When this was over I ran my fingers down the monkey's tail and felt two sausage-shaped swellings, each as long as the first joint of my little finger and about the same circumference. I showed these to my companion, and then parted the hair so that she could see the circular, porthole-like opening at the end of each swelling. Looking through the porthole into the interior of the swelling, you could see something white and loathsome moving. I explained, with my best Harley Street air, that a certain forest fly lays it eggs on the fur of various animals, and when the maggot hatches it burrows down into the flesh of its host and lives there, fattening like a pig in a sty, getting air through the porthole, and, when it finally leaves to turn into a fly, the host has a hole the circumference of a cigarette in its flesh, which generally becomes a suppurating sore. I showed my helper, who was by now quite pale, that it was impossible to hook these maggots out. I got the needle and, parting the hair, showed her the creature lying in its burrow like a miniature barrage balloon; as soon as the tip of the needle touched it, however, it just compressed itself into a wrinkled blob, folding up like a concertina, and slid back into the depths of the monkey's tail. Then I showed her how to get them out – a method I had invented: pushing the nozzle of the anaesthetic tube into the porthole, I squirted the liquid inside until I had frozen the maggot into immobility; then, with a scalpel, I enlarged the porthole slightly, stabbed the maggot with the end of the needle and withdrew it from its lair. As I pulled the wrinkled white horror out of the bloodstained hole, my helper left me suddenly and precipitately. I removed the second maggot, disinfected the gaping holes they had left and then joined her at the other side of the camp clearing. She explained that she was late for a lunch date, thanked me for a most interesting morning, and took her leave, never to visit us again. I always think it rather a pity that people don't learn more about the drawbacks of life in the jungle before prating about the cruelty of captivity.

One of the most delightful monkeys we had was a baby moustached Guenon, whom Smith procured on a trip up-country. He was the smallest monkey I had ever seen, and, except for his long slender tail, he could fit comfortably into a tea-cup. He was a greenish-grey colour, with buttercup-yellow cheek-patches and a white shirt-front. But the most remarkable thing about him was his face, for across his upper lip was a broad, curving band of white hair that made him look as though he had an impressive moustache. For his size, his mouth was enormous, and could quite easily accommodate the teat of the feeding-bottle. It was a most amusing sight to see this tiny, moustached animal hurl himself on to the bottle when it arrived, uttering shrill squeaks of joy, wrap his arms and legs round it tightly, and lie there with his eyes closed, sucking away frantically. It looked rather as though he was being suckled by a large white airship, for the bottle was three times his size. He was very quick to learn, and it was not long before we had taught him to drink his milk out of a saucer. He would be put on the camp table to be fed, and the moment he saw the saucer approaching he would get quite hysterical with excitement, trembling and twitching, and screaming at the top of his voice. As soon as the saucer was placed before him he would, without any hesitation, dive head first into it. He would push his face completely under the milk, and only come up for air when he could hold out no longer. Sometimes, in his greed, he would wait too long, and a shower of bubbles would break the surface, and he would follow them, coughing and sneezing and spattering himself and the table with a fountain of milk. There were times during his meal when he would become convinced that you were hanging around waiting an opportunity to take his saucer away from him, and, giving a quavering scream of rage, he would frustrate your plan by the simple expedient of leaping into the air and landing in the centre of the saucer with a splash, where he would sit glaring at you triumphantly. At meal-times he would get his head and face so covered with milk that it was only with difficulty you could tell where his moustache began and ended, and the table would look as though someone had milked a large and healthy cow over it.

The two most forceful characters in our monkey collection were, of course, the chimpanzees Mary and Charlie. Charlie had been the pet of a planter before he came to us, so he was fairly domesticated. He had a small, wrinkled, sorrowful face and melting brown eyes; he looked as though the world had treated him harshly but that he was too much of a saint to complain. This wounded, dejected air was a lot of moonshine, for in reality Charlie, far from being an ill-treated, misunderstood ape, was a disgraceful little street urchin, full of low cunning and deceit. Every day we used to let him out of his cage for exercise, and he would roam about the camp looking radiantly innocent until he thought he had lulled you into believing in his integrity. Then he would wander nonchalantly towards the food-table, give a quick glance round to see if he was observed, grab the largest bunch of bananas within reach and dash madly away towards the nearest tree. If you gave chase he would drop the fruit and skid to a standstill. Then he would sit in the dust while you scolded him, gazing up at you sorrowfully, the picture of injured innocence, the expression on his face showing quite plainly that he was being wrongfully accused of a monstrous crime, but that he was far too noble to point that out to you if you were too obtuse to realise it. Wave the bunch of stolen fruit under his nose and he would regard it with faint surprise, mingled with disgust. Why should you imagine that he had stolen the fruit? his expression seemed to say. Were you not aware of the fact that he disliked bananas? Never in his whole life (devoted to philanthropy and self-denial) had he felt the slightest inclination to even sample the loathsome fruit, much less steal any. The scolding over, Charlie would rise, give a deep sigh, throw you a look of compassion tinged with disgust, and lope off to the kitchen to see what he could steal there. He was quite incorrigible, and his face was so expressive that he could carry on a long conversation with you without any need of speech.

Charlie's greatest triumph came when we received a visit from the High Commissioner for the Cameroons, who was passing through on one of his periodical visits of inspection. He came down to our camp accompanied by a vast army of secretaries and other supporters, and was greatly interested in our large array of beasts. But the animal that attracted him most was Charlie. While we explained to H.E. what a disgusting hypocrite the ape was, Charlie was sitting in his cage, holding the great man's hand through the bars, and gazing up at him with woe-begone expression and pleading eyes, begging that His Excellency would not listen to the foul slander we were uttering. When His Excellency left, he invited Smith and myself to his At Home, which was to take place the following evening. The next morning a most impressive messenger, glittering with golden buttons, delivered an envelope from the District Office. Inside was a large card which informed us, in magnificent twirly writing, that His Excellency, the High Commissioner for the Cameroons, requested the pleasure of Charlie's presence during his At Home, between the hours of six and eight. When we showed it to Charlie he was sitting in his cage meditating, and he gave it a brief glance and then ignored it. His attitude told us he was quite used to being showered with such invitations, but that these things were too worldly to be of any interest to him. He was, he implied, far too busy with his saint-like meditations to get excited about invitations to drinking-orgies with mere High Commissioners. As he had been into the kitchen that morning and stolen six eggs, a loaf of bread and a leg of cold chicken, we did not believe him.

Mary was a chimp of completely different character. She was older than Charlie, and much bigger, being about the size of a two-year-old human. Before we bought her she had been in the hands of a Hausa trader, and I am afraid she must have been teased and ill-treated, for at first she was sullen and vicious, and we feared we would never be able to gain her confidence as she had developed a deep-rooted mistrust of anything human, black or white. But after a few months of good food and kind handling she delighted us by blossoming forth into a chimp with much charm, a sunny disposition and a terrific sense of humour. She had a pale pink, rather oafish face, and a large pot belly. She reminded me rather of a fat barmaid, who was always ready to laugh uproariously at some bawdy jest. After she got to know and trust us, she developed a trick which she thought was frightfully funny. She would lie back in her cage, balanced precariously on her perch, and present an unmentionable part of her anatomy to the bars. You were then expected to lean forward and blow hard whereupon Mary would utter a screech of laughter and modestly cover herself up with her hands. Then she would give you a coy look from over the mound of her stomach, and uncover herself again, and you were expected to repeat this mirth-provoking action. This became known to both us and the staff as Blowing Mary's Wicked Parts, and no matter how many times a day you repeated it, Mary still found it exceedingly funny; she would throw back her head and open her mouth wide, showing vast areas of pink gum and white teeth, hooting and tittering with hysterical laughter.

Although Mary treated us and the staff with great gentleness, she never forgot that she had a grudge against Africans in general, and she used to pick on any strange ones that came to camp. She would grin at them ingratiatingly and slap her chest, or turn somersaults – anything to gain their attention. By her antics she would lure them closer and closer to the cage, looking the picture of cheerful good humour, while her shrewd eyes judged the distance carefully. Suddenly the long and powerful arm would shoot out through the bars, there would be a loud ripping noise, a yelp of fright from the African, and Mary would be dancing round her cage triumphantly waving a torn shirt or singlet that she had pulled off her admirer's back. Her strength was extraordinary, and it cost me a small fortune in replacements until I put her cage in such a position that she could not commit these outrages.

The monkey collection kept up a continuous noise all through the day, but in the afternoon, at about four-thirty, this rose to a crescendo of sound that would tax the strongest nerves, for it was at this time that the monkeys had their milk. About four they would start to get impatient, leaping and jumping about their cages, turning somersaults, or sitting with their faces pressed to the bars making mournful squeaks. As soon as the line of clean pots was laid out, however, and the great kerosene tin full of warm milk, malt and cod-liver oil, sugar and calcium came in sight, a wave of excitement would sweep the cages and the uproar would be deafening. The chimps would be giving prolonged hoots through pursed lips and thumping on the sides of their cages with their fists, the Drills would be uttering their loud and penetrating, 'Ar-ar-ar-ar-ar-erererer!' cries, like miniature machine-guns, the Guenons would be giving faint, bird-like whistles and trills, the Patas monkeys would be dancing up and down like mad ballerinas, shouting 'Proup . . . proup' plaintively, and the beautiful Colobus, with her swaying shawl of white and black hair, would be calling 'Arroup! arroup! arroup! ye-ye-ye-ye!' in a commanding tone of voice. As we moved along the cages, pushing the pots of milk through the doors, the noises would gradually cease, until all that could be heard was a low snorting, sucking sound, interspersed by an occasional cough as some milk went down the wrong way. Then, the pots empty, the monkeys would climb up on to their perches and sit there, their bellies bulging, uttering loud and satisfied belches at regular intervals. After a while they would all climb down again on to the floor to examine their pots and make quite sure there was no milk left in them, even picking them up and looking underneath. Then they would curl up on their perches in the evening sun and fall into a bloated stupor, while peace came to the camp.

One of the things that I find particularly endearing about monkeys is the fact that they are completely uninhibited, and will perform any action they feel like with an entire lack of embarrassment. They will urinate copiously, or bend down and watch their own faeces appear with expressions of absorbed interest; they will mate or masturbate with great freedom, regardless of any audience. I have heard embarrassed human beings call monkeys dirty, filthy creatures when they have watched them innocently perform these actions in public, and it is an attitude of mind that I always find difficult to understand. After all, it is we, with our superior intelligence, who have decided that the perfectly natural functions of our bodies are something unclean; monkeys do not share our view.

Similarly, one of the things I liked about the Africans was this same innocent attitude towards the functions of the body. In this respect they were extremely like the monkeys. I had a wonderful example of this one day when a couple of rather stuffy missionaires came to look round the camp.

I showed them our various animals and birds, and they made a lot of unctuous comments about them. Then we came to the monkeys, and the missionaries were delighted with them.

Presently, however, we reached a cage where a monkey was sitting on the perch in a curious hunched-up attitude.

'Oh! What's *he* doing?' cried the lady gaily, and before I could prevent her she had bent down to get a better look. She shot up again, her face a deep, rich scarlet, for the monkey had been whiling away the hours to meal time by sitting there and sucking himself.

We hurried through the rest of the monkey collection in record time, and I was much amused by the expression of frozen disgust that had replaced the look of benevolent delight on the lady missionary's face. They might be God's creatures, her expression implied, but she wished He would do something about their habits. However, as we rounded the corner of the marquee we were greeted by another of God's creatures in the shape of a lanky African hunter. He was a man who had brought in specimens regularly each week, but for the past fortnight he had not come near us.

'Iseeya, Samuel!' I greeted him.

'Iseeya, Masa,' he said, coming towards us.

'Which side you done go all dis time?' I asked; 'why you never bring me beef for two weeks, eh?'

'Eh! Masa, I done get sickness,' he explained.

'Sickness? Eh, sorry, my friend. Na what sickness you get?'

'Na my ghonereah, Masa,' he explained innocently, 'my ghonereah de worry me *too much*.'

The missionaries were among the people who never called twice at the camp site.

●

## *The Lion*

Oh, weep for Mr and Mrs Bryan!
He was eaten by a lion;
Following which, the lion's lioness
Up and swallowed Bryan's Bryaness.

**Ogden Nash**

'That pooch really put up a tough battle when I put him out last night, honey!'

**Donald Orehek**

# *All Things Bright and Beautiful*

## James Herriot

There was one marvellous thing about the set-up in Darrowby. I had the inestimable advantage of being a large animal practitioner with a passion for dogs and cats. So that although I spent most of my time in the wide outdoors of Yorkshire there was always the captivating background of the household pets to make a contrast.

I treated some of them every day and it made an extra interest in my life; interest of a different kind, based on sentiment instead of commerce and because of the way things were it was something I could linger over and enjoy. I suppose with a very intensive small animal practice it would be easy to regard the thing as a huge sausage machine, an endless procession of hairy forms to prod with hypodermic needles. But in Darrowby we got to know them all as individual entities.

Driving through the town I was able to identify my ex-patients without difficulty; Rover Johnson, recovered from his ear canker, coming out of the ironmonger's with his mistress, Patch Walker, whose broken leg had healed beautifully, balanced happily on the back of his owner's coal wagon, or Spot Briggs who was a bit of a rake anyway and would soon be tearing himself again on barbed wire, ambling all alone across the market place cobbles in search of adventure. I got quite a kick out of recalling their ailments and mulling over their characteristics. Because they all had their own personalities and they were manifested in different ways.

One of those was their personal reaction to me and my treatment. Most dogs and cats appeared to bear me not the slightest ill will despite the fact that I usually had to do something disagreeable to them.

But there were exceptions and one of these was Magnus, the Miniature Dachshund from the Drovers' Arms.

He was in my mind now as I leaned across the bar counter.

'A pint of Smith's, please, Danny,' I whispered.

The barman grinned. 'Coming up, Mr Herriot.' He pulled at the lever and the beer hissed gently into the glass and as he passed it over the froth stood high and firm on the surface.

'That ale looks really fit tonight,' I breathed almost inaudibly.

'Fit? It's beautiful!' Danny looked fondly at the brimming glass. 'In fact it's a shame to sell it.'

I laughed, but pianissimo. 'Well it's nice of you to spare me a drop.' I took a deep pull and turned to old Mr Fairburn who was as always sitting at the far corner of the bar with his own fancy flower-painted glass in his hand.

'It's been a grand day, Mr Fairburn,' I murmured sotto voce.

The old man put his hand to his ear. 'What's that you say?'

'Nice warm day it's been.' My voice was like a soft breeze sighing over the marshes.

I felt a violent dig at my back. 'What the heck's the matter with you, Jim? Have you got laryngitis?'

I turned and saw the tall bald-headed figure of Dr Allinson, my medical adviser and friend. 'Hello, Harry,' I cried. 'Nice to see you.' Then I put my hand to my mouth.

But it was too late. A furious yapping issued from the manager's office. It was loud and penetrating and it went on and on.

'Damn, I forgot,' I said wearily. 'There goes Magnus again.'

'Magnus? What are you talking about?'

'Well, it's a long story.' I took another sip at my beer as the din continued from the office. It really shattered the peace of the comfortable bar and I could see the regulars fidgeting and looking out into the hallway.

Would that little dog ever forget? It seemed a long time now since Mr Beckwith, the new young manager at the Drovers', had brought Magnus in to the surgery. He had looked a little apprehensive.

'You'll have to watch him, Mr Herriot.'

'What do you mean?'

'Well, be careful. He's very vicious.'

I looked at the sleek little form, a mere brown dot on the table. He would probably turn the scale at around six pounds. And I couldn't help laughing.

'Vicious? He's not big enough, surely.'

'Don't you worry!' Mr Beckwith raised a warning finger. 'I took him to the vet in Bradford where I used to manage the White Swan and he sank his teeth into the poor chap's finger.'

'He did?'

'He certainly did! Right down to the bone! By God I've never heard such language but I couldn't blame the man. There was blood all over the place. I had to help him to put a bandage on.'

'Mm, I see.' It was nice to be told before you had been bitten and not after. 'And what was he trying to do to the dog? Must have been something pretty major.'

'It wasn't, you know. All I wanted was his nails clipped.'

'Is that all? And why have you brought him today?'

'Same thing.'

'Well honestly, Mr Beckwith,' I said. 'I think we can manage to cut his nails without bloodshed. If he'd been a Bull Mastiff or an Alsatian we might have had a problem, but I think that you and I between us can control a Miniature Dachshund.'

The Manager shook his head. 'Don't bring me into it. I'm sorry, but I'd rather not hold him, if you don't mind.'

'Why not?'

'Well, he'd never forgive me. He's a funny little dog.'

I rubbed my chin. 'But if he's as difficult as you say and you can't hold him, what do you expect me to do?'

'I don't know, really . . . maybe you could sort of dope him . . . knock him out?'

'You mean a general anaesthetic? To cut his claws . . . ?'

'It'll be the only way, I'm afraid.' Mr Beckwith stared gloomily at the tiny animal. 'You don't know him.'

It was difficult to believe but it seemed pretty obvious that this canine morsel was the boss in the Beckwith home. In my experience many dogs had occupied this position but none as small as this one. Anyway, I had no more time to waste on this nonsense.

'Look,' I said. 'I'll put a tape muzzle on his nose and I'll have this job done in a couple of minutes.' I reached behind me for the nail clippers and laid them on the table, then I unrolled a length of bandage and tied it in a loop.

'Good boy, Magnus,' I said ingratiatingly as I advanced towards him.

The little dog eyed the bandage unwinkingly until it was almost touching his nose then, with a surprising outburst of ferocity, he made a snarling leap at my hand. I felt the draught on my fingers as a row of sparkling teeth snapped shut half an inch away, but as he turned to have another go my free hand clamped on the scruff of his neck.

'Right, Mr Beckwith,' I said calmly. 'I have him now. Just pass me that bandage again and I won't be long.'

But the young man had had enough. 'Not me!' he gasped. 'I'm off!' He turned the door handle and I heard his feet scurrying along the passage.

Ah well, I thought, it was probably best. With boss dogs my primary move was usually to get the owner out of the way. It was surprising how quickly these tough guys calmed down when they found themselves alone with a no-nonsense stranger who knew how to handle them. I could recite a list who were raving tearaways in there own homes but apologetic tail-waggers once they crossed the surgery threshold. And they were all bigger than Magnus.

Retaining my firm grip on his neck I unwound another foot of bandage and as he fought furiously, mouth gaping, lips retracted like a scaled-down Siberian wolf, I slipped the loop over his nose, tightened it and tied the knot behind his ears. His mouth was now clamped shut and just to make sure, I applied a second bandage so that he was well and truly trussed.

This was when they usually packed in and I looked confidently at the dog for signs of submission. But above the encircling white coils the eyes glared furiously and from within the little frame an enraged growling issued, rising and falling like the distant droning of a thousand bees.

Sometimes a stern word or two had the effect of showing them who was boss.

'Magnus!' I barked at him. 'That's enough! Behave yourself!' I gave his neck a shake to make it clear that I wasn't kidding but the only response was a sidelong squint of pure defiance from the slightly bulging eyes.

I lifted the clippers. 'All right,' I said wearily. 'If you won't have it one way you'll have it the other.' And I tucked him under one arm, seized a paw and began to clip.

He couldn't do a thing about it. He fought and wriggled but I had him as in a vice. And as I methodically trimmed the overgrown nails, wrathful bubbles escaped on either side of the bandage along with his splutterings. If dogs could swear I was getting the biggest cursing in history.

I did my job with particular care, taking pains to keep well away from the sensitive core of the claw so that he felt nothing, but it made no difference. The indignity of being mastered for once in his life was insupportable.

Towards the conclusion of the operation I began to change my tone. I had found in the past that once dominance has been established it is quite easy to work up a friendly relationship, so I started to introduce a wheedling note.

'Good little chap,' I cooed. 'That wasn't so bad, was it?'

I laid down the clippers and stroked his head as a few more resentful bubbles forced their way round the bandage. 'All right, Magnus, we'll take your muzzle off now.' I began to loosen the knot, 'You'll feel a lot better then, won't you?'

So often it happened that when I finally removed the restraint the dog would apparently decide to let bygones be bygones and in some cases would even lick my hand. But not so with Magnus. As the last turn of bandage fell from his nose he made another very creditable attempt to bite me.

'All right, Mr Beckwith,' I called along the passage. 'You can come and get him now.'

My final memory of the visit was of the little dog turning at the top of the surgery steps and giving me a last dirty look before his master led him down the street.

It said very clearly, 'Right, mate, I won't forget you.'

That had been weeks ago but ever since that day the very sound of my voice was enough to set Magnus yapping his disapproval. At first the regulars treated it as a big joke but now they had started to look at me strangely. Maybe they thought I had been cruel to the animal or something. It was all very embarrassing because I didn't want to abandon the Drovers'; the bar was always cosy even on the coldest night and the beer very consistent.

Anyway if I had gone to another pub I would probably have started to do my talking in whispers and people would have looked at me even more strangely then.

How different it was with Mrs Hammond's Irish Setter. This started with an urgent phone call one night when I was in the bath. Helen knocked on the bathroom door and I dried off quickly and threw on my dressing gown. I ran upstairs and as soon as I lifted the receiver an anxious voice burst in my ear.

'Mr Herriot, it's Rock! He's been missing for two days and a man has just brought him back now. He found him in a wood with his foot in a gin trap. He must . . .' I heard a half sob at the end of the line. 'He must have been caught there all this time.'

'Oh. I'm sorry! Is it very bad?'

'Yes, it is.' Mrs Hammond was the wife of one of the local bank managers and a capable, sensible woman. There was a pause and I imagined her determinedly gaining control of herself. When she spoke her voice was calm.

'Yes, I'm afraid it looks as though he'll have to have his foot amputated.'

'Oh, I'm terribly sorry to hear that.' But I wasn't really surprised. A limb compressed in one of those barbarous instruments for 48 hours would be in a critical state. These traps were now mercifully illegal but in those days they often provided me with the kind of jobs I didn't want and the kind of decisions I hated to make. Did you take a limb from an uncomprehending animal to keep it alive or did you bring down the merciful but final curtain of euthanasia? I was responsible for the fact that there were several three-legged dogs and cats running around Darrowby and though they seemed happy enough and their owners still had the pleasure of their pets, the thing, for me, was clouded with sorrow.

Anyway, I would do what had to be done.

'Bring him straight round, Mrs Hammond,' I said.

Rock was a big dog but he was the lean type of Setter and seemed very light as I lifted him on to the surgery table. As my arms encircled the unresisting body I could feel the rib cage sharply ridged under the skin.

'He's lost a lot of weight,' I said.

His mistress nodded. 'It's a long time to go without food. He ate ravenously when he came in, despite his pain.'

I put a hand beneath the dog's elbow and gently lifted the leg. The vicious teeth of the trap had been clamped on the radius and ulna but what worried me was the grossly swollen state of the foot. It was at least twice its normal size.

'What do you think, Mr Herriot?' Mrs Hammond's hands twisted anxiously at the handbag which every woman seemed to bring to the surgery irrespective of the circumstances.

I stroked the dog's head. Under the light, the rich sheen of the coat glowed red and gold. 'This terrific swelling of the foot. It's partly due to inflammation but also to the fact that the circulation was pretty well cut off for the time he was in the trap. The danger is gangrene – that's when the tissue dies and decomposes.'

'I know,' she replied. 'I did a bit of nursing before I married.'

Carefully I lifted the enormous foot. Rock gazed calmly in front of him as I felt around the metacarpals and phalanges, working my way up to the dreadful wound. 'Well, it's a mess,' I said. 'But there are two good things. First, the leg isn't broken. The trap has gone right down to the bone but there is no fracture. And second and more important, the foot is still warm.'

'That's a good sign?'

'Oh yes. It means there's still some circulation. If the foot had been cold and clammy the thing would have been hopeless. I would have had to amputate.'

'You think you can save his foot, then?'

I held up my hand. 'I don't know, Mrs Hammond. As I say,

he still has some circulation but the question is how much. Some of this tissue is bound to slough off and things could look very nasty in a few days. But I'd like to try.'

I flushed out the wound with a mild antiseptic in warm water and gingerly explored the grisly depths. As I snipped away the pieces of damaged muscle and cut off the shreds and flaps of dead skin the thought was uppermost that it must be extremely unpleasant for the dog; but Rock held his head high and scarcely flinched. Once or twice he turned his head towards me enquiringly as I probed deeply and at times I felt his moist nose softly brushing my face as I bent over the foot, but that was all.

The injury seemed a desecration. There are few more beautiful dogs than an Irish Setter and Rock was a picture; sleek coated and graceful with silky feathers on legs and tail and a noble, gentle-eyed head. As the thought of how he would look without a foot drove into my mind I shook my head and turned quickly to lift the sulphanilamide powder from the trolley behind me. Thank heavens this was now available, one of the new revolutionary drugs, and I packed it deep into the wound with the confidence that it would really do something to keep down the infection. I applied a layer of gauze then a light bandage with a feeling of fatalism. There was nothing else I could do.

Rock was brought in to me every day. And every day he endured the same procedure; the removal of the dressing which was usually adhering to the wound to some degree, then the inevitable trimming of the dying tissues and the rebandaging. Yet, incredibly, he never showed any reluctant to come. Most of my patients came in very slowly and left at top speed, dragging their owners on the end of the leads; in fact some turned tail at the door, slipped their collar and sped down Trengate with their owners in hot pursuit. Dogs aren't so daft and there is doubtless a dentist's chair type of association about a vet's surgery.

Rock, however, always marched in happily with a gentle waving of his tail. In fact when I went into the waiting room and saw him sitting there he usually offered me his paw. This had always been a characteristic gesture of his but there seemed something uncanny about it when I bent over him and saw the white-swathed limb outstretched towards me.

After a week the outlook was grim. All the time the dead tissue had been sloughing and one night when I removed the dressing Mrs Hammond gasped and turned away. With her nursing training she had been very helpful, holding the foot this way and that intuitively as I worked, but tonight, she didn't want to look.

I couldn't blame her. In places the white bones of the metacarpals could be seen like the fingers of a human hand with only random strands of skin covering them.

'Is it hopeless, do you think?' she whispered, still looking away.

I didn't answer for a moment as I felt my way underneath the foot. 'It does look awful, but do you know, I think we have reached the end of the road and are going to turn the corner soon.'

'How do you mean?'

'Well, all the under surface is sound and warm. His pads are perfectly intact. And do you notice, there's no smell tonight? That's because there is no more dead stuff to cut away. I really think this foot is going to start granulating.'

She stole a look. 'And do you think those . . . bones . . . will be covered over?'

'Yes, I do.' I dusted on the faithful sulphanilamide. 'It won't be exactly the same foot as before but it will do.'

And it turned out just that way. It took a long time but the new healthy tissue worked its way upwards as though determined to prove me right and when, many months later, Rock came into the surgery with a mild attack of conjunctivitis he proferred a courteous paw as was his wont. I accepted the civility and as we shook hands I looked at the upper surface of the foot. It was hairless, smooth and shining, but it was completely healed.

'You'd hardly notice it, would you?' Mrs Hammond said.

'That's right, it's marvellous. Just this little bare patch. And he walked in without a limp.'

Mrs Hammond laughed. 'Oh, he's quite sound on that leg

now. And do you know, I really think he's grateful to you – look at him.'

I suppose the animal psychologists would say it was ridiculous even to think that the big dog realised I had done him a bit of good; that lolling-tongued open mouth, warm eyes and outstretched paw didn't mean anything like that.

Maybe they are right, but what I do know and cherish is the certainty that after all the discomforts I had put him through Rock didn't hold a thing against me.

I have to turn back to the other side of the coin to discuss Timmy Butterworth. He was a wire-haired Fox Terrier who resided in Gimber's yard, one of the little cobbled alleys off Trengate, and the only time I had to treat him was one lunch time.

I had just got out of the car and was climbing the surgery steps when I saw a little girl running along the street, waving frantically as she approached. I waited for her and when she panted up to me her eyes were wide with fright.

'Ah'm Wendy Butterworth,' she gasped. 'Me mam sent me. Will you come to our dog?'

'What's wrong with him?'

'Me mam says he's et summat!'

'Poison?'

'Ah think so.'

It was less than a hundred yards away, not worth taking the car. I broke into a trot with Wendy by my side and within seconds we were turning into the narrow archway of the 'yard.' Our feet clattered along the tunnel-like passage then we emerged into one of the unlikely scenes which had surprised me so much when I first came to Darrowby; the miniature street with its tiny crowding houses, strips of garden, bow windows looking into each other across a few feet of cobbles. But I had no time to gaze around me today because Mrs Butterworth, stout, red-faced and very flustered, was waiting for me.

'He's in 'ere, Mr Herriot!' she cried and threw wide the door of one of the cottages. It opened straight into the living room and I saw my patient sitting on the hearth rug looking somewhat thoughtful.

'What's happened, then?' I asked.

The lady clasped and unclasped her hands. 'I saw a big rat run down across t'yard yesterday and I got some poison to put down for 'im.' She gulped agitatedly. 'I mixed it in a saucer full o' porridge then somebody came to t'door and when ah came back, Timmy was just finishin' it off!'

The terrier's thoughtful expression had deepened and he ran his tongue slowly round his lips with the obvious reflection that that was the strangest porridge he had ever tasted.

I turned to Mrs Butterworth. 'Have you got the poison tin there?'

'Yes, here it is.' With a violently trembling hand she passed it to me.

I read the label. It was a well known name and the very look of it sounded a knell in my mind recalling the many dead and dying animals with which it was associated. Its active ingredient was zinc phosphide and even today with our modern drugs we are usually helpless once a dog has absorbed it.

I thumped the tin down on the table. 'We've got to make him vomit immediately! I don't want to waste time going back to the surgery – have you got any washing soda? If I push a few crystals down it'll do the trick.'

'Oh dear!' Mrs Butterworth bit her lip. 'We 'aven't such a thing in the house . . . is there anything else we could . . .'

'Wait a minute!' I looked across the table, past the piece of cold mutton, the tureen of potatoes and a jar of pickles. 'Is there any mustard in that pot?'

'Aye, it's full.'

Quickly I grabbed the pot, ran to the tap and diluted the mustard to the consistency of milk.

'Come on!' I shouted. 'Let's have him outside.'

I seized the astonished Timmy, whisked him from the rug, shot through the door and dumped him on the cobbles. Holding his body clamped tightly between my knees and his jaws close together with my left hand I poured the liquid mustard into the side of his mouth whence it trickled down to the back of his throat. There was nothing he could do about it, he had to swallow the disgusting stuff, and when about a teaspoon had gone down I released him.

After a single affronted glare at me the terrier began to retch then to lurch across the smooth stones. Within seconds he had deposited his stolen meal in a quiet corner.

'Do you think that's the lot?' I asked.

'That's it,' Mrs Butterworth replied firmly. 'I'll fetch a brush and shovel.'

Timmy, his short tail tucked down, slunk back into the house and I watched him as he took up his favourite position on the hearthrug. He coughed, snorted, pawed at his mouth, but he just couldn't rid himself of that dreadful taste; and increasingly it was obvious that he had me firmly tagged as the cause of all the trouble. As I left he flashed me a glance which said quite plainly, 'You rotten swine!'

There was something in that look which reminded me of Magnus, from the Drovers', but the first sign that Timmy, unlike Magnus, wasn't going to be satisfied with vocal disapproval came within a few days. I was strolling meditatively down Trengate when a white missile issued from Gimber's Yard, nipped me on the ankle and disappeared as silently as he had come. I caught only a glimpse of the little form speeding on his short legs down the passage.

I laughed. Fancy him remembering! But it happened again and again and I realised that the little dog was indeed lying in wait for me. He never actually sank his teeth into me – it was a gesture more than anything – but it seemed to satisfy him to see me jump as he snatched briefly at my calf or trouser leg. I was a sitting bird because I was usually deep in thought as I walked down the street.

And when I thought about it, I couldn't blame Timmy. Looking at it from his point of view he had been sitting by his fireside digesting an unusual meal and minding his own business when a total stranger had pounced on him, hustled him from the comfort of his rug and poured mustard into him. It was outrageous and he just wasn't prepared to let the matter rest there.

For my part there was a certain satisfaction in being the object of a vendetta waged by an animal who would have been dead without my services. And unpleasantly dead because the victims of phosphorus poisoning had to endure long days and sometimes weeks of jaundice, misery and creeping debility before the inevitable end.

So I suffered the attacks with good grace. But when I remembered I crossed to the other side of the street to avoid the hazard of Gimber's Yard; and from there I could often see the little white dog peeping round the corner waiting for the moment when he would make me pay for that indignity.

Timmy, I knew, was one who would never forget.

●

## *Couplet for a Dog's Collar*

I am his Highness' Dog at Kew;
Pray tell me Sir, whose Dog are you?

**Alexander Pope**

# *Groucho and Me*

## Groucho Marx

*Come back next Thursday with a Specimen of your Money*

As I get further along with this chronicle of trivia, it's beginning to dawn on me that writing is an extremely tough racket. In my day, I've written many allegedly comic pieces for magazines and newspapers, but to keep going for enough pages to fill a book is a new experience for me. I used to play golf daily and badly, take long walks with two expensive, flea-bitten poodles and even ride a horse occasionally. It seems to me that I don't do anything now but write. And anybody who has ever written knows that writing requires thinking. And everybody knows that thinking is easily the most distasteful way of spending the day. But I keep plugging along. I must say the subject of this book has never seemed to me the most entrancing topic in the world. I'm just curious now to learn whether I have the stamina and will power to see it through to the end.

Some time ago I read Stefan Zweig's *Life of Balzac*. The only way Balzac sustained himself through his lifetime of writing was to have his valet chain him to the bedpost at night and unchain him in the morning. To keep himself awake, he would drink twenty or thirty cups of coffee. Benzedrine and the other more potent stimulants had not yet been discovered. He finally died of coffee poisoning. There is a medical name for this, but I don't remember what it is, and I'm not going to phone and ask my doctor about it. If I do, he'll charge me for a visit.

I don't know how it is in the hinterlands, but in Beverly Hills the old country doctor with his horse and buggy and his little black bag has gone the way of the horse and buggy. I saw a man leaving my country club yesterday in a chauffeur-driven El Dorado Cadillac. As he rode away, I asked the parking attendant what business this man was in. I knew he must be a rich man, because a Cadillac and a chauffeur in these days of virtual tax confiscation can be a very expensive mode of travel. The attendant said the man was a doctor.

'A doctor!' I exclaimed. 'And he can afford a Cadillac and a chauffeur? What kind of a doctor is he?'

'He's an allergist,' the boy answered.

I guess most of you know what an allergist is. If not, I'll describe one to you briefly. Let's say, for example, that your skin turns slightly blue when you eat cucumbers. You, being the average man (or jerk, as the case may be), wake up one morning, look in the mirror and discover that your entire carcass is covered in blue patches. A pretty picture, I must say.

Naturally, you have no idea what's wrong with you. All you know is, this is not the way Mother Nature intended you to look. Alarmed, you feverishly call up your family physician. He is busy taking X-rays of his nurse, who by an odd coincidence turns out to be a very beautiful girl with precisely the same measurements as Sophia Loren. You say, 'Doctor, what shall I do? I'm turning blue all over.'

'Hmmm,' he answers. 'Blue, eh?'

While phoning, you're shivering in the cold bedroom. You know you should get your clothes on, but the sight of your blue body fascinates you.

You repeat, 'Well, Doc, what should I do?'

The doctor says, 'Drop by tomorrow!'

You say, 'Doc, you don't understand. I told you I'm turning blue. I must see you immediately. I'll be over there in twenty minutes. Is that OK?'

The doctor is not crazy about this impending intrusion, for he isn't through taking the nurse's X-rays. Also, he has to move fast because his wife has promised to look in on him some time that morning. You're still standing there naked, and now in addition to turning blue, your body is beginning to acquire ridges. You're beginning to look like a relief map of northern

Greece. The doctor, meanwhile, anxious to get back to his X-rays, has solved his side of the problem by hanging up. Not only by hanging up, but by leaving the receiver off the hook.

You quickly get dressed, and after a hasty breakfast of nothing, you rush to your doctor's office, hoping against hope that you will arrive there before you croak. As you enter the office, the nurse is putting the receiver back on the hook. The doctor is pretty annoyed at your showing up so quickly, and the fact that you still owe him eighty-five dollars from last month doesn't help bridge the gulf between you.

'What's the matter with you?' he asks querulously.

'Oh nothing much,' you reply sarcastically. 'I'm just turning blue all over.'

'Blue, eh? Well, take off your clothes and we'll have a look at you.'

The 'we' puzzles you. Does he mean you and the doctor, you and the nurse or the doctor and the nurse?

'Sit up!' he orders. After eyeing you for a few minutes he proceeds to tap you sharply with a small hammer. Sitting on a cold bench, naked, with basic low blood pressure – this is not the easiest way to keep warm. 'Hmmm,' he says. 'Something is definitely the matter with you. You're blue all over.'

Now there's a hot piece of news! Your gardener (to whom you also owe money) could have told you that.

Meanwhile, the nurse is getting pretty impatient, and at a nod from her the doctor says, 'I'll get right to the point. I can't do anything for you. What you need is an allergist.'

'An allergist? I thought *you* were a doctor,' you reply.

'I *am* a doctor, but this is not my field. Let me explain it to you. There is evidently somthing that doesn't agree with you.'

You say, 'Let's keep my wife out of this.' (This isn't much of a joke; but you must remember, he isn't much of a doctor.)

'No,' he shakes his head impatiently. 'I mean there's something you *eat* that doesn't agree with you.'

'There is nothing I eat that agrees with me – but what's that got to do with my turning blue?'

'We'll have to take some tests to find out what you should avoid.'

You think to yourself, 'What I should avoid is this quack.' But since you're naked you are obviously in no position to defend yourself, so you decide to let sleeping dogs lie.

As soon as you get your clothes on, the doctor hands you a card. It reads, Dr Hugo Schmaltz, Allergist.

'Doctor Schmaltz is a leader in his field,' he says. 'A good man . . . world-famous . . . Vienna, you know. Oh, by the way, be sure to tell him I sent you.' You know what that means. It means he's getting a cut of whatever Schmaltz soaks you.

Sophia Loren then makes an immediate appointment for you to see Dr Schmaltz.

Ten minutes later you're over at Schmaltz's Allergy Emporium. The doc is about five feet three, and his Adam's apple is almost the same size as his head. From his looks, you're sure he's wanted in Vienna. Not by his former patients, but by the police.

'Well, Mr Marx,' he says, 'what brings you here?' (I forgot to tell you – your name is Marx. So is mine, by the way.)

Now there's a great beginning for a world-famous allergist!

'Why don't you take off your clothes and we'll have a look at you.' To idle away the time while you're undressing, he asks, 'What seems to be the trouble?'

'Oh, nothing much,' you chuckle. 'I'm just turning blue all over.'

'Blue? Hmmmm.'

This news seems to unsettle him. Apparently some of his past experiences with blue patients haven't been happy ones. Then he fools you. You thought he was going to bring out the little hammer. Not Schmaltz. He's from Vienna. He brings out a stethoscope. He doesn't use it on you. He just hangs it around his neck. He probably thinks this makes him look more like a doctor. 'What have you been eating?' he asks.

'Well,' you begin, 'I had nothing for breakfast . . .'

'What did you have for dinner last night?' he interrupts.

'Let's see now. There was Norman Krasna and his wife, Mr and Mrs Nunnally Johnson and the Sheekmans,' you reply.

His tone grows sharper. 'Maybe I don't make myself clear,' he says. 'Tell me everything you *ate* last night.'

'Oh,' you say. 'Well, I had spaghetti and meat-balls, some frozen fish-sticks and a cucumber salad.'

'And how often do you have cucumber salad?' he inquires. But before you can answer, he starts walking around the room, humming to himself, 'Cucumbers and fish-sticks. Cucumbers and fish-sticks.' He's probably thinking it's not a bad idea for a Calypso song. He wheels on you sharply. 'When can you come again?'

'When can I come *again*?' you exclaim. 'I'm here right now!'

'*Ja*,' he says. Apparently this is the first time he realises you are in his office.

'Why can't you tell me what's wrong with me?' you insist.

He looks at you pityingly. 'Mr Marx, it don't go that fast. Already first we're going to have to take some allergy tests. You may have to come every day for a month.'

'Every day!' you repeat. 'Didn't you tell me it was cucumbers?'

'Not at all,' he replies. '*You* said you ate cucumbers, but that don't mean that from cucumbers you are turning blue.'

This makes sense to you. Everyone knows that cucumbers are green. But you continue hopefully, 'Well, I'll just cut out cucumbers.'

'No,' he says patiently. 'You don't understand. It could be the cucumbers. On the other hand, it could be also the meat-balls.' Then he laughs heartily. 'It could even the fish-sticks be. So! You see what we are up against?'

It's always embarrassing to ask a doctor what his fee is, but if you are going to have to make daily visits to Joe Allergy, you'd better find out how much you're going to be rooked. You decide that if it's going to be more than twenty-five bucks a day, you'll just have to remain blue. In your mind you rapidly multiply thirty days by twenty-five dollars a throw. Seven hundred and fifty dollars a month! The price of a pretty good second-hand car. Clearing your throat and averting your gaze, you ask, 'Doc, what do you get for each visit?'

'Well,' he says, 'my regular fee is fifty dollars, but since you have to come every day for a month, we'll make it twenty-five dollars.'

'Now just a moment,' you say. 'Suppose you find out by the third day what's wrong with me? Why do I have to come every day for a month?'

'Don't you worry,' he replies happily. 'It'll take a month all right!'

I hope this will explain why Dr Schmaltz was seen leaving the country club in his chauffeur-driven El Dorado Brougham Cadillac.

●

'Yes, it's true. You were adopted.'

HENRY MARTIN

## *The Rabbit*

The rabbit has a charming face:
Its private life is a disgrace.
I really dare not name to you.
The awful things that rabbits do;
Things that your paper never prints –
You only mention them in hints.
They have such lost, degraded souls
No wonder they inhabit holes;
When such depravity is found
It can only live underground.

**Anon. (20th century)**

## *Part Four*

# YOUNG THINGS

There was an old maid of Duluth
Who wept when she thought of her youth,
  And the glorious chances
  She'd missed at school dances
And once in a telephone booth.

**Anon.**

# *The Story-Teller*

## Saki

It was a hot afternoon, and the railway carriage was correspondingly sultry, and the next stop was at Templecombe, nearly an hour ahead. The occupants of the carriage were a small girl, and a smaller girl, and a small boy. An aunt belonging to the children occupied one corner seat, and the further corner seat on the opposite side was occupied by a bachelor who was a stranger to their party, but the small girls and small boy emphatically occupied the compartment. Both the aunt and the children were conversational in a limited, persistent way, reminding one of the attentions of a housefly that refused to be discouraged. Most of the aunt's remarks seemed to begin with 'Don't,' and nearly all of the children's remarks began with 'Why?' The bachelor said nothing out loud.

'Don't, Cyril, don't,' exclaimed the aunt, as the small boy began smacking the cushions of the seat, producing a cloud of dust at each blow.

'Come and look out of the window,' she added.

The child moved reluctantly to the window. 'Why are those sheep being driven out of that field?' he asked.

'I expect they are being driven to another field where there is more grass,' said the aunt weakly.

'But there is lots of grass in that field,' protested the boy; 'there's nothing else but grass there. Aunt, there's lot of grass in that field.'

'Perhaps the grass in the other field is better,' suggested the aunt fatuously.

'Why is it better?' came the swift, inevitable question.

'Oh, look at those cows!' exclaimed the aunt. Nearly every field along the line had contained cows or bullocks, but she spoke as though she was drawing attention to a rarity.

'Why is the grass in the other field better?' persisted Cyril.

The frown on the bachelor's face was deepening into a scowl. He was a hard, unsympathetic man, the aunt decided in her mind. She was utterly unable to come to any satisfactory decision about the grass in the other field.

The smaller girl created a diversion by beginning to recite 'On the Road to Mandalay.' She only knew the first line, but she put her limited knowledge to the fullest possible use. She repeated the line over and over again in a dreamy but resolute and very audible voice; it seemed to the bachelor as though someone had had a bet with her that she could not repeat the line aloud two thousand times without stopping. Whoever it was who had made the wager was likely to lose his bet.

'Come over here and listen to a story,' said the aunt, when the bachelor had looked twice at her and once at the communication cord.

The children moved listlessly towards the aunt's end of the carriage. Evidently her reputation as a story-teller did not rank high in their estimation.

In a low, confidential voice, interrupted at frequent intervals by loud, petulant questions from her listeners, she began an unenterprising and deplorably uninteresting story about a little girl who was good, and made friends with every one on account of her goodness, and was finally saved from a mad bull by a number of rescuers who admired her moral character.

'Wouldn't they have saved her if she hadn't been good?' demanded the bigger of the small girls. It was exactly the question that the bachelor had wanted to ask.

'Well, yes,' admitted the aunt lamely, 'but I don't think they would have run quite so fast to her help if they had not liked her so much.'

'It's the stupidest story I've ever heard,' said the bigger of the small girls, with immense conviction.

'I didn't listen after the first bit, it was so stupid,' said Cyril.

The smaller girl made no actual comment on the story, but

she had long ago recommended a murmured repetition of her favourite line.

'You don't seem to be a success as a story-teller,' said the bachelor suddenly from his corner.

The aunt bristled in instant defence at his unexpected attack.

'It's a very difficult thing to tell stories that children can both understand and appreciate,' she said stiffly.

'I don't agree with you,' said the bachelor.

'Perhaps *you* would like to tell them a story,' was the aunt's retort.

'Tell us a story,' demanded the bigger of the small girls.

'Once upon a time,' began the bachelor, 'there was a little girl called Bertha, who was extraordinarily good.'

The children's momentarily-aroused interest began at once to flicker; all stories seemed dreadfully alike, no matter who told them.

'She did all that she was told, she was always thoughful, she kept her clothes clean, ate milk puddings as though they were jam tarts, learned her lessons perfectly, and was polite in her manners.'

'Was she pretty?' asked the bigger of the small girls.

'Not as pretty as any of you,' said the bachelor, 'but she was horribly good.'

There was a wave of reaction in favour of the story; the word horrible in connection with goodness was a novelty that commended itself. It seemed to introduce a ring of truth that was absent from the aunt's tales of infant life.

'She was so good,' continued the bachelor, 'that she won several medals for goodness, which she always wore, pinned on to her dress. There was a medal for obedience, another medal for punctuality, and a third for good behaviour. They were large metal medals and they clicked against one another as she walked. No other child in the town where she lived had as many as three medals, so everybody knew that she must be an extra good child.'

'Horribly good,' quoted Cyril.

'Everybody talked about her goodness, and the Prince of the country got to hear about it, and he said that as she was so very good she might be allowed once a week to walk in his park, which was just outside the town. It was a beautiful park, and no children were ever allowed in it, so it was a great honour for Bertha to be allowed to go there.'

'Were there any sheep in the park?' demanded Cyril.

'No,' said the bachelor, 'there were no sheep.'

'Why weren't there any sheep?' came the inevitable question arising out of that answer.

The aunt permitted herself a smile, which might almost have been described as a grin.

'There were no sheep in the park,' said the bachelor, 'because the Prince's mother had once had a dream that her son would either be killed by a sheep or else by a clock falling on him. For that reason the prince never kept a sheep in his park or a clock in his palace.'

The aunt suppressed a gasp of admiration.

'Was the Prince killed by a sheep or by a clock?' asked Cyril.

'He is still alive, so we can't tell whether the dream will come true,' said the bachelor unconcernedly; 'anyway, there were no sheep in the park, but there were lots of little pigs running all over the place.'

'What colour were they?'

'Black with white faces, white with black spots, black all over, grey with white patches, and some were white all over.'

The story-teller paused to let a full idea of the park's treasures sink into the children's imaginations; then he resumed:

'Bertha was rather sorry to find that there were no flowers in the park. She had promised her aunts, with tears in her eyes, that she would not pick any of the kind Prince's flowers, and she had meant to keep her promise, so of course it made her feel silly to find that there were no flowers to pick.'

'Why weren't there any flowes?'

'Because the pigs had eaten them all,' said the bachelor promptly. 'The gardeners had told the Prince that you couldn't have pigs and flowers, so he decided to have pigs and no flowers.'

There was a murmur of approval at the excellence of the

Prince's decision; so many people would have decided the other way.

'There were lots of other delightful things in the park. There were ponds with gold and blue and green fish in them, and trees with beautiful parrots that said clever things at a moment's notice, and humming birds that hummed all the popular tunes of the day. Bertha walked up and down and enjoyed herself immensely, and thought to herself: 'If I were not so extraordinarily good I should not have been allowed to come into this beautiful park and enjoy all that there is to be seen in it,' and her three medals clinked against one another as she walked and helped to remind her how very good she really was. Just then an enormous wolf came prowling into the park to see if it could catch a fat little pig for its supper.'

'What colour was it?' asked the children, amid an immediate quickening of interest.

'Mud-colour all over, with a black tongue and pale grey eyes that gleamed with unspeakable ferocity. The first thing that it saw in the park was Bertha; her pinafore was so spotlessly white and clean that it could be seen from a great distance. Bertha saw the wolf and saw that it was stealing towards her, and she began to wish that she had never been allowed to come into the park. She ran as hard as she could, and the wolf came after her with huge leaps and bounds. She managed to reach a shrubbery of myrtle bushes and she hid herself in one of the thickest of the bushes. The wolf came sniffing among the branches, its black tongue lolling out of its mouth and its pale grey eyes glaring with rage. Bertha was terribly frightened, and thought to herself: "If I had not been so extraordinarily good I should have been safe in the town at this moment." However, the scent of the myrtle was so strong that the wolf could not sniff out where Bertha was hiding, and the bushes were so thick that he might have hunted about in them for a long time without catching sight of her, so he thought he might as well go off and catch a little pig instead. Bertha was trembling very much at having the wolf prowling and sniffing so near her, and as she trembled the medal for obedience clinked against the medals for good conduct and punctuality. The wolf was just moving away when he heard the sounds of the medals clinking and stopped to listen; they clinked again in a bush quite near him. He dashed into the bush, his pale grey eyes gleaming with ferocity and triumph, and dragged Bertha out and devoured her to the last morsel. All that was left of her were her shoes, bits of clothing, and the three medals for goodness.'

'Were any of the little pigs killed?'

'No, they all escaped.'

'The story began badly,' said the smaller of the small girls, 'but it had a beautiful ending.'

'It is the most beautiful story that I ever heard,' said the bigger of the small girls, with immense decision.

'It is the *only* beautiful story I have ever heard,' said Cyril.

A dissentient opinion came from the aunt.

'A most improper story to tell to young children! You have undermined the effect of years of careful teaching.'

'At any rate,' said the bachelor, collecting his belongings preparatory to leaving the carriage, 'I kept them quiet for ten minutes, which was more than you were able to do.'

'Unhappy woman!' he observed to himself as he walked down the platform of Templecombe station; 'for the next six months or so those children will assail her in public with demands for an improper story!'

●

There was a young man of Montrose,
Who had pockets in none of his clothes.
When asked by his lass
Where he carried his brass,
He said: 'Darling, I pay through the nose.'

**Arnold Bennett**

# *The Growing Pains of Adrian Mole*

## Sue Townsend

**Monday June 21st**
*Longest Day. New Moon*
Mr Scruton summoned the whole school into the assembly hall this morning. Even the teachers who are atheists were forced to attend.

I was dead nervous. It's ages since I broke a school rule but Scruton makes you feel dead guilty somehow. When the doors were closed and the whole school was lined up in rows Scruton nodded to Mrs Figges, who was sitting at the piano, and she started playing 'Hallelujah!'

Some of the fifth years (including Pandora) sang along using different words: 'Hallelujah! What's it to you?' etc. It was quite impressive. Though I thought it was time that the blind piano tuner called again.

When the singing stopped and Mrs Figges was still, Mr Scruton walked up to his lectern, paused, and then said, 'Today is a day that will go down in history.' He paused long enough for a rumour to travel along the rows that he was resigning, then he shouted, 'Quiet!' and continued, 'Today at three minutes to nine a future King of England was born.' All the girls, apart from Pandora, (she is a republican) said, 'Ooh! Lady Di's 'ad it!'

Claire Neilson shouted: 'How much did he weigh?'

Mr Scruton smiled and ignored her.

Pandora shouted, 'How much will he *cost*?' and Mr Scruton suddenly developed good hearing and ordered her out of the assembly hall.

Poor Pandora, her face was as red as the Russian flag as she walked along the rows to the exit door, when she passed me I tried to give her a supportive smile, but it must have come out wrong because she whispered, 'Still leering at me, Adrian?'

Mr Scruton dismissed the school after giving us a talk on what a good job the Royal Family do for British exports.

Went to bed early; it had been a long day.

**Tuesday June 22nd**

The new prince left the hospital today. My father is hoping that he will be called George, after him. My mother said that it's time the Royal Family came up to date and called the Prince Brett or Jason.

Scotland are out of the World Cup. They drew 2–2 with Russia. My father called the Russian team 'those Commie bastards'. He was not a bit gracious in defeat.

**Wednesday June 23rd**

Pandora has been put into isolation at school. She is working at a desk outside Scruton's office. I left the following note on her peg in the cloakroom:

> Pandora,
> A short note to say that I admired your spirited stand on Monday.
> From Adrian Mole, your ex-lover
> P.S. My mother is with child.

**Thursday June 24th**
*Midsummer Day (Quarter Day)*
Found a note on my peg at break this morning.

> Adrian,
> We were never lovers so it was inaccurate, indeed libellous,

of you to sign your note 'ex-lover'. However, I thank you for your note of support.

Pandora

P.S. I am shocked to learn that your mother is *enceinte*. Tell her to ring the Clinic.

**Friday June 25th**

My thing is 14cm extended and about 3cm in its unwoken state. I am dead worried. Donkey Dawkins of 5P says his thing comes off the end of a ruler, yet he is only a week older than me.

**Saturday June 26th**

It was with great pleasure that I saw Mr Roy Hattersley on television tonight. Once again I was struck by his obvious sincerity and good vocabulary. Mr Hattersley was predicting that there will be an early election. He denied that Mr Michael Foot is too scruffy to be the next Prime Minister.

**Sunday June 27th**
*Third After Trinity*
I can't go on with this charade of churchgoing every Sunday. I will have to tell Grandma that I have become an agnostic atheist. If there *is* a God then He/She must know that I am a hypocrite. If there isn't a God then, of course, it doesn't matter.

**Monday June 28th**
*Moon's First Quarter*
Bert rang me when I got home from school to bellow that Social Services had paid for him to have a phone installed in his pensioner's bungalow. Bert told me that he had already phoned one of his daughters in Melbourne, Australia, and Queenie had phoned her eldest son in Ontario, Canada. They had listened to

Dial-a-Disc, the Recipe for the Day, the Weather Forecast, the Cricket News, and they were both looking forward to listening to the GPO's Bedtime Story. I pointed out to Bert that he would have to pay for each phone call he made, but he laughed his wheezy laugh and said, 'I shall probably be a gonner before the bill comes in.' (Bert is nearly ninety.)

**Tuesday June 29th**

Usual last-minute discussion about where we are going for our summer holiday. My father said, 'It'll probably be our last. This time next year we'll have the nipper.' My mother got dead mad, she said that having a baby was not going to restrict her. She said that if she felt like walking in the Hindu Kush next year, then she would strap the baby on her back to go.

The Hindu Kush! She moans if she has to walk to the bus stop.

I suggested the Lake District. I wanted to see if living there for a bit would help my poetry.

My father suggested Skegness. My mother suggested Greece. Nobody could agree, so we each wrote our choice on a scrap of old till roll and put them into a Tupperware gravy maker. We didn't trust each other to make the draw so my mother went and fetched Mrs Singh.

Mrs Singh and all the little Singhs came and stood in our kitchen. Mrs Singh asked, 'Why are you having this procedure, Mrs Mole? Can't your husband decide?' My mother explained that Mr Mole had no superior status in our house. Mrs Singh looked shocked, but she drew a piece of paper out of the hat. It said 'Skegness'. Worse luck!

Mrs Singh excused herself, saying that she must get back to prepare her husband's meal. As she left I noticed my father glance wistfully at her in her pretty sari and jewelled sandals.

I also noticed him looking sadly at my mother in her overalls and ankle boots. My mother said, 'That poor downtrodden woman.'

My father sighed and said, 'Yes.'

**Wednesday June 30th**

My mother wants to move. She wants to sell the house that I have lived in all my life. She said that we will need more room 'for the baby'. How stupid can you get? Babies hardly take any space at all. They are only about twenty-one inches long.

**Thursday July 1st**
*Dominion Day (Canada)*
Nigel has arranged for me to have a blind date with Sharon Botts. I am meeting her at the roller-skating rink on Saturday. I am dead nervous. I don't know how to roller-skate – let alone make love.

**Friday July 2nd**

Borrowed Nigel's disco-skates and practised skating on the pavement in our cul-de-sac. I was OK so long as I had a privet hedge to grab at, but I dreaded skating past the open-plan gardens where there is nothing to hold on to.

I wanted to wear my skates in the house so that I would develop confidence, but my father moaned about the marks the wheels made on the cushion floor in the kitchen.

**Saturday July 3rd**

*12.15 p.m.* Got up at 6 a.m. for more roller-skating practice. Mr O'Leary shouted abuse because of the early morning noise, so I went to the little kids' play park and practised there, but I had to give up. There was so much broken glass and dog muck lying about that I feared for the ballbearings in the skates. I waited for the greengrocer's to open, bought a pound of grapes, went home, had a bath, washed my hair and cut my toenails etc. Then I put my entire wardrobe of clothes on to the bed and tried to decide what to wear.

It was a pitiful collection. By the time I had eliminated my school uniform I was left with: three pairs of flared jeans (FLARES! Yuk! Yuk! Nobody wears flares except the worst kind of moron), two shirts, both with long pointed collars (LONG POINTS! Yuk!), four of Grandma's handknitted jumpers (HAND-KNITTED! Ugh!). The only possible clothes were my bottle-green elephant cords and my khaki army sweater. But which shoes? I had left my trainers at school and I can't wear my formal wedding shoes to a roller-skating rink, can I?

At 10.30 I rang Nigel and asked him what youths wore at roller-skating rinks. He said, 'They wear red satin side vent running shorts, sleeveless satin vests, white knee socks, Sony Walkman earphones and one gold earring.' I thanked him, put the phone down and went and had another look at my clothes.

The nearest I could get were my black PE shorts, my white string vest and my grey knee socks. I am the only person in the world not to have a Sony Walkman and I haven't had my ears pierced so I couldn't manage those two items, but I hope that Sharon Bott won't mind too much.

Do I go in my shorts etc. or do I change when I get to the rink? And how will I know which girl is Sharon Bott? I've only seen her in school uniform and in my experience girls are unrecognisable when they are in civilian clothes.

Must stop, it's time to go.

*6 p.m.* That's the first and last time I go roller-skating. Sharon Bott is an expert. She went whizzing off at 40 mph, only stopping now and again to do the splits in mid-air.

She sometimes slowed down to say, 'Let go of the barrier, Dumbo,' but she didn't stay long enough for me to divert her into having a longer conversation. When it was time for the under-twelves to monopolise the rink, she sped to the barrier and helped me into the coffee bar. We had a Coke then I clumped off to the cloakroom to get the grapes. When I gave her them she said, 'Why have you bought me grapes? I'm not poorly.' I dropped a hint by looking knowingly at her figure in its lycra body stocking and miniskirt but then the roller disco started and she sped off to do wild disco dancing on her skates.

She was soon surrounded by tall skated youths in satin shorts so I staggered off to get changed.

I rang Nigel when I got home. I complained that Sharon Bott was a dead loss. He said that Sharon Bott had already rung him to complain that I had showed her up by dressing in my school PE kit.

Nigel said that he is giving up matchmaking.

**Sunday July 4th**

*Fourth After Trinity. American Independence Day*

I was just starting to get my Sunday dinner when Bert Baxter rang and asked me to go round urgently. I bolted my spaghetti bolognese down as quickly as I could and ran round to Bert's.

Sabre, the vicious Alsatian, was standing at the door looking worried. As a precaution I gave him a dog choc and hurried into the bungalow. Bert was sitting in the living room in his wheelchair, the television was switched off so I knew something serious had happened. He said, 'Queenie's had a bad turn.' I went into the tiny bedroom. Queenie was lying in the big saggy bed looking gruesome (she hadn't put her artificial cheeks or lips on). She said, 'You're a good lad to come round, Adrian.' I asked her what was wrong. She said, 'I've been having pains like red hot needles in my chest.'

Bert interrupted, 'You said the pains were like red-hot knives five minutes ago!'

I asked Bert if he had called the doctor. He said he hadn't because Queenie was frightened of doctors. I rang my mother and asked for her advice. She said she'd come round.

While we waited for her I made a cup of tea and fed Sabre and made Bert a beetroot sandwich.

My mother and father came and took over. My mother phoned for an ambulance. It was a good job they did because while it was coming Queenie went a bit strange and started talking about ration books and stuff.

Bert held her hand and called her a 'daft old bat.'

The ambulance men were just shutting the doors when Queenie shouted out, 'Fetch me pot of rouge. I'm not going until I've got me rouge.' I ran into the bedroom and looked on the dressing table. The top was covered in pots and hair nets and hairpins and china dishes and lace mats and photos of babies and weddings. I found the rouge in a little drawer and took it to Queenie. My mother went off in the ambulance and me and my father stayed behind to comfort Bert. Two hours later my mother rang from the hospital to say that Queenie had had a stroke and would be in hospital for ages.

Bert said, 'What am I going to do without my girl to help me?'

Girl! Queenie is seventy-eight.

Bert wouldn't come home with us. He is scared that the council will take his bungalow away from him.

**Monday July 5th**
*Independence Day Holiday (USA)*
Queenie can't speak. She is sort of awake but she can't move her mouth muscles. My mother has been round at Bert's all day cleaning and cooking. My father is going to call in every day on his way home from the canal. I have promised to take horrible Sabre for his morning and evening walks.

**Tuesday July 7th**
*Full Moon*
Bert's social worker, Katie Bell, has been to see Bert. She wants Bert to go back into the Alderman Cooper Sunshine Home temporarily. Bert said he 'would prefer death to that morgue.'

Katie Bell is coming round to see us tomorrow. She is checking Bert's lie that my mother and father and me are providing twenty-four hour care for him. Queenie is still very poorly.

**Wednesday July 7th**

Katie Bell is a strange woman. She talks (and looks) a bit like

Rick Lemon. She was wearing a donkey jacket and denim jeans and she had long greasy hair parted down the middle. Her nose is long and pointed (from poking into other people's business my father said). She sat in our lounge rolling a cigarette in one hand and taking notes with the other.

She said Bert was stubborn and suffering from slight senile dementia and that what he needed was to see a consultant psychogeriatrician. My mother got dead mad and shouted, 'What he needs is a day- and a night-nurse.' Katie Bell went red and said, 'Day and night care is prohibitively expensive.'

My father asked how much it would cost to put an old person in an old people's home. Katie Bell said, 'It costs about two hundred pounds a week.'

My father shouted, 'Give me two hundred pounds a week and I'll move in and look after the old bugger.'

Katie Bell said, 'I can't relocate funds, Mr Mole.' As she was going she said, 'Look, I don't like the system any more than you do. I know it stinks, but what can I do?'

My mother said, 'You could wash your hair, dear, you'd feel much better without it straggling around your face.'

**Thursday July 8th**

I left a note on Pandora's peg today. It said:

> Pandora,
> Queenie Baxter is in hospital after a stroke. Bert is on his own in the bungalow. I am going round and doing what I can, but it would be nice if you could visit him for a bit. He is dead sad. Have you got any photos of Blossom?
> Yours, as ever,
> Adrian

**Friday July 9th**

A brilliant day today. School broke up for eight fabbo weeks.

Then something *even better* happened tonight.

I was in the middle of ironing Bert's giant underpants when Pandora walked into the living room. She was carrying a jar of home-pickled beetroot. I was transfixed. She gets more beautiful every day. Bert cheered up no end. He sent me off to make some tea. I could hardly keep my hands still. I felt as if I'd had an electric shock. I looked yearningly at Pandora as I handed her her tea. And she looked yearning back at me!!!!!!!!

We sat around looking at photos of Blossom, Pandora's ex-pony. Bert droned on about ponies and horses he had known when he was an ostler.

At 9.30 I washed Bert, sat him on the commode and then put him to bed. We sat by the electric coal fire until he started snoring, then we fell into each other's arms with little sighs and moans. We stayed like that until Bert's clock struck 10 p.m. Sex didn't cross my mind once. I just felt dead calm and comfortable.

On the way home I asked Pandora when she realised that she still loved me. She said, 'When I saw you ironing those horrible underpants. Only a superior type of youth could have done it.'

It has just been on the news that a man has been found in the Queen's bedroom. Radio Four said that the man was an intruder and was previously unknown to the Queen. My father said: 'That's her story.'

●

*'Of course, quads were quite a shock at first.'*

*'Look, Dad, I've made the Mary Rose out of matches.'*

# *Unreliable Memoirs*

## Clive James

Whatever lay beyond the back fence, I was always tunnelling towards it. The back patch was the site of my unflagging efforts to get back to the womb by digging into the earth. I started this at quite an early age, attaining more proficiency as time went on. My early burrows were simple dug-outs roofed over with box tops, after which the earth was heaped back on. There was just room for me. I would persaude my mother to cover up the entrance and leave me down there all afternoon. It didn't matter if the thing collapsed – it was only a few inches of dirt. Older children had been known to try the same trick in sand dunes, with fatal results. She probably reasoned that it was better to let me indulge these fantasies where she could keep an eye on me.

Over the next few years, the back patch started looking like the Ypres Salient. I would dig complicated networks of trenches, roof them over, and continue tunnelling from inside, honey-combing the clay all the way down to the water table. Other boys in the street were fascinated. It became known that I was taking my Donald Duck comics down there and reading them by torchlight. They, too, turned up with armfuls of comics. Suddenly I had friends. I had stumbled on one of the secrets of leadership – start something, then let people know you are doing them a favour by bringing them in on it. Candidates for my tunnel club had to go through a probationary period of hovering on the outskirts. It was like being put up for the Garrick. Finally half the small boys in the district were spending the whole weekend somewhere under our back yard. Similar scenes must have occurred on the night of the Great

Escape from Stalug Luft III. I overdid it when I started letting the little kids down there. Little kids, I should have known, ruin things. Geoffrey Teichmann was only about four years old. Crawling somewhere down around Level 7 off Shaft 4, he brushed against one of the fruit-case slats I used for pit-props. The whole system fell on him. Parents arrived from everywhere to dig the little twerp out. That was the end of that.

But my new-found acceptability was strictly a local phenomenon. School was a still a nightmare. I went to Kogarah Infants' School and then to Kogarah Primary. They were both in the same place, near Kogarah station, more than a mile away on the trolley bus. The fare was a penny. The trolley bus went down Rocky Point Road, through a shopping centre called the Bundy, then turned left to cut across Prince's Highway and climb over the hill to the station, where it either turned around at the Loop or went on to Rockdale. There were shops at the Loop, including Parry's Milk Bar, the centre of local night life for years to come. Being bought a fruit sundae in Parry's late at night was pretty well the most luxurious thing that could happen to you.

Two minutes' walk up the hill from the Loop was the school. I could make that two minutes last an hour – sometimes a whole day. If it had not been for another boy called McGowan, I would have been cast as the school's problem child. Luckily McGowan was so disturbed that I seemed unobtrusive by comparison. A ginger shambles, McGowan wore glasses with one lens covered up by brown sticky paper, presumably to correct a fault of vision. He screamed without provocation, frothed at the mouth, bit pieces out of other children and kicked teachers in the stomach. In the playground he would run at the supervising teacher while her back was turned, so that he would be going at full speed when she wheeled at the sound of his running footsteps. He was thus able to get plenty of force behind the kick. The teacher would be taken away on a stretcher. Eventually there were no longer any members of the staff willing to take on the job of supervising any classroom or playground with McGowan in it, so he was removed. That left me looking more conspicuous.

The only thing I liked about school was skipping around in circles until the music stopped, then lying down on the floor for Quiet Time. I was very good at Quiet Time. Otherwise it was all a bit hopeless. I piddled on the floor when it was my turn to sing. Conversely, I got caught drinking my daily bottle of milk in the lavatory. For some reason this was regarded as a fearful crime. My mother used to pick me up after school. One day we missed each other and I went home on the bus. Meanwhile my mother was going frantic at the school. There were mutual tears that night. Next day when I answered my name at the morning assembly roll-call, the headmistress said, 'Ah yes, that's the little boy who ran away from his mother.' Thanks a lot, witch. I kacked my pants on the spot.

The whole secret of kacking your pants, incidentally, is to produce a rock-solid blob which will slide down your leg in one piece and can be rolled away into hiding at the point of the toe. That way, your moment of shame can be kept to the proportions of a strictly local disaster. But if you let go with anything soft, it takes two teachers to clean you up and the whole affair attracts nation-wide publicity. You get people interviewing you.

## *Dib, Dib, Dib, Dib*

Somewhere about this time I was in the Cubs. When the time came for graduations to the Scouts, I was not accepted, and thus became, for the brief time before I tossed the whole thing in, the oldest Cub in the First Kagorah Wolf Cub Pack and probably the world. Lacking the precious gift of taciturnity, I could never achieve the grim face essential to success in paramilitary organisations. Considering this fatal flaw, it is remarkable how many of them I tried to get into. The Cubs were merely the first in a long line. My mother made my scarf. It had to be in First Kogarah colours – maroon with yellow piping. She made me a woggle out of leather. Every Cub had to have a woggle. It held your scarf on. As well as the woggle, there were special sock-tops – called something like fuggles –

which always fell down. After you passed your Tenderfoot you got a wolf's head, or diggle, to wear on your cap. Also on the cap went a scraggle for each year of service. In addition to woggles, fuggles, diggles and scraggles, successful Cubs had the right, indeed obligation, to wear a whole collection of insignia and badges. The second in command of a sub-pack of six Cubs was called a Seconder and wore a yellow stripe on his sleeve. The commander of a sub-pack was called a Sixer and wore two stripes. A sixer in his final year would be so covered in decorations that promotion to the Scouts became a physical necessity, lest he expire under the weight.

Ruling over the whole pack was Akela. Her name was taken from *The Jungle Book*. She wore a brown uniform with a Scout hat. Otherwise she, too, was burdened down with woggles and fuggles. At the beginning of our weekly meetings, we Cubs would squat in a circle and worship her. While squatting, we made wolf-head signs with our fingers and pointed them at the floor. Then we chanted, 'Akela, we'll do our best. We'll dib dib dib dib. We'll dob dob dob dob . . .' This routine was climaxed by a mass throwing back of heads and emitting of supposedly vulpine howls. I used to get through the dibbing and dobbing all right but during the howling I usually rolled over backwards.

My lack of poise could possibly have stemmed from a never-to-be-satisfied wonderment about what dibbing and dobbing might actually consist of, but more probably it was just the result of an overwhelmingly love for Akela. I adored her. A school teacher in real life, she was a mother figure with none of the drawbacks. For her own part, she must have found me a problem, since I trailed her around everywhere. The theory of Scouting, or in this case Cubbing, was that boys should become independent through the acquisition of woodcraft and related skills. All I ever learned was how to attach myself to Akela's skirt. This made it hard for Akela and Baloo to be alone. Baloo the Bear was a young adult King's Scout who visited the pack once a month. Decorated like a combination of Boris Godunov and General MacArthur, a King's Scout in full regalia could be looked at only through smoked glass.

Baloo also accompanied us on camps. We went on a camp to

Heathcote, in the National Park. My mother came along to help. I had talked her into coming by telling her that every other mother would be there and that the camp site was yards from the station. It was seven thousand yards from the station. Mine was the only mother large-hearted enough to contribute her services. The trek to the camp site was along bush tracks and down cliffs. Swinging white-lipped from vines, my mother vowed to pick a bone with me later. By the time we got to the camp site she was too far gone to expend any of her remaining energy remonstrating with me. She cooked the sausages while Akela and Baloo put up the tents. It took Akela and Baloo about an hour's walk in the bush to find each tent pole. Meanwhile my mother doled out the exploding sausages and bandaged the hands of those Cubs – all of them heavily decorated with badges denoting proficiency in woodcraft – who had burned themselves picking up aluminium mugs of hot tea.

That night it rained like the Great Flood. The river rose. Tents collapsed. All the Cubs ended up in one big tent with my mother. Akela ended up in a pup tent with Baloo. Shortly afterwards they were married. Presumably Akela gave birth to either a bear or a wolf. By that time I had left the Cubs. You couldn't get into the Scouts without a certain number of badges. My own score was zero. Besides, I couldn't face a change of Akelas.

# *The Conscience-Pudding*

## Edith Nesbit

It was Christmas, nearly a year after mother died. I cannot write about mother – but I will just say one thing. If she had only been away for a little while, and not for always, we shouldn't have been so keen on having a Christmas. I didn't understand this then, but I am much older now, and I think it was just because everything was so different and horrid we felt we *must* do something; and perhaps we were not particular enough *what*. Things make you much more unhappy when you loaf about than when you are doing events.

Father had to go away just about Christmas. He had heard that his wicked partner, who ran away with his money, was in France, and he thought he could catch him, but really he was in Spain, where catching criminals is never practised. We did not know this till afterwards.

Before father went away he took Dora and Oswald into his study, and said:

'I'm awfully sorry I've got to go away, but it is very serious business, and I must go. You'll be good while I'm away, kiddies, won't you?'

We promised faithfully. Then he said:

'There are reasons – you wouldn't understand if I tried to tell you – but you can't have much of a Christmas this year. But I've told Matilda to make you a good plain pudding. Perhaps next Christmas will be brighter.'

(It was; for the next Christmas saw us the affluent nephews and nieces of an Indian uncle – but that is quite another story, as good old Kipling says.)

When father had been seen off at Lewisham Station with his

bags, and a plaid rug in a strap, we came home again, and it was horrid. There were papers and things littered all over his room where he had packed. We tidied the room up – it was the only thing we could do for him. It was Dicky who accidentally broke his shaving-glass, and H.O. made a paper boat out of a letter we found out afterwards father particularly wanted to keep. This took us some time, and when we went into the nursery the fire was black out, and we could not get it alight again, even with the whole *Daily Chronicle*. Matilda, who was our general then, was out, as well as the fire, so we went and sat in the kitchen. There is always a good fire in kitchens. The kitchen hearthrug was not nice to sit on, so we spread newspapers on it.

It was sitting in the kitchen, I think, that brought to our minds my father's parting words – about the pudding, I mean.

Oswald said, 'Father said we couldn't have much of a Christmas for secret reasons, and he said he had told Matilda to make us a plain pudding.'

The plain pudding instantly cast its shadow over the deepening gloom of our young minds.

'I wonder *how* plain she'll make it?' Dicky said.

'As plain as plain, you may depend,' said Oswald. 'A here-am-I-where-are-you-pudding – that's her sort.'

The others groaned, and we gathered closer round the fire till the newspapers rustled madly.

'I believe I could make a pudding that *wasn't* plain, if I tried,' Alice said. 'Why shouldn't we?'

'No chink,' said Oswald, with brief sadness.

'How much would it cost?' Noël asked, and added that Dora had twopence and H.O. had a French halfpenny.

Dora got the cookery-book out of the dresser drawer, where it lay doubled up among clothes-pegs, dirty dusters, scallop shells, string, penny novelettes, and the dining-room corkscrew. The general we had then – it seemed as if she did all the cooking on the cookery-book instead of on the baking-board, there were traces of so many bygone meals upon its pages.

'It doesn't say Christmas pudding at all,' said Dora.

'Try plum,' the resourceful Oswald instantly counselled.

Dora turned the greasy pages anxiously.

'"Plum-pudding, 518.

'"A rich, with flour, 517.

'"Christmas, 517.

'"Cold brandy sauce for, – 241."

'We shouldn't care about that, so it's no use looking.'

'"Good without eggs, 518.

'"Plain, 518."

'We don't want *that* anyhow, "Christmas, 517" – that's the one.'

It took her a long time to find the page. Oswald got a shovel of coals and made up the fire. It blazed up like the devouring elephant the *Daily Telegraph* always calls it. Then Dora read: '"Christmas plum-pudding. Time six hours."'

'To eat it in?' said H.O.

'No, silly! to make it.'

'Forge ahead, Dora,' Dicky replied.

Dora went on:

'"2072. One pound and a half of raisins; half a pound of currants; three quarters of a pound of breadcrumbs; half a pound of flour; three quarters of a pound of beef suet; nine eggs; one wineglassful of brandy; half a pound of citron and orange peel; half a nutmeg; and a little ground ginger." I wonder *how* little ground ginger.'

'A teacupful would be enough, I think,' Alice said; 'we must not be extravagant.'

'We haven't got anything yet to be extravagant *with*,' said Oswald, who had toothache that day. 'What would you do with the things if you'd got them?'

'You'd "chop the suet as fine as possible" – I wonder how fine that is?' replied Dora and the book together – '"and mix it with the breadcrumbs and flour; add the currants washed and dried."'

'Not starched, then,' said Alice.

'"The citron and orange peel cut into thin slices" – I wonder what they call thin? Matilda's thin bread-and-butter is quite different from what I mean by it – "and the raisins stoned and divided." How many heaps would you divide them into?'

'Seven, I suppose,' said Alice; 'one for each person and one for the pot – I mean pudding.'

'"Mix it all well together with the grated nutmeg and ginger. Then stir in nine eggs well beaten, and the brandy" – we'll leave that out, I think – "and again mix it thoroughly together that every ingredient may be moistened; put it into a buttered mould, tie over tightly, and boil for six hours. Serve it ornamented with holly and brandy poured over it."'

'I should think holly and brandy poured over it would be simply beastly,' said Dicky.

'I expect the book knows. I dare say holly and water would do as well though. "This pudding may be made a month before" – it's no use reading about that though, because we've only got four days to Christmas.'

'It's no use reading about any of it,' said Oswald, with thoughtful repeatedness, 'because we haven't got the things, and we haven't got the coin to get them.'

'We might get the tin somehow,' said Dicky.

'There must be lots of kind people who would subscribe to a Christmas pudding for poor children who hadn't any,' Noël said.

'Well I'm going skating at Penn's,' said Oswald. 'It's no use thinking about puddings. We must put up with it plain.'

So he went, and Dicky went with him.

When they returned to their home in the evening the fire had been lighted again in the nursery, and the others were just having tea. We toasted our bread-and-butter on the bare side, and it gets a little warm among the butter. This is called French toast. 'I like English better, but it is more expensive.' Alice said:

'Matilda is in a frightful rage about your putting those coals on the kitchen fire, Oswald. She says we shan't have enough to last over Christmas as it is. And father gave her a talking to before he went about them – asked her if she ate them, she says – but I don't believe he did. Anyway, she's locked the coal-cellar door, and she's got the key in her pocket. I don't see how we can boil the pudding.'

'What pudding?' said Oswald dreamily. He was thinking of a chap he had seen at Penn's who had cut the date 1899 on the ice with four strokes.

'*The* pudding,' Alice said. 'Oh, we've had such a time, Oswald! First Dora and I went to the shops to find out exactly what the pudding would cost – it's only two and elevenpence halfpenny, counting in the holly.'

'It's no good,' Oswald repeated; he is very patient and will say the same thing any number of times. 'It's no good. You know we've got no tin.'

'Ah,' said Alice, 'but Noël and I went out, and we called at some of the houses in Granville Park and Dartmouth Hill – and we got a lot of sixpences and shillings, beside pennies, and one old gentleman gave us a half-a-crown. He was so nice. Quite bald, with a knitted red and blue waistcoat. We've got eight-and-sevenpence.'

Oswald did not feel quite sure father would like us to go asking for shillings and sixpences, or even half-crowns from strangers, but he did not say so. The money had been asked for and got and it couldn't be helped – and perhaps he wanted the pudding – I am not able to remember exactly why he did not speak up and say, 'This is wrong,' but anyway he didn't.

Alice and Dora went out and bought the things next morning. They bought double quantities, so that it came to five shillings and elevenpence, and was enough to make a noble pudding. There was a lot of holly left over for decorations. We used very little for the sauce. The money that was left we spent very anxiously in other things to eat, such as dates and figs and toffee.

We did not tell Matilda about it. She was a red-haired girl, and apt to turn shirty at the least thing.

Concealed under our jackets and overcoats we carried the parcels up to the nursery, and hid them in the treasure-chest we had there. It was the bureau drawer. It was locked up afterwards because the treacle got all over the green baize and the little drawers inside it while we were waiting to begin to make the pudding. It was the grocer told us we ought to put treacle in the pudding, and also about not so much ginger as a teacupful.

When Matilda had begun to pretend to scrub the floor (she pretended this three times a week so as to have an excuse not to let us in the kitchen, but I know she used to read novelettes most of the time, because Alice and I had a squint through the window more than once), we barricaded the nursery and set to work. We were very careful to be quite clean. We washed our hands as well as the currants. I have sometimes thought we did not get all the soap off the currants. The pudding smelt like a washing-day when the time came to cut it open. And we washed a corner of the table to chop the suet on. Chopping suet looks easy till you try.

Father's machine he weighs letters with did to weigh out the things. We did this very carefully, in case the grocer had not done so. Everything was right except the raisins. H.O. had carried them home. He was very young then, and there was a hole in the corner of the paper bag and his mouth was sticky.

Lots of people have been hanged to a gibbet in chains on evidence no worse than that, and we told H.O. so till he cried. This was good for him. It was not unkindness to H.O., but part of our duty.

Chopping suet as fine as possible is much harder than any one would think, as I said before. So is crumbling bread – especially if your loaf is new, like ours was. When we had done them the breadcrumbs and the suet were both very large and lumpy, and of a dingy grey colour, something like pale slate pencil.

They looked a better colour when we had mixed them with the flour. The girls had washed the currants with Brown Windsor soap and the sponge. Some of the currants got inside the sponge and kept coming out in the bath for days afterwards. I see now that this was not quite nice. We cut the candied peel as thin as we wish people would cut our bread-and-butter. We tried to take the stones out of the raisins, but they were too sticky, so we just divided them up in seven lots. Then we mixed the other things in the wash-hand basin from the spare bedroom that was always spare. We each put in our own lot of raisins and turned it all into a pudding basin, and tied it up in one of Alice's pinafores, which was the nearest thing to a proper pudding-cloth we could find – at any rate clean. What was left sticking to the wash-hand basin did not taste so bad.

'It's a little bit soapy,' Alice said; 'but perhaps that will boil out; like stains in tablecloths.'

It was a difficult question how to boil the pudding. Matilda proved furious when asked to let us, just because some one happened to knock her hat off the scullery door and Pincher had got it and done for it. However, part of the embassy nicked a saucepan while the others were being told what Matilda thought about the hat, and we got hot water out of the bathroom and made it boil over our nursery fire. We put the pudding in – it was now getting on towards the hour of tea – and let it boil. With some exceptions – owing to the fire going down, and Matilda not hurrying up with coals – it boiled for an hour and a quarter. Then Matilda came suddenly in and said, 'I'm not going to have you messing about in here with my saucepans'; and she tried to take it off the fire. You will see that we couldn't stand this; it was not likely. I do not remember who it was that told her to mind her own business, and I think I have forgotten who caught hold of her first to make her chuck it. I am sure no needless violence was used. Anyway, while the struggle progressed, Alice and Dora took the saucepan away and put it in the boot-cupboard under the stairs and put the key in their pocket.

This sharp encounter made every one hot and cross. We got over it before Matilda did, but we brought her round before bedtime. Quarrels should always be made up before bedtime. It says so in the Bible. If this simple rule was followed there would not be so many wars and martyrs and lawsuits and inquisitions and bloody deaths at the stake.

All the house was still. The gas was out all over the house except on the first landing, when several darkly shrouded figures might have been observed creeping downstairs to the kitchen.

On the way, with superior precaution, we got out our saucepan. The kitchen fire was red, but low; the coal-cellar was locked, and there was nothing in the scuttle but a little coal-dust and the piece of brown paper that is put in to keep the coals from tumbling out through the bottom where the hole is. We put the saucepan on the fire and plied it with fuel – two

*Chronicles*, a *Telegraph* and two *Family Herald* novelettes were burned in vain. I am almost sure the pudding did not boil at all that night.

'Never mind,' Alice said. 'We can each nick a piece of coal every time we go into the kitchen tomorrow.'

This daring scheme was faithfully performed, and by night we had nearly half a waste-paper basket of coal, coke, and cinders. And in the depth of night once more we might have been observed this time with our collier-like waste-paper basket in our guarded hands.

There was more fire left in the grate that night, and we fed it with the fuel we had collected. This time the fire blazed up, and the pudding boiled like mad. This was the time it boiled two hours – at least I think it was about that, but we dropped alseep on the kitchen tables and dresser. You dare not be lowly in the night in the kitchen, because of the beetles. We were aroused by a horrible smell. It was the pudding-cloth burning. All the water had secretly boiled itself away. We filled it up at once with cold, and the saucepan cracked. So we cleaned it and put it back on the shelf and took another and went to bed. You see what a lot of trouble we had over the pudding. Every evening till Christmas, which had now become only the day after tomorrow, we sneaked down in the inky midnight and boiled that pudding for as long as it would.

On Christmas morning we chopped the holly for the sauce, but we put hot water (instead of brandy) and moist sugar. Some of them said it was not so bad. Oswald was not one of these.

Then came the moment when the plain pudding father had ordered smoked upon the board. Matilda brought it in and went away at once. She had a cousin out of Woolwich Arsenal to see her that day, I remember. Those far-off days are quite distinct in memory's recollection still.

Then we got our own pudding from its hiding-place and gave it one last hurried boil – only seven minutes, because of the general impatience which Oswald and Dora could not cope with.

We had found means to secrete a dish, and we now tried to dish the pudding up, but it stuck to the basin, and had to be dislodged with a chisel. The pudding was horribly pale. We poured the holly sauce over it, and Dora took up the knife and was just cutting it when a few simple words from H.O. turned us from happy and triumphing cookery artists to persons in despair.

He said: 'How pleased all those kind ladies and gentlemen would be if they knew *we* were the poor children they gave the shillings and sixpences and things for!'

We all said, *'What?'* It was no moment for politeness.

'I say,' H.O. said, 'they'd be glad if they knew it was us was enjoying the pudding, and not dirty little, really poor children.'

'You should say "you were," not "you was,"' said Dora, but it was as in a dream and only from habit.

'Do you mean to say' – Oswald spoke firmly, yet not angrily – 'that you and Alice went and begged for money for poor children, and then *kept* it?'

'We didn't keep it,' said H.O., 'we spent it.'

'We've kept the *things*, you little duffer!' said Dicky, looking at the pudding sitting alone and uncared for on its dish. 'You begged for money for poor children, and then *kept* it. It's stealing, that's what it is. I don't say so much about you – you're only a silly kid – but Alice knew better. Why did you do it?'

He turned to Alice, but she was now too deep in tears to get a word out.

H.O. looked a bit frightened, but he answered the question. We have taught him this. He said:

'I thought they'd give us more if I said poor children than if I said just us.'

'*That's* cheating,' said Dicky – 'downright beastly, mean, low cheating.'

'I'm not,' said H.O.; 'and you're another.'

Then he began to cry too. I do not know how the others felt, but I understand from Oswald that he felt that now the honour of the House of Bastable had been stamped on in the dust, and it didn't matter what happened. He looked at the beastly holly that had been left over from the sauce and was stuck up over the pictures. It now apppeared hollow and disgusting, though it had got quite a lot of berries, and some of it was the varied kind –

green and white. The figs and dates and toffee were set out in the doll's dinner service. The very sight of it all made Oswald blush sickly. He owns he would have liked to cuff H.O., and, if he did for a moment wish to shake Alice, the author, for one, can make allowances.

Now Alice choked and spluttered, and wiped her eyes fiercely, and said, 'It's no use ragging H.O. It's my fault. I'm older than he is.'

H.O. said, 'It couldn't be Alice's fault. I don't see as it was wrong.'

'That, not as,' murmured Dora, putting her arms round the sinner who had brought this degrading blight upon our family tree, but such is girls' undetermined and affectionate silliness. 'Tell sister all about it, H.O. dear. Why couldn't it be Alice's fault?'

H.O. cuddled up to Dora and said snuffingly in his nose:

'Because she hadn't got nothing to do with it. I collected it all. She never went into one of the houses. She didn't want to.'

'And then took all the credit for getting the money,' said Dicky savagely.

Oswald said, 'Not much *credit*,' in scornful tones.

'Oh, you are *beastly*, the whole lot of you, except Dora!' Alice said, stamping her foot in rage and despair. 'I tore my frock on a nail going out, and I didn't want to go back, and I got H.O. to go the houses alone, and I waited for him outside. And I asked him not to say anything because I didn't want Dora to know about the frock – it's my best. And *I* don't know what he said inside. He never told me. But I'll bet anything he didn't *mean* to cheat.'

'You said lots of kind people would be ready to give money to get pudding for poor children. So I asked them to.'

Oswald, with his strong right hand, waved a wave of passing things over.

'We'll talk about that another time,' he said; 'just now we've got weightier things to deal with.'

He pointed to the pudding, which had grown cold during the conversation to which I have alluded. H.O. stopped crying, but Alice went on with it. Oswald now said:

'We're a base and outcast family. Until that pudding's out of the house we shan't be able to look any one in the face. We must see that that pudding goes to the poor children – not grisling, grumpy, whiney-piney, pretending poor children – but real poor ones, just as poor as they can stick.'

'And the figs too – and the dates,' said Noël with regretting tones.

'Every fig,' said Dicky sternly. 'Oswald is quite right.'

This honourable resolution made us feel a bit better. We hastily put on our best things, and washed ourselves a bit, and hurried out to find some really poor people to give the pudding to. We cut it in slices ready, and put it in a basket with figs and dates and toffee. We would not let H.O. come with us at first because he wanted to. And Alice would not come because of him. So at last we had to let him. The excitement of tearing into your best things heals the hurt that wounded honour feels, as the poetry writer said – or at any rate it makes the hurt feel better.

We went out into the streets. They were pretty quiet – nearly everybody was eating its Christmas dessert. But presently we met a woman in an apron. Oswald said very politely:

'Please, are you a poor person?' And she told us to get along with us.

The next we met was a shabby man with a hole in his left boot.

Again Oswald said, 'Please, are you a poor person, and have you any poor little children?'

The man told us not to come any of our games with him, or we should laugh on the wrong side of our faces. We went on sadly. We had no heart to stop and explain to him that we had no games to come.

The next was a young man near the Obelisk. Dora tried this time.

She said, 'Oh, if you please we've got some Christmas pudding in this basket, and if you're a poor person you can have some.'

'Poor as Job,' said the young man in a hoarse voice, and he had to come up out of a red comforter to say it.

We gave him a slice of the pudding, and he bit into it without thanks or delay. The next minute he had thrown the pudding slap in Dora's face, and was clutching Dicky by the collar.

'Blime if I don't chuck ye in the river, the whole bloomin' lot of you!' he exclaimed.

The girls screamed, the boys shouted, and though Oswald threw himself on the insulter of his sister with all his manly vigour, yet but for a friend of Oswald's, who is in the police, passing at that instant, the author shudders to think what might have happened, for he was a strong young man, and Oswald is not yet come to his full strength, and the Quaggy runs all too near.

Our policeman led our assailant aside, and we waited anxiously, as he told us to. After long uncertain moments the young man in the comforter loafed off grumbling, and our policeman turned to us.

'Said you gave him a dollop o' pudding, and it tasted of soap and hair-oil.'

I suppose the hair-oil must have been the Brown Windsoriness of the soap coming out. We were sorry, but it was still our duty to get rid of the pudding. The Quaggy was handy, it is true, but when you have collected money to feed poor children and spent it on pudding it is not right to throw that pudding in the river. People do not subscribe shillings and sixpences and half-crowns to feed a hungry flood with Christmas pudding.

Yet we shrank from asking any more people whether they were poor persons, or about their families, and still more from offering the pudding to chance people who might bite into it and taste the soap before we had time to get away.

It was Alice, the most paralysed with disgrace of all of us, who thought of the best idea.

She said, 'Let's take it it the workhouse. At any rate they're all poor people there, and they mayn't go out without leave, so they can't run after us to do anything to us after the pudding. No one would give the leave to go out to pursue people who had brought them pudding, and wreck vengeance on them, and at any rate we shall get rid of the conscience-pudding – it's a sort of conscience-money, you know – only it isn't money but pudding.'

The workhouse is a good way, but we stuck to it, though very cold, and hungrier than we thought possible when we started, for we had been so agitated that we had not even stayed to eat the plain pudding our good father had so kindly and thoughfully ordered for our Christmas dinner.

The big bell at the workhouse made a man open the door to us, when we rang it. Oswald said (and he spoke because he is next eldest to Dora, and she had had jolly well enough of saying anything about pudding) – he said:

'Please we've brought some pudding for the poor people.'

He looked us up and down, and he looked at our basket, then he said: 'You better see the Matron.'

We waited in a hall, feeling more and more uncomfy, and less and less like Christmas. We were very cold indeed, especially our hands and our noses. And we felt less and less able to face the Matron if she was horrid, and one of us at least wished he had chosen the Quaggy for the pudding's long home, and made it up to the robbed poor in some other way afterwards.

Just as Alice was saying earnestly in the burning cold ear of Oswald, 'Let's put down the basket and make a bolt for it. Oh, Oswald, *let's*!' a lady came along the passage. She was very upright, and she had eyes that went through you like blue gimlets. I shouldn't like to be obliged to thwart that lady if she had any design, and mine was opposite. I am glad this is not likely to occur.

She said, 'What's all this about a pudding?'

H.O. said at once, before we could stop him, 'They say I've stolen the pudding, so we've brought it here for the poor people.'

'No, we didn't!' 'That wasn't why!' 'The money was given!' 'It was meant for the poor!' 'Shut up, H.O.!' said the rest of us all at once.

Then there was an awful silence. The lady gimleted us again one by one with her blue eyes.

Then she said: 'Come into my room. You all look frozen.'

She took us into a very jolly room with velvet curtains and a big fire, and the gas lighted, because now it was almost dark, even out of doors. She gave us chairs, and Oswald felt as if his was a dock, he felt so criminal, and the lady looked so Judgular.

Then she took the armchair by the fire herself, and said, 'Who's the eldest?'

'I am,' said Dora, looking more like a frightened white rabbit than I've ever seen her.

'Then tell me all about it.'

Dora looked at Alice and began to cry. That slab of pudding in the face had totally unnerved the gentle girl. Alice's eyes were red, and her face was puffy with crying; but she spoke up for Dora and said:

'Oh, please let Oswald tell. Dora can't. She's tired with the long walk. And a young man threw a piece of it in her face, and—'

The lady nodded, and Oswald began. He told the story from the very beginning, as he has always been taught to, though he hated to lay bare the family honour's wound before a stranger, however judge-like and gimlet-eyed.

He told all – not concealing the pudding-throwing, nor what the young man said about soap.

'So,' he ended, 'we want to give the conscience-pudding to you. It's like conscience-money – you know what that is, don't you? But if you really think it is soapy and not just the young man's horridness, perhaps you'd better not let them eat it. But the figs and things are all right.'

When he had done the lady said, for most of us were crying more or less:

'Come, cheer up! It's Christmas-time, and he's very little – your brother, I mean. And I think the rest of you seem pretty well able to take care of the honour of the family. I'll take the conscience-pudding off your minds. Where are you going now?'

'Home, I suppose,' Oswald said. And he thought how nasty and dark and dull it would be. The fire out most likely and father away.

'And your father's not at home, you say,' the blue-gimlet lady went on. 'What do you say to having tea with me, and then seeing the entertainment we have got up for our old people?'

Then the lady smiled and the blue gimlets looked quite merry. The room was so warm and comfortable and the invitation was the last thing we expected. It was jolly of her, I do think.'

No one thought quite at first of saying how pleased we should be to accept her kind invitation. Instead we all just said 'Oh!' but in a tone which must have told her we meant 'Yes, please,' very deeply.

Oswald (this has more than once happened) was the first to restore his manners. He made a proper bow like he had been taught, and said:

'Thank you very much. We should like it very much. It is very much nicer than going home. Thank you very much.'

I need not tell the reader that Oswald could have made up a much better speech if he had had more time to make it up in, or if he had not been so filled with mixed flusteredness and furification by the shameful events of the day.

We washed our faces and hands and had a first-rate muffin and crumpet tea, with slices of cold meats, and many nice jams and cakes. A lot of other people were there, most of them people who were giving the entertainment to the aged poor.

After tea it was the entertainment. Songs and conjuring and a play called 'Box and Cox,' very amusing, and a lot of throwing things about in it – bacon and chops and things – and nigger minstrels. We clapped till our hands were sore.

When it was over we said good-bye. In between the songs and things Oswald had had time to make up a speech of thanks to the lady.

He said:

'We all thank you heartily for your goodness. The entertainment was beautiful. We shall never forget your kindness and hospitableness.'

The lady laughed, and said she had been very pleased to have us. A fat gentleman said:

'And your teas? I hope you enjoyed those – eh?'

Oswald had not had time to make up an answer to that, so he answered straight from the heart, and said:

'Ra-*ther*!'

And every one laughed and slapped us boys on the back and kissed the girls, and the gentleman who played the bones in the nigger minstrels saw us home. We ate the cold pudding that night and H.O. dreamed that something came to eat him, like it advised you to in the advertisements on the hoardings. The grown-ups said it was the pudding, but I don't think it could have been that because, as I have said more than once, it was so very plain.

Some of H.O.'s brothers and sisters thought it was a judgement on him for pretending about who the poor children were he was collecting the money for. Oswald does not believe such a little boy as H.O. would have a real judgement made just for him and nobody else, whatever he did.

But it certainly is odd. H.O. was the only one who had bad dreams, and he was also the only one who got any of the things we bought with that ill-gotten money, because, you remember, he picked a hole in the raisin-paper as he was bringing the parcel home. The rest of us had nothing, unless you count the scrapings of the pudding-basin, and those don't really count at all.

●

*'I know it's a bit late, but looking at our Nigel,*
*I think I'm starting a post-natal depression.'*

# *Part Five*

# LIFE SENTENCES

It's hard for me to get used to these changing times. I can remember when the air was clean and sex was dirty.

**George Burns**

# *Military Affairs*

## David Niven

In the months that followed, my military ambitions suffered a certain seepage as, slowly, but surely, it dawned on me that there was very little point in being a keen young officer. The Army list was kept in the Mess and the pages devoted to the Highland Light Infantry were grubby from the probing fingers that had endlessly traced the inevitable promotions that would come in the long, long years ahead.

However, there was so much new, so much to enjoy that it was almost two years before the deadening horror of the whole thing finally descended upon me and enveloped me like a black Bedouin tent. In the meanwhile Trubshawe's guidance continued apace. He explained to me that I could hire polo ponies for fifteen shillings a month and that apart from buying some mallets, I had nothing to worry about financially, the grooms being soldiers and the ponies all being on the regimental strength as officers' chargers. In addition, as I got better at the game, he assured me that many naval officers would be delighted to lend me their ponies just to keep them exercised during the long periods they would be away at sea.

All this was indeed true and I found myself quite soon with as many mounts as I could play and quite a respectable handicap.

The Marsa Polo Club was the smart place to be – smart in the most colonial sense of the word; it was mounted suburbia. It was parasols and fraightfully refained voices. It was 'Boy, bring me a stingar', and naval wives who announced with a smirk – 'We're going in to have our bottom scrubbed next week,' but it was still heady stuff compared with what I had been exposed to before and I thrived on it. Girls there were in plenty. Apart from the resident ones, daughters of senior officers and officials, there were also for several months a year hundreds of young and lonely naval officers' wives. There was in addition the 'Fishing Fleet', a motley collection of passed-over debs and pink-cheeked country cousins who annually timed their arrival to coincide with the return, after many months at sea, of several thousand sex-starved mariners. Finally, there were the whores, and Valletta was full of professionals busily catering to the needs of all ranks of the biggest fleet in the world. Many were mid-Europeans or Russians, refugees of impeccable lineage with sisters plying the same desperate trade in Singapore and fathers driving taxis in Paris.

There was a professionally languid Captain in the Headquarters wing who wore a monocle. His wife was very pretty in a sort of chocolate boxy way and could have been described in polite society as a flirt; anywhere else she would have been called a cock teaser.

I had, it is true, nibbled her ear and snapped her garter a couple of times while watching the polo from her car, but nothing more, so I was all unsuspecting when a runner informed me that the Captain wished to see me immediately in his company office. I entered and saluted. He was busy looking over some ammunition returns with the Quartermaster Sergeant. I fidgeted around for a while but he still did not look up. Finally, head still down, he spoke.

'Niven, are you very much in love with my wife?'

My toes tried to grip the floor through my brogues to stop me from keeling over.

'No, sir . . . not at all, sir.' I murmured and then, for no apparent reason, I added,

'Thank you very much, sir.'

'Well, if you're not,' said the Captain, putting some papers in a folder, 'be a good chap, don't go on telling her you are . . . upsets her, you know. Now, Quartermaster Sergeant, about the Range Allotment of 303 . . . .'

I saluted the top of his head and withdrew.

After that I decided to be a good deal more selective in my nibbling and snapping.

The Fleet was sailing for several weeks of exercises off the Greek islands, leaving behind literally hundreds of ladies in different stages of availability. I discussed the situation with the wife of the Signals Officer of a destroyer who had made it very obvious that she had no intention of sitting around twiddling her thumbs during his absence.

It was a nasty little intrigue really but quite exciting especially when the husband gave a party in his cabin before he sailed and said to me, 'Look after Eunice for me till I get back.'

'I certainly will,' I said, avoiding his eye.

When sailing time came, Eunice and I climbed to the top of the cliffs and watched the splendid spectacle of the entire Mediterranean Fleet steaming out of the harbour, Royal Marine bands playing and bunting fluttering.

We used my field glasses and paid particular attention to her husband's destroyer. He was on the bridge. We had told him where we would be watching and with his binoculars he found us. Lots of waving went on and we even staged a big amorous embrace to make him laugh. I wish I could report that I felt a twinge of shame at that moment but I didn't. I had other feelings of a more animal nature to contend with.

The Fleet sailed away into the sunset and disappeared over the horizon bearing the poor cuckold-to-be towards Corfu; never had a safer stage been set for infidelity but Eunice was in no rush and decided to savour the moment. After all, we had at least six weeks ahead of us in which to indulge ourselves so she insisted that I take her to the Sliema Club to a party with some others, escort her home to her house and then . . .

So we danced close and drank champagne and toasted each other over the rim of our glasses, all very high powered romantic stuff; finally I found myself in her bed.

Some far from routine thrashing around was going on because Eunice was an expert at prolonging everything when suddenly she went rigid.

'Christ!' she hissed, 'he's back!'

He was too and downstairs in the sitting room.

'Get in that cupboard,' ordered Eunice.

It was pretty ridiculous because my clothes were all over the floor but I did as I was told and stood quaking in a black hole that smelled of mothballs.

I didn't have time to reflect on the old French farce situation that I was in. All I could think of was certain death that would soon come up those stairs.

Eunice was made of different stuff. She went down naked to meet him.

'Darling, how did you get back?'

'Stripped a bloody turbine thirty miles out . . . towed back.'

Somehow she persuaded him to get in the car and go and get a bottle of champagne so they could celebrate.

I dressed in about eleven seconds and with my shoes on the wrong feet shot downstairs and out of the house. I was impotent for days.

●

# *On Being Small*

## Ronnie Corbett

Actually, in the first place, I suppose we should determine what we mean by a 'Small Man'. The whole thing is relative. If you live in England, where the national average is about five foot eight, and you are only five foot two – you are small. Whereas I was reading about a chap, smaller than myself, who went to live with a tribe of pygmies in the Congo, where he was known locally as Bwana M'Bongo M'Gongo, 'He who walks with his head in the clouds'. While that might be all very nice for some people, I personally don't feel inclined to trudge around the rain forests living on grubs and berries, just so I can look down on someone. Anyway my wife says, 'It's too far from Sainsbury's,' so that's that.

I'm not sure it was M'Bongo M'Gongo – it might have been M'Gongo M'Bongo – but you get the general idea, don't you? Actually it doesn't really matter unless you're a pygmy, and if you happen to be a pygmy reading this book, well, Hullo Shorty!

Anyway that has cleared that point up, whatever it was.

So without further ado let's get right on with Chapter One, 'The Small Man's Guide to Self-Defence'. (I think I was right the first time, M'Bongo M'Gongo), but I digress.

Self-Defence. I suppose the obvious approach to the problem of survival for the Small Man is to avoid trouble in the first place, but unless you are going to join an enclosed order based on the teachings of St. Tyrone the Terrified and live in a cellar in Tibet, you might as well face the fact that eighty-seven point eight of all looping right-handers thrown in places of amusement – pubs – dance halls – other people's bedrooms etc – are thrown by *big* men and received my *small* men. And if you are going to go through life with beautiful thoughts about faith in human nature or memories of David and Goliath, you are going to spend more time in Casualty than some of the nurses.

Actually, it is an interesting fact that prior to World War Two, there existed a code of ethics that frowned upon the practice of big men hitting small men – especially *small men with glasses*. Then the Japanese declared war on us and suddenly half the world was full of *small men with glasses* running around, bent on doing a mischief to everybody. And it was during those dark days that society reconsidered the status of the smaller man and replaced the pat on the head, with a punch in the earhole.

Actually, there is more than one opinion regarding the merits of self-defence and the Small Man. There is one theory that the bigger the struggle you put up the bigger the whacking you are going to get. So the perfect ploy could be, as soon as the trouble starts, throw yourself down and pretend to be dead. This could possibly have the effect of frightening your assailant so much that, overcome with fear and remorse, he will immediately leave the premises and perhaps even the country. However, there's an old saying that murderers return to the scene of the crime, so just don't be sitting up at the bar giggling about it when he comes back or you might pay a surprise visit to the coroner after all.

There was a case recently of a certain S.M. who had learned Karate from a book, purchased in good faith from no less than W.H. Smith, or one of his Sons, and he happened to enter licensed premises where a multi-storey punchup was in progress. Our friend stood quietly for a few moments on the fringe of the mêlée, a confident smile on his little features, considering whether to start his contribution to the action with a bit of fun; (chapters four and five) 'How to bring about temporary paralysis by dislocation'. Or to go straight in with lesson 28, '*For Advanced Students Only*!' 'How to kill without causing unnecessary suffering'. When someone hit him in the face with the landlord's dog, and as there had been no mention in the book about countering a blow with twenty pounds of cross-bred bull-terrier, he panicked, went to pieces and stared shouting, 'Help! Police! My doze is mleeding!' and 'The drinks are on me!'

Later his wife had to supply a photograph of what he used to look like before they could put him together again.

In any case the business of learning the Martial Arts from a book is very much over-rated.

Put yourself in the place of our friend, foolhardy little twit. You have survived the encounter with the aerial pooch, and gone in with lesson 28. Figs. 1, 2, 3 and 4, starting with Fig. 1. Grip your opponent's lapel firmly in the right hand, now, pivoting on your left foot – (is it possible your opponent hasn't got a lapel? Some suits don't have them these days! Hard luck, you've picked a snazzy dresser!) but by the time you have digested this information you are already into Fig. 2 and pivoting gracefully on the left foot, and unless your opponent is completely lost and overcome by the grace and beauty of it all, he is now in a position to give you a kick from behind that could leave you speechless for a fortnight with all your hair falling out.

Therefore it almost immediately becomes obvious that all those hours you spent in your little room giving a hard time to a couple of pillows inside an old raincoat, followed by the occasional Flying Lotus at Mummy while she is straining the greens, has got you precisely nowhere, and if you continue along this path you will eventually become a burden on the National Health.

'But what,' you may well ask, 'about those schools where they teach Kung Fu and Judo and all that jazz?' Good question, and very nicely put, because therein lies the answer to our problem.

It was indeed a lucky day for me when in the spring of '75 I made the decision to become a student of the Kung Fu School of Martial Arts.

The Kung Fu School of Martial Arts is situated, as you may know, between the New Swedish Massage Parlour and the Novelty Sex Emporium, Dean Street, London W.1. When I entered the front office that morning I was greeted by a Chinese girl of such incredible loveliness – I think she was Chinese but she could have been Japanese. They say you can tell the difference but I've never personally believed it – anyway she was so lovely that I had to go outside again and check the name over the doorway, because I thought for a moment that I had walked into the wrong place and was about to put myself down for some novelty sex or a massage by Bibi and Babs that might leave me even more vulnerable than I was already.

Anyway I said to her, 'I'd like to – er – learn a bit of the old Judo.' I've heard it said that you can't tell what the Chinese are thinking, because their faces are so impassive. But I could tell immediately that this one was thinking: 'By the Sacred Buddha, we have a right one here.'

'One cannot learn a *bit* of the old Judo,' she replied, in a voice like the evening breeze rustling the cherry blossom.

I said, 'Well, I can't learn it all, dear, I'm a busy man, I've more important things to do. I just want to learn a couple of grips and armlocks and things to put a few of 'em in their place and stop them drinking my beer and fiddling the dart scores.'

She looked very sad.

'Look, if I really like it and I get a bit more time I might go on to the more advanced bit, how to break their arms, etcetera.'

I thought his might cheer her up a bit.

'Judo,' she whispered, 'is not for breaking the arms, but for strengthening the body and beautifying the mind.' Her lovely fingers fluttered to indicate which was her body and which was her mind.

'Well,' I said, 'I think we can cut that bit by half, because while the body is obviously ready for some slight improvement I do happen to possess one of the most beautiful minds between here and the London Palladium. A puppy in a shop window brings an immediate lump to my throat and I have to be tranquillised every time I see Bette Davis in "Dark Victory", so let's not worry about the mind, but concentrate the age-old skills and wisdom of the Orient on stopping me getting duffed up quite so frequently. Now let's say half a dozen lessons and see how we go from there. O.K.?'

She bowed her exquisite little head to the Occidental ability to make up one's mind and pay the bill in 'readies', and wrote me a nicely headed Kung Fu appointment card. Then we relaxed a bit and had a little general conversation during which she told me she was married to a Karate instructor, which was the end of that.

But I always think that the few quid I spent that morning were the wisest I ever spent in my life.

I never actually got around to attending a lesson. I simply lost the appointment card several times in the various venues that I frequented and by the time somebody found it, and returned same, the whisper had gone round, 'Don't take any liberties with him. He's a student of the Martial Arts.'

●

Behind every successful man stands a surprised mother-in-law.

**Hubert Humphrey**

Two in every one people in this country are schizophrenic.

**Graffito**

# *The Night the Ghost Got In*

## James Thurber

The ghost that got into our house on the night of November 17th, 1915, raised such a hullabaloo of misunderstandings that I am sorry I didn't just let it keep on walking, and go to bed. Its advent caused my mother to throw a shoe through a window of the house next door and ended up with my grandfather shooting a patrolman. I am sorry, therefore, as I have said, that I ever paid any attention to the footsteps.

They began about a quarter past one o'clock in the morning, rhythmic, quick-cadenced walking around the dining-room table. My mother was asleep in one room upstairs, my brother Herman in another; grandfather was in the attic, in the old walnut bed which, as you will remember, once fell on my father. I had just stepped out of the bathtub and was busily rubbing myself with a towel when I heard the steps. They were the steps of a man walking rapidly around the dining-room table downstairs. The light from the bathroom shone down the back steps, which dropped directly into the dining-room; I could see the faint shine of plates on the plate-rail; I couldn't see the table. The steps kept going round and round the table; at regular intervals a board creaked, when it was trod upon. I supposed at first that it was my father or my brother Roy, who had gone to Indianapolis but were expected home at any time. I suspected next that it was a burglar. It did not enter my mind until later that it was a ghost.

After the walking had gone on for perhaps three minutes, I tiptoed to Herman's room. 'Psst!' I hissed, in the dark, shaking him. 'Awp', he said, in the low, hopeless tone of a despondent beagle – he always half suspected that something would 'get him' in the night. I told him who I was. 'There's something downstairs!' I said. He got up and followed me to the head of the back stairs. We listened together. There was no sound. The steps had ceased. Herman looked at me in some alarm: I had only the bath towel around my waist. He wanted to go back to bed, but I gripped his arm. 'There's something down there', I said. Instantly the steps began again, circled the dining-room table like a man running, and started up the stairs towards us, heavily, two at a time. The light still shone palely down the stairs: we saw nothing coming; we only heard the steps. Herman rushed to his room and slammed the door. I slammed shut the door at the stairs top and held my knee against it. After a long minute, I slowly opened it again. There was nothing there. There was no sound. None of us ever heard the ghost again.

The slamming of the door had aroused mother: she peered out of her room. 'What on earth are you boys doing?' she demanded. Herman ventured out of his room. 'Nothing', he said gruffly, but he was, in colour, a light green. 'What was all that running around downstairs?' said mother. So she had heard the steps, too! We just looked at her. 'Burglars!' she shouted, intuitively. I tried to quiet her by starting lightly downstairs.

'Come on, Herman,' I said.

'I'll stay with mother', he said. 'She's all excited.'

I stepped back on to the landing.

'Don't either of you go a step', said mother. 'We'll call the police.' Since the phone was downstairs, I didn't see how we were going to call the police – nor did I want the police – but mother made one of her quick, incomparable decisions. She flung up a window of her bedroom which faced the bedroom windows of the house of a neighbour, picked up a shoe, and whammed it through a pane of glass across the narrow space that separated the two houses. Glass tinkled into the bedroom occupied by a retired engraver named Bodwell and his wife. Bodwell had been for some years in rather a bad way and was subject to mild 'attacks'. Most everybody we knew or lived near had *some* kind of attacks.

It was now about two o'clock of a moonless night; clouds hung black and low. Bodwell was at the window in a minute, shouting, frothing a little, shaking his fist. 'We'll sell the house and go back to Peoria', we could hear Mrs Bodwell saying. It was some time before mother 'got through' to Bodwell. 'Burglars!' she shouted. 'Burglars in the house!' Herman and I hadn't dared to tell her that it was not burglars but ghosts, for she was even more afraid of ghosts than of burglars. Bodwell at first thought that she meant that there were burglars in his house, but finally he quieted down and called the police for us over an extension phone by his bed. After he had disappeared from the window, mother suddenly made as if to throw another shoe, not because there was further need of it, but, as she later explained, because the thrill of heaving a shoe through a window glass had enormously taken her fancy. I prevented her.

The police were on hand in a commendably short time: a Ford sedan full of them, two on motorcycles, and a patrol wagon with about eight in it and a few reporters. They began banging at our front door. Flashlights shot streaks of gleam up and down the walls, across the yard, down the walk between our house and Bodwell's. 'Open up!' cried a hoarse voice. 'We're men from headquarters!' I wanted to go down and let them in, since there they were, but mother wouldn't hear of it. 'You haven't a stitch on', she pointed out. 'You'd catch your death.' I wound the towel around me again. Finally the cops put their shoulders to our big heavy front door with its thick bevelled glass and broke it in: I could hear a rending of wood and a splash of glass on the floor of the hall. Their lights played all over the living-room and criss-crossed nervously in the dining-room, stabbed into hallways, shot up the front stairs, and finally up the back. They caught me standing in my towel at the top. A heavy policeman bounded up the steps. 'Who are you?' he demanded. 'I live here', I said. 'Well, whattsa matta, ya hot?' he asked. It was, as a matter of fact, cold; I went to my room and pulled on some trousers. On my way out, a cop stuck a gun into my ribs. 'Whatta you doin' here?' he demanded. 'I live here', I said.

The officer in charge reported to mother. 'No sign of nobody, lady', he said. 'Musta got away – whatt'd he look like?' 'There were two or three of them', mother said, 'whooping and carrying on and slamming doors.' 'Funny', said the cop. 'All ya windows and doors was locked on the inside tight as a tick.'

Downstairs, we could hear the tramping of the other police. Police were all over the place; doors were yanked open, drawers were yanked open, windows were shot up and pulled down, furniture fell with dull thumps. A half-dozen policemen emerged out of the darkness of the front hallway upstairs. They began to ransack the floor; pulled beds away from the walls, tore clothes off hooks in the closets, pulled suitcases and boxes off shelves. One of them found an old zither that Roy had won in a pool tournament. 'Looky here, Joe', he said, strumming it with a big paw. The cop named Joe took it and turned it over. 'What is it?' 'It's an old zither our guinea pig used to sleep on', I said. It was true that a pet guinea pig we once had would never sleep anywhere except on the zither, but I should never had said so. Joe and the other cop looked at me a long time. They put the zither back on a shelf.

'No sign o' nothing', said the cop who had first spoken to mother. 'This guy', he explained to the others, jerking a thumb at me, 'was nekked. The lady seems historical.' They all nodded, but said nothing; just looked at me. In the small silence we all heard a creaking in the attic. Grandfather was turning over in bed. 'What's 'at?' snapped Joe. Five or six cops sprang for the attic door before I could intervene or explain. I realised that it would be bad if they burst in on grandfather unannounced, or even announced. He was going through a phase in which he believed that General Meade's men, under steady hammering by Stonewall Jackson, were beginning to retreat and even desert.

When I got to the attic, things were pretty confused. Grandfather had evidently jumped to the conclusion that the police were deserters from Meade's army, trying to hide away in his attic. He bounded out of bed wearing a long flannel nightgown over long woollen underwear, a nightcap, and a leather jacket around his chest. The cops must have realised at once that the indignant white-haired old man belonged in the house, but they had no chance to say so. 'Back ye cowardly dogs!' roared grandfather. 'Back t' the lines, ye goddam lily-livered cattle!' With that he fetched the officer who found the zither a flat-handed smack alongside his head that sent him sprawling. The others beat a retreat, but not fast enough; grandfather grabbed zither's gun from his holster and let fly. The report seemed to crack the rafters; smoke filled the attic. A cop cursed and shot his hand to his shoulder. Somehow, we all finally got downstairs again and locked the door against the old gentleman. He fired once or twice more in the darkness and then went back to bed. 'That was grandfather', I explained to Joe, out of breath. 'He thinks you're deserters.' 'I'll say he does', said Joe.

The cops were reluctant to leave without getting their hands on somebody besides grandfather; the night had been distinctly a defeat for them. Furthermore, they obviously didn't like the 'layout'; something looked – and I can see their viewpoint – phony. They began to poke into things again. A reporter, a thin-faced, wispy man, came up to me. I had put on one of mother's blouses, not being able to find anything else. The reporter looked at me with mingled suspicion and interest. 'Just what the hell is the real lowdown here, Bud?' he asked. I decided to be frank with him. 'We had ghosts', I said. He gazed at me a long time as if I were a slot machine into which he had, without results, dropped a nickel. Then he walked away. The cops followed him, the one grandfather shot holding his now-bandaged arm, cursing and blaspheming. 'I'm gonna get my gun back from that old bird', said the zither-cop. 'Yeh', said Joe. 'You – and who else?' I told them I would bring it to the station house the next day.

'What was the matter with that one policeman?' mother asked, after they had gone. 'Grandfather shot him', I said. 'What for?' she demanded. I told her he was a deserter. 'Of all things!' said mother. 'He was such a nice-looking young man.'

Grandfather was fresh as a daisy and full of jokes at breakfast next morning. We thought at first he had forgotten all about

# *My Best Friend is a Dog*

## Groucho Marx

A man in my position (horizontal at the moment) is likely to hear strange stories about himself. For example, it was rumored a few years ago that I made a pig of myself drinking champagne out of Sophia Loren's slipper. This is sheer, slanderous nonsense. I am willing to concede that I tried to drink the bubbly stuff out of her slipper but she wouldn't take the damn shoe off her foot. So, while she wasn't looking, I drank it out of her handbag and nearly choked to death when I accidentally swallowed her lipstick along with the wine.

And now they say I am not a dog lover. Not a dog lover, indeed! Why, if I have a friend in the world it's my Great Dane bitch, Zsa-Zsa. We have been absolutely inseparable for years. The only reason she didn't come with me when I went to New York recently was that she didn't have the bus fare. Meanwhile, New York is a very lonely place without my dog. Actually, it's so lonely that when I see a pretty girl with a dog in the hotel lobby, tears come into my eyes and I invite the hound into the bar for a drink.

In the eight years we've been together, Zsa-Zsa and I have never quarrelled. Oh, occasionally she bites me but when she does I bite her right back. I'll teach her who's head of the house!

I don't spend any more on Zsa-Zsa's wardrobe than I have ever spent on any other girl, but she has never once asked me for a new collar just because the dog across the alley has a new collar. She has never sat in a night club with me and whined that Fred Astaire does the Twist and he's no kid so why can't I get off my butt and shake those old bones?

I give you my word that Zsa-Zsa has never said, 'Dear, why don't you take a few dancing lessons? Really, nobody does the Bunny Hug any more.'

Don't get me wrong. I am not suggesting that dogs will ever replace the fairest sex that blossoms in this great country of ours. That is something that every man will have to decide for himself. Personally, I don't see why a man can't have a dog *and* a girl. But if you can afford only one, get a dog. For example, if your dog sees you playing with another dog, does he rush to his lawyer and bark that your marriage is on the rocks and that he wants 600 bones a month alimony, the good car, and the little forty-thousand-dollar home that still has a nineteen-thousand-dollar mortgage on it?

Only once has a dog disappointed me. That was the time I took Alonzo, a big Saint Bernard, home from the studio. He had been working in a picture, earning twelve dollars a day, and he seemed lonely. I would have been even happier to take home a dog who earned fifteen hundred bucks a week. Lassie, for instance. But those dogs go with a much classier set than the crowd I hang around with.

At any rate, Alonzo was a very intelligent beast and his habit of running off with our brandy was, I suppose, typical of Saint Bernards, although many of my two-footed friends have done the same thing.

I was a little annoyed when Alonzo refused to eat the grub at my house. He said he preferred to take his meals at a nearby delicatessen. (Not that the food at my house isn't any good; I don't want people to get that idea, even though many of them have pointed it out to me. One woman said, 'Your food isn't fit for a dog.' Alonzo happened to be present that night and I think that's why he decided to eat out.)

Naturally my feelings were hurt when Alonzo walked out, but I kept my trap shut. After all, he was earning twelve dollars a day, which was eight dollars more than I was making at the time.

After he had been with me a week, I got the shock of my life. On Saturday night, just as I got through marking the liquor level on my brandy bottles, a little man stuck his head out of

Alonzo's skin and asked for his salary – twelve dollars a day! Of course I should have suspected something was wrong the day my girl friend came into the living room with the cat. Instead of chasing the cat, as a dog should, Alonzo chased my girl.

Possibly it was this incident which gave rise to the ugly rumour that I am not a dog lover. People stopped inviting me to their homes – the same people who hadn't been inviting me for years. Ladies walked by without troubling to curtsy, and even my barber cut me. That hurt most. Nevertheless, to me it was enough that my dog kept his faith in me.

My overwhelming affection for dogs does not mean, of course, that I have no love for other pets. All my life I have had animals of one kind or another around the house, even if it was only a small distant relative or a skunk. (And believe me, there's not a great deal of difference.)

Once, when I was a child, I was given a pair of guinea pigs which, with a little difficulty, I learned to love like brothers. Incidentally, learning to love my brothers was much more difficult. Well, the two guinea pigs settled down in our cellar and one afternoon I discovered the celler floor literally covered with the little creatures.

In those days my heart was smaller than it is now and I was able to love, at most, no more than thirty or forty guinea pigs. I was in a quandary. Did you ever spend an afternoon in a quandary with ninety-six guinea pigs?

'Sell them,' my brother Harpo suggested.

'If that,' I replied, 'is all you have to say, you ought never to bother to speak again.'

To this day Harpo has remained silent, and I can't tell you how pleased I've been.

Another brother, Gummo, came down to the cellar and he, too, said, 'Sell them.'

Since none of my brothers had any enthusiasm for these furry rodents, I took the hint and went to a near-by pet shop where I offered to sell my ninety-six guinea pigs for a paltry twenty dollars.

The dealer scratched his head. He then paced up and down the shop, kicking two guinea pigs who happened to be in his path. 'Tell you what I'll do,' he said. 'I'll give you a hundred guinea pigs for nothing, throw in a cockatoo, and pay you three dollars in cash.'

But let's get to the point of this story. For a good year-round pet, there is nothing to compare with a simple, unpedigreed chorus girl. Like the Maltese cat, the chorus girl becomes attached to any man who feeds her. But, unfortunately, there the resemblance ends, for whereas you can take a Maltese cat to the basement for a saucer of milk the chorus girl insists on eating at the Pavillion on '21' where two people can get a good meal for around sixty-eight dollars. That is, if you don't tip the waiter.

A poor man's pet is definitely not a chorus girl, but nevertheless some day I hope to own one.

●

# *The Most of S.J. Perelman*

## S.J. Perelman

### *Country Life*

According to recent figures compiled by trained statisticians working under filtered oatmeal, the first thing ninety-four per cent of the population does on acquiring a country place is to build some sort of swimming pool. The other six per cent instantly welshes on the deal and stops payment. I tried to, but the previous owner beat me to the bank. My checkbook had hardly ceased thrashing about in its final agony before I was out in honey-coloured corduroy leggings, barking orders at a team of mules and a scoop and shovel. I didn't want anything showy, just a fiord about the size of Lake Huron deep enough to float a yawl. In my overheated imagination I saw our anemic little creek transformed into a crystal mirror bordered by gay cabañas. I could almost hear the bevy of Powers models sighing with envy as my tanned, muscular form flashed off the spring-board in a perfect swan dive. I even wired the Department of the Interior that if Grand Coulee proved insufficient, I could furnish water power to keep the wheels turning for a year or two.

What I had when the gang of workmen departed was a small, shrunken buffalo wallow infested with every variety of poison-ous snake known to man, including several found only in the upper reaches of the Orinoco. Its surface was covered with an attractive green film dotted with decaying stumps and half-submerged oilcans. At night a dense mist shrouded the tarn, eerie lights flickered in the rushes, ghostly chuckles were audible, and if you ventured too close, you were liable to encounter a transparent citizen carrying his head under his arm. Thirteen families of ground hogs had set up light housekeeping in the dam itself, a massive affair of earth and logs that looked like the Union breastworks before Vicksburg. Every time it rained, the water boiled up, punching another hole in the structure, and I ran down the valley to pay the neighbours for the chickens it swept away. My children went hungry and unshod while I poured tons of cement into the coffers to make them hold. One morning I caught myself cackling hysterically and ramming an old mattress into the dam, and I knew I was licked. I called in the local dynamiter, indicated the project with a careless wave, and commanded him to erase it from the face of the earth.

The moment word was bruited about that Loch Wampum was doomed, the local savants gathered on the banks for a gleeful death watch. The man who had done the excavating was especially triumphant. 'I could have told him it wouldn't work,' he crowed. 'By rights he should have dug out that gully where they dump the swill. Good stone bottom there.' I asked him why he hadn't mentioned it earlier. 'It don't pay to poke your nose in other people's business,' he replied virtuously.

It took a day and a half for the dynamiter to drill the charges and string red flags across the township. On the appointed morning, the place was busier than New London during the Harvard-Yale regatta. Whole clans of Mennonites and Amish bearing box lunches arrived from the back country in ancient buckboards. Sightseers wandered through the garden poking sly fun at our vegetables, and one bystander mimicked my gait and speech so cleverly that I could not help sharing the general merriment. When everything was ready, I retired to the toolshed with my family and made them lie flat on the floor. With a warning, 'Stand clear, all!' the dynamiter threw his switch. The blast which followed tore the roof off the springhouse and broke windows in the county seat sixteen miles away. Its only effect on the damn, however, was to harden the cement in it. My specialist bit his lip in chagrin. 'I must have cut her a bit too fine,' he confessed; 'I'll fix her tomorrow, by cracky.'

He kept his word. When the dust finally settled, I had enough firewood for the next fifty years, most of it right inside the house where I could get at it. And when *I* finally settled, the man next door had a new front porch and a glass eye you couldn't tell from the other one. Of course it's a bit unwieldy for five people to take a bath in a washtub, particularly at one time, but at least you don't have to look out for copperheads.

Outside of a spring lamb trotting into a slaughterhouse, there is nothing in the animal kingdon as innocent and foredoomed as the new purchaser of a country place. The moment he scratches his signature on the deed, it is open season and no limit to the bag. At once, Nature starts cutting him down to size. Wells that bubbled over for two hundreds years mysteriously go dry, stone walls develop huge fissures, and chimneys sag out of plumb. Majestic elms which have withstood the full fury of the hurricane and the Dutch blight begin shedding their leaves; oaks dating from the reign of Charles II fade like cheap calico. Meanwhile, the former owner is busy removing a few personal effects. He rolls up the lawn preparatory to loading it on flat-cars, floats the larger trees downstream, and carts off the corncrib, woodshed and toolhouse. When I first viewed my own property, my dewy naïveté was incredible – even Dewey Naïveté, the agent who showed me around, had to suppress a smile. What sealed the choice was a decrepit hen-house occupied by a flock of white Wyandottes. According to my estimate, it needed only a vigorous dusting and a small can of enamel to transform it into a snug guest cottage. Shading my eyes, I could see the magnificent wistaria, heavy with blooms, creeping up a lattice any amateur could construct with ten cents' worth of nails. As soon as I took possession, though, I discovered it must have been on casters, for all that greeted me was a yawning pit trimmed with guano and eggshells.

This baptism, however, was merely a prelude to the keelhauling the natives had in store. Like any greenhorn from the city, I used to choke up freely at the sight of the man with the hoe. Every bumpkin I encountered reminded me of Daniel Webster; his dreariest platitude had the dignity and sweep of Walt

Whitman's verse. Selecting one noble old patriarch, who I was sure had served with John Brown at Harpers Ferry, I commissioned him to paint the barn. Several days later, he notified me that forty-seven gallons were exhausted. 'No use skimpin',' he warned. 'A hickory stump, a widow woman and a barn has to be protected from the weather.' I was chuckling over this bit of folk wisdom without quite understanding it when I detected a slight bulge under his coat similar to that caused by a five-gallon drum. He intercepted my glance and informed me fluently that he usually picked a few cranberries during his lunch hour. Apparently he lunched on Cape Cod, five hundred miles to the north, but since he never took more than half an hour, I overlooked it and ordered more paint. A week afterward, his barn burst forth in a shade of red identical with mine.

'Looks like new, don't it?' He grinned. 'Durned if I can tell 'em apart.' I knew what he meant.

I have been taken to the cleaners since by some notable brigands, but the most brazen of the lot was the kinsman of Jesse James who repaired our road. Edward Mittendorf and his merry men spent a fortnight lounging about in well-cut slacks, pitching quoits and reading Kierkegaard. Occasionally one of the more enterprising workmen would saunter over and deposit a pinch of gravel daintily in the ruts. Whenever my wife passed by, the crew appraised her charms whistling and clucking spiritedly. I entered a mild demurrer and received the following instructions: 'You tell 'em, corset; you've been around the ladies.' The day of settlement dawned on schedule, and with Mittendorf watching me beadily. I began to examine his bill. It was a closely typewritten document resembling the annual report of the Federal Reserve. Among other items he listed depreciation on shovels, lemonades for the men, and some bridgework his niece had ordered.

'Who's Ed Mittendorf?' I inquired, indicating a salary in excess of Cary Grant's.

'Mu cousin – the little fat feller,' he explained.

'Is he the same as Eddie Mittendorf?' I asked.

'No, that's my dad,' he returned smoothly, 'and Ned

Mittendorf there, he's my uncle. I'm Edward – got that straight?'

'I should,' I snapped. 'Your name's down here twice.'

'Is it?' he gasped. 'Well, I swan.'

I swanned also on reading the total, but I paid through the nose, a locale which was rapidly taking on the aspect of a teller's window. If you ever drive up the lane, be careful. Those diamonds raise hell with your treads.

I wouldn't live in the city if you paid me a million dollars a year – well, let's say forty-two dollars a year. How people can exist side by side with utter disregard for each other, never prying into anybody's business, is beyond me. In the country, folks are more matey; there is always an extra stiletto for the newcomer and a friendly hand ready to tighten around his throat. The moving men have hardly kicked the rungs out of your Chippendale chairs before neighbours spring up like mushrooms, eager to point out any flaws you may have missed in your place and gloat over your predicament. My wife and I were still knee-deep in a puddle outside our front door, exchanging shrill taunts and questioning each other's legitimacy, when our first visitor drove up. Shearing off an irreplaceable dogwood, he pulled into a flower bed and got out. From the expression of mingled condescension, malice and envy, I knew at once he must be another city man turned farmer. As his gaze travelled slowly over the *estancia*, he took on the look of one who has just bitten into an unripe persimmon.

'Finally unloaded it, did they?' he remarked with a ghoulish smirk.

'What do you mean?' I asked, my hackles rising to attention.

'The old pesthouse,' he said intimately. 'So they found a simp to take it off their hands.'

'Oh, I don't know,' I said with what started out as dignity but wound up a girlish toss of the head. He examined my clothes intently. 'You the hired man?' he asked at length.

'No, the simp,' I snarled. There was a brief interval during which I could hear his watch ticking.

'No hard feelings, brother,' he said eventually. Nice little spot you've got here. My name's Grundy.' He held out his hand.

'Mine's Frankenstein,' I said, ignoring it, 'and this is the Monster,' I added, indicating my wife.

'Glad to know you, Mrs Monster,' he acknowledged. 'I see you're having trouble with your foundation.'

'I *beg* your pardon,' she snapped with considerable hauteur, furtively smoothing her hips.

'I mean, of the house,' Grundy corrected himself. 'I saw your husband creeping around under the porch a while ago.'

'Oh, we was just rooting for truffles,' she said sweetly. As she stalked off, Grundy smacked his lips. 'Some package,' he commented. 'Where'd a little shrimp like you ever meet her?'

'Listen here, my friend,' I began, taking a step toward him.

'Yes,' he said thoughtfully, 'you've got plenty of things to worry about. You'll never be able to drink the water – it's tainted. And that woodwork of yours is alive with termites. What did you give for this root cellar?'

'Nothing,' I lied. 'We took it for a bad debt.'

'Well, you were stung,' said Grundy. 'Come here.' He approached one of the windows, and whipping out a jackknife, slashed at the casings. Several panes of glass shivered into fragments on the ground. 'Putty's rotten,' he said triumphantly. 'It's the talk of the countryside. And that's not all. See that stream down there? Every spring it rises to the second storey. You'll be doubled up with rheumatism, if the mosquitoes don't get you first. You know, I never saw the shack by daylight before; no wonder they say it's haunted. Now, you take my place –'

We took his place. It had thirty-five rooms and ten baths – snug but adequate for his needs. The attic was hand-hewn out of solid cherry, with burled walnut doors. For odd jobs he employed a lineal descendant of Cellini, whom he paid off in green trading stamps; the latter had just remodelled the barn into a game room and servants' quarters at a total cost of $2.76. The soil was none too fertile, he admitted – it took a week for tomatoes to bear and his dahlias were only a foot across. But there were so many trout in his creek that you could walk across without wetting your feet.

'Tell you what I'd do if I were you,' he concluded. 'I'd pitch a tent outside and use the dwelling for a cow stable. Only watch out where you camp; the grass is full of black widows.' He left, whistling the 'Dead March' from *Saul*, and I entered the house to find my wife in tears. She cried for six days and on the seventh created apple butter. It was good, but not like the woman's next door.

# *Army Days*

## Peter Ustinov

Our next duty was to try and capture the town of Maidstone from the Home Guard, that civilian task force of veterans and the infirm who were supposed to harass the Germans in case of a landing, and hold vital positions until better-armed units of the army could be deployed.

We were, on this occasion, supposed to be German. As soon as the battle began, I detached myself from my unit, and advanced along to the centre of the town by the simple expedient of knocking on people's doors. When they were opened, invariably by men in pyjamas or women in night-dresses, for it was a little before six in the morning, I would explain the vital nature of the manoeuvre, without ever revealing which side I was on. Flushed with patriotism, the good burghers of Maidstone forgot their annoyance at being woken so early, and let me through their houses, and into their gardens. Here I would climb into a neighbouring garden, and knock on the back door of another house. These people would then let me out of their front doors. Looking both ways, I would then race across the road and knock at another front door, and the process would repeat itself. It took me over two hours to penetrate into the centre of the city at right angles, as it were, to the traffic.

There, I suddenly found myself before the Home Guard headquarters. A choleric general emerged. I aimed my rifle at him, and fired. Since the rifle was empty, it only produced a click, which neither he nor the umpire, a very stout lieutenant, heard. I consequently shouted 'Bang!' and then informed the general, politely, that he was dead.

Death was the farthest thing from the general's mind, and he spluttered, 'Don't talk such tommyrot. Who are you, anyway?'

The umpire turned out to have a terrifying stammer. His face scarlet with effort and apology, he told the general that he was indeed d . . ., but the word simply would not come.

It was the delay in the verdict which more than anything seemed to enrage the general. 'Look here,' he snorted, 'it's not good enough. Fellow points a gun at me and says bang. May be a bad shot for all I know. Might have come out of the encounter unscathed, what?'

'Would you have preferred me to use ammunition?' I asked.

The general lost his head. 'Who asked your advice?' he blustered. 'Haven't you done enough harm?'

'D . . . ead!' the umpire managed at length.

'I won't accept it. Won't accept it, d'you hear? Not from a mere lieutenant.'

It was the lieutenant's turn to be annoyed. 'I am the acc . . . the . . . of . . .acc . . .'

'I don't give a damn about all that,' ranted the general. 'I'm off to inspect the forward positions, and I'd like to see the chap who's going to stop me.'

*'Sie sind tot!'* I cried.

The general spun on me, suspicious for the first time. 'What did you say?'

*'Sie sind, tot, Herr General!'*

'Are you talking some foreign language, or something?' asked the general, as though he was on the trail of something big.

*'Ich bin Deutscher.'*

'German, eh?' the general asked, his eyes narrowing.

'Acc . . . redited umpire of this exc . . . exc . . . sss,' the lieutenant declared.

Just then, some other Home Guards appeared out of headquarters.

'I've caught a German prisoner,' cried the general. 'Put him under lock and key,' and then, brushing the umpire aside, he jumped into his staff car, and told the driver to leave the scene of his humiliation as quickly as possible.

The umpire was boiling with frustration.

'I'm s . . . so . . . so . . .' he hissed.

'So am I, sir,' I said as I was led away.

A Home Guard major read all my correspondence, culled from my pockets, and then began a cross-examination.

I refused to answer in any language but German.

The major became very irritated. 'Now look here, I'm going to report you to your unit if you don't pull up your socks and answer a few questions.'

'*Das ist mir egal,*' I rasped.

'That's your final word?' he asked, evilly.

'*Heil Hitler!*' I shouted.

'That does it.'

They chose to lock me in the armoury.

I seized a Sten gun, broke open the door, upset the staff table, smeared ink on the maps and plans of the local high command, before I was overpowered by a cohort of old gentlemen, to whom I wished no harm, and therefore allowed myself to be locked into a disused scullery. They were all very angry indeed, and I felt that the frontier between fact and fiction had become unclear. One or two of them looked at me as though indeed I was a Nazi.

In the mid-afternoon, the colonel of my battalion arrived. He was a man whose voice rarely rose above a whisper, and whose head emerged from the front of his uniform at such an extravagant angle that from the side one could read the name of his tailor inside the jacket. He had the curious prehistoric look of a bemused turtle, and I always felt that if we ever had to face actual warfare in the company of this gentleman, he might well, in a moment of difficulty, disappear into his uniform until the storm blew over.

'Now what is all this?' he asked me almost inaudibly.

I explained, as so often, my version of the truth.

'I see,' he murmured. 'But was it really necessary to confuse the issue by speaking in German?'

'It's a manner in which the Germans are likely to confuse the issue, sir, if they should ever land in Maidstone,' I suggested.

'See what you mean,' he said, 'although that's an eventuality I consider to be most unlikely, don't you?'

I was a little suprised to be consulted, but decided to suggest that if there was no likelihood of the Germans landing in Maidstone, we were all wasting our time.

'Quite, quite,' he agreed absently, then smiled briefly. 'Full marks.'

On his way out, he hesitated a moment. 'You are one of my men, are you?'

'I'm wearing the uniform, sir,' I pointed out.

'Yes, yes. I just thought you might belong to the Home Guard. But then, of course, there'd be absolutely no point in your talking German.'

Muttering confirmations of his own opinion, he left the room, and secured my release by suggesting the Home Guard should all learn German in order to know how to deal with recalcitrant prisoners if, of course, the Germans ever had the bad taste to come to Maidstone.

Something happened to the British army around this time. While it was loath to abandon the extraordinary abstract attitude of many of its officers, to which it believed it owed many of its successes in history, it was nevertheless exasperated by the endless retreats before Germans and Japanese, who seemed to have got hold of something new by way of battle procedure. The result of these meditations in high places took various forms, all of them immensely unpleasant. It was determined that a new, more aggressive fighting man would arise like a khaki phoenix from the fires of abandoned supplies and gutted citadels. We were made to rush up and down the pebbled beaches barefoot in what were called 'foot-'ardening hexecises' by the non-commissioned officers who ran by our side, boots on their feet, encouraging us to ignore the pain of jagged stones, broken glass and desiccated seaweed. Then there were the battle courses, usually converted golf-courses, in which the conditions and some of the idiocy of battle were simulated, officers lying in ambush among the bushes with pots of animal blood which they would try to spray you with in order, so they declared, to get a man used to the sight of blood.

These traps were quite easy to avoid, since the officers were not very adept at concealment, and had no great faith in the psychological soundness of their task. Machine-guns would blast away over our heads to give us confidence in covering fire, which didn't prevent them from shooting dead a man running near me. Those repsonsible had negligently mounted their guns on sand, and when they began firing these automatically dug themselves in, with the result that instead of giving us covering fire they were merely shooting through us. This may be another reason why the officers lay low with their pots of blood.

Then there was a new secret weapon called Battle Drill, in which an infantry unit was sub-divided into platoons, each man having a specific and prescribed duty during an advance on an enemy position. I have no idea what was supposed to happen during a retreat, because we never practised those any more. Anyway, linking the activities of this combat group was a runner, who was supposed to charge over exposed ground with vital messages. My battalion was selected to produce the demonstration squad which would inject the whole South-Eastern Command with this new formula for success. My Battalion Commander selected my Company for the honour of forming this squad. The Company Commander then picked my platoon, and I need hardly add that I found myself in the demonstration squad, not as one of the chess men, but as the connecting runner! Out of the entire South-Eastern Command, they had to pick on me as a runner, with my heredity. Their horribly fallacious theory was that, being an actor, I was trained to commit long and complicated messages to memory. What they failed to realise was that, on eventual arrival at my destination, I was far too out of breath to deliver the message, and that by the time I had recovered my breath, I had forgotten the message.

All over the counties of Surrey, Sussex, Middlesex, and Kent we travelled in lorries in order to demonstrate this new method of defeating the Germans. I must have run hundreds of useless miles carrying information I was unable to deliver. For many years, before the advent of new highways, I was never lost in these counties. I recognised evey hedgerow as a refuge where I had panted my lungs out, with the grass going in and out of focus as I stared at it in order to avoid looking at the corporal who cast his shadow over my wheezing form.

'Deliver the fucking message, damn you!'

I recognised every hillock as an obstacle I had had to run across, doubled up, in order to lessen the target. I recognised every ditch as a gaping mouth ready to snatch my ankle in its jaws. Dante had his inferno, I had mine.

There was still one lesson to learn.

When eventually an application arrived to join Carol Reed, in Scotland in order to write a film about the techniques of Combined Operations, I was marched in to see the colonel. He vaguely recognised me from somewhere, Singapore, Kuala Lumpur, Maidstone . . .

'You don't want to leave us, do you?'

'Yes, sir, I do.'

'How very odd.'

He informed me that I could leave the very next day after lunch, and after a morning spent in the rifle butts. I was so intoxicated with relief at being able to leave this Alice-in-Wonderland unit that I shot like a sheriff in a Western, fast and furious and carefree. When they fetched my target, it was revealed that I had shot all ten bullets in the same hole. The centre of the target was just demolished. The colonel affixed the target to his notice-board, my posting was cancelled, and I was sent on a sniper's course. Not only did Great Britain have Battle Drill up its sleeve, it also had a Wyatt Earp. The only trouble, as they were to find out, was that however good a shot I might be, I needed the help of ten men to lift me into a position from where I could wreak havoc. A few days later I left for Scotland after all.

And here is the lesson I learned in the army. If you want to do a thing badly, you have to work as hard at it as though you want to do it well.

●

# *Life's Rich Pageant*

## Arthur Marshall

As was the custom in all schools, we played every day, except Sundays (walks), some game, or boxed, or ran, or did gymnastics and I once, to my great surprise, found myself taking part in a cricketing 'stand'. In some ways the authorities at Stirling Court encouraged individuality, or perhaps it was simply because they got tired of struggling away, day after day, to make us conform to a pattern, and at cricket many of us had been at pains to acquire a little speciality that was all our own. A boy called Mould bowled sneaks of a really sensational speed and accuracy, varying them with lofted deliveries that appeared to descend from the stratosphere. A boy called Westmore used to pretend to have hurt his ankle and, playing at mid-off, limped quite a bit, encouraging members of opposing school teams to try to snatch a single where no single was (there were no fewer than five Run Outs in a needle match against Fairfields). I regret to say, but truth is truth, that Murphy, who fielded at point year after year (our positions were never changed) had perfected a range of noises of a kind that I do not wish to discuss and which considerably unsettled prim batsmen from more sedate schools. My special friend, Williamson, was our wicket-keeper and, when called upon to bat, had developed, for use against umpires, a stare so compelling and imperious and disturbing that few ever dared to give him out even though, bulky as he was, he was plainly constantly impeding the straight passage of ball to stump. I freely confess that the cricketing tone of Stirling Court could not be counted among the best.

My own 'thing' was, and I cannot recommend it too highly for those readers who still indulge in our national game, to use the bat the wrong way round and present the triangular side to the ball. The results pass all expectation, the ball ricocheting quite unpredictably, now here, now there, and, as often as not, flying to the boundary to the amazement of all. During the stand of which I speak, I found myself at the crease with Williamson and playing, as so often, our great rivals, Dumbleton Park. Williamson had already survived four confident and fully justified appeals for LBW and one of the umpires had started to twitch nervously (another of Williamson's devastating ploys, anticipating Potter, was to request umpires, and especially after a No Ball, to 'speak up, please!'). On my going out to bat and join Williamson, he approached me and muttered a few words which I dare say onlookers took to be sage advice about which way the ball was swinging, or whatever, but which, knowing him, were probably a brisk run-down of the edible items that he later intended to purchase with his Saturday pocket-money. We then settled to our task, and Williamson's scowls at the umpires (he sometimes asked for an unusual guard: 'Off stump, please') and my wrong-sided bat produced between them 18 runs. This was, to us, a notable total and I expect that in the long winter evenings at Stirling Court they speak of it still.

At Stirling Court we 'did' Genesis in the sixth form (it was probably considered too sensational and disturbing for younger boys) and here Williamson came into his own for he had a splendidly enquiring and, when necessary, slightly dirty mind and was not at all averse to asking questions, especially when he suspected, and how right he usually was, that the full truth was being, for some adult reason, withheld from him. He had already caused considerable consternation among the teaching staff by insisting on having the word 'whore' explained to him ('an immoral woman who sells herself for gold and I don't want to hear another word from you this lesson, Williamson') and he had followed it up with 'eunuch', which he mistakenly pronounced ee-unch ('a handicapped male person sometimes in the service of an eastern prince and come and see me after prayers, Williamson').

As soon as, in Genesis, we reached the Cities of the Plain and

Sodom in particular, Williamsons's alert mind spotted that we were not being told All. The story, as watered down for our youthful ears, was feeble in the extreme. Everything hung, as you'll recall, on a secondary meaning of the verb 'to know'. This, we were told by a young and blushing Mr Sinclair, just meant 'getting to know you' merely indicated a chummy approach – one imagined a sort of exchange of names and visiting cards ('I'm Uz, and this is my friend, Obal'). But why then the fire and brimstone and why, most revealing of all, these blushes? Williamson kept up a fine barrage of 'But, sir . . .', Mr Sinclair countering strongly with 'Oh do shut up, Williamson!' As soon as the lesson was over, Williamson flew to the school library and searching, in a high state of excitement, through Chambers's invaluable dictionary, found what he was looking for ('To have sexual commerce with') and next day a fresh persecution of poor Mr Sinclair began, by now in deep trouble over Lot's unconventional behaviour in the mountains behind Zoar. 'Please sir, what does "commerce" mean?' 'It depends in what sense, Williamson. And why do you ask?' And so on.

Among the enticing literary treats that I have either had, through pressure of work or absence of time, to forgo or which have never, as in this case, come within my reach, a novel called *Apples of Sodom* ranks pretty high. It was the work of a woman, a Miss Mary Bramston, it was written about 1870, and she sold the world rights for £20. Somewhere there lurk, presumably, critical evaluations of the work ('Miss Bramston casts a bright and wholesome light on a dark corner of biblical history') but its chief interest lies in the fact that its authoress was at the same time, governess to the children of those unusually bizarre Benson parents. It isn't every day that the Master of Wellington College, later Archbishop of Canterbury, marries a basically homosexual bride half his age and they then produce between them, in conditions that the sensitive will prefer not to dwell on, three highly gifted and queer sons, among them E.F. Benson to whom we owe the marvellous Miss Mapp and Lucia books, and much else. There was also a homicidal maniac daughter. Believers in predestination will enjoy picturing God arranging all that elaborate little tangle, so very different from conditions at Oundle.

One does so wonder whether the oddities of the Benson background and the tendencies of her charges inspired or influenced to some extent the authoress of *Apples of Sodom*. Who, do you suppose, can be the main character? It can hardly be Mrs Lot of whom vivid details are really rather scarce and whom one sees as a somewhat shadowy and nervous figure, twitching a goodish bit and probably locking herself in a hidden recess while all that clamouring and banging was going on at their door ('Do see who that is, dear. Tell them we've got visitors. If you want me, I'm in the airing cupboard'), though she does of course in the end have her moment of glory as a Challenge to Cerebos. We know much more, rather too much in fact, about her husband and especially his last unfortunate days in that cave, though here his childless and incestuous daughters were much to blame and he, poor man, lying there in a drunken stupor, was literally more sinned against than sinning. None of these persons would, however, tempt the pen of a governess in the saintly public school household of a future archbishop, so the leading figure must have been somebody else. Or do you think that *Apples of Sodom* was in fact a 'modern' novel but with an, er, Sodom theme?

Twice a term, matron would appear in the dormitories while we were getting up and deciding it was too cold to wash and, looking for her fairly ferocious, handed out brimming mugs of Gregory Powder, an appallingly explosive purgative. And in addition to this, we were all issued (6d on the bill) with an improving little booklet called 'Self Helps to Self and Fitness' which aimed at producing both the mind serene and the body beautiful. After a foreword on the importance of regular habits, the opening sentence of the main body of the work ran: 'On waking, trumpet vigorously to clear nostrils'. 'To trumpet', we learned, meant to snort noisily outwards. The author was a master at the school, a deviate giant who taught French extremely well and added to this ability various unscheduled extras when opportunity presented itself. Whenever out in the open, he chose to trumpet and snuffle without benefit of handkerchief, finger and thumb to nose. I have seen others do this since and as a spectacle I haven't ever come to love it. With the aid of the Self Helps, we ran here, doubled there, threw this and held that, our minds sullenly unreceptive and by no means serene. We benefited, I don't doubt, bodily but I've never enjoyed being coerced into any violent physical movement, apart from those that come quite naturally such as running for a bus or nimbly dodging cars or playing Scrabble, and since leaving the school (it was 1924) and abandoning Self Helps, I've rather let that side of things slide.

●

## *Part Six*

# EXIT LAUGHTER

It's a funny old world – a man's lucky if he gets out of it alive.

**W.C. Fields**

# *A Linguistic Experiment*

## Jerome K. Jerome

On Monday afternoon Harris came round; he had a cycling paper in his hand.

I said: 'If you take my advice, you will leave it alone.'

Harris said: 'Leave what alone?'

I said: 'That brand-new, patent, revolution in cycling, record-breaking, tomfoolishness, whatever it may be, the advertisement of which you have there in your hand.'

He said: 'Well, I don't know; there will be some steep hills for us to negotiate; I guess we shall want a good brake.'

I said: 'We shall want a brake, I agree; what we shall not want is a mechanical surprise that we don't understand, and that never acts when it is wanted.'

'This thing,' he said, 'acts automatically.'

'You needn't tell me,' I said. 'I know exactly what it will do, by instinct. Going uphill it will jamb the wheel so effectively that we shall have to carry the machine bodily. The air at the top of the hill will do it good, and it will suddenly come right again. Going downhill it will start reflecting what a nuisance it has been. This will lead to remorse, and finally to despair. It will say to itself; "I'm not fit to be a brake. I don't help these fellows; I only hinder them. I'm a curse, that's what I am"; and, without a word of warning, it will "chuck" the whole business. That is what that brake will do. Leave it alone. You are a good fellow,' I continued, 'but you have one fault.'

'What?' he asked indignantly.

'You have too much faith,' I answered. 'If you read an advertisement, you go away and believe it. Every experiment that every fool has thought of in connection with cycling you have tried. Your guardian angel appears to be a capable and conscientious spirit, and hitherto she has seen you through; take my advice and don't try her too far. She must have had a busy time since you started cycling. Don't go on till you make her mad.'

He said: 'If every man talked like that there would be no advancement made in any department of life. If nobody ever tried a new thing the world would come to a standstill. It is by . . .'

'I know all that can be said on that side of the argument,' I interrupted. 'I agree in trying new experiments up to thirty-five; *after* thirty-five I consider a man is entitled to think of himself. You and I have done our duty in this direction, you especially. You have been blown up by a patent gas lamp . . .'

He said: 'I really think, you know, that was my fault; I think I must have screwed it up too tight.'

I said: 'I am quite willing to believe that if there was a wrong way of handling the thing that is the way you would handle it. You should take that tendency of yours into consideration; it bears upon the argument. Myself, I did not notice what you did; I only know we were riding peacefully and pleasantly along the Whitby Road, discussing the Thirty Years War, when your lamp went off like a pistol shot. The start sent me into the ditch; and your wife's face, when I told her there was nothing the matter and that she was not to worry, because the two men would carry you upstairs, and the doctor would be round in a minute bringing the nurse with him, still lingers in my memory.'

He said: 'I wish you had thought to pick up the lamp. I should like to have found out what was the cause of its going off like that.'

I said: 'There was not time to pick up the lamp. I calculated it would have taken two hours to have collected it. As to its "going off," the mere fact of its being advertised as the safest lamp ever intended would of itself, to anyone but you, have suggested accident. Then there was that electric lamp,' I continued.

'Well, that really did give a fine light,' he replied; 'you said so yourself.'

I said: 'It gave a brilliant light in the King's Road, Brighton, and frightened a horse. The moment we got into the dark beyond Kemp Town it went out, and you were summoned for riding without a light. You may remember that on sunny afternoons you used to ride about with that lamp shining for all it was worth. When lighting-up time came it was naturally tired, and wanted a rest.'

'It was a bit irritating, that lamp,' he murmured; 'I remember it.'

I said: 'It irritated me; it must have been worse for you. Then, there are saddles,' I went on – I wished to get this lesson home to him. 'Can you think of any saddle ever advertised that you have *not* tried?'

He said: 'It has been an idea of mine that the right saddle is to be found.'

I said: 'You give up that idea; this is an imperfect world of joy and sorrow mingled. There may be a better land where bicycle saddles are made out of rainbow, stuffed with cloud; in this world the simplest thing is to get used to something hard. There was that saddle you bought in Birmingham; it was divided in the middle, and looked like a pair of kidneys.'

He said: 'You mean that one constructed on anatomical principles.'

'Very likely,' I replied. 'The box you bought it in had a picture on the cover, representing a sitting skeleton – or rather that part of a skeleton which does sit.'

He said: 'It was quite correct; it showed you the true position of the . . .'

I said: 'We will not go into details; the picture always seemed to me indelicate.'

He said: 'Medically speaking, it was right.'

'Possibly,' I said, 'for a man who rode in nothing but his bones. I only know that I tried it myself, and that to a man who wore flesh it was agony. Every time you went over a stone or a rut it nipped you; it was like riding on an irritable lobster. You rode that for a month.'

'I thought it only right to give it a fair trial,' he answered.

I said: 'You gave your family a fair trial also; if you will allow me the use of slang. Your wife told me that never in the whole course of your married life had she known you so bad tempered, so unchristian-like, as you were that month. Then you remember that other saddle, the one with the spring under it.'

He said: 'You mean "the Spiral." '

I said: 'I mean the one that jerked you up and down like a jack-in-the-box; sometimes you came down again in the right place, and sometimes you didn't. I am not referring to these matters merely to recall painful memories, but I want to impress you with the folly of trying experiments at your time of life.'

He said: 'I wish you wouldn't harp so much on my age. A man at thirty-four . . .'

'A man at what?'

He said: 'If you don't want the thing, don't have it. If your machine runs away with you down a mountain, and you and George get flung through a church roof, don't blame me.'

'I cannot promise for George,' I said; 'a little thing will sometimes irritate him, as you know. If such an accident as you suggest happens, he may be cross, but I will undertake to explain to him that it was not your fault.'

'Is the thing all right?' he asked.

'The tandem,' I replied, 'is well.'

He said: 'Have you overhauled it?'

I said: 'I have not, nor is anyone else going to overhaul it. The thing is now in working order, and it is going to remain in working order till we start.'

I have had experience of this 'overhauling.' There was a man at Folkestone; I used to meet him on the Lees. He proposed one evening we should go for a long bicycle ride together on the following day, and I agreed. I got up early, for me; I made an effort, and was pleased with myself. He came half an hour later: I was waiting for him in the garden. It was a lovely day. He said:

'That's a good-looking machine of yours. How does it run?'

'Oh, like most of them!' I answered; 'easily enough in the morning; goes a little stiffly after lunch.'

He caught hold of it by the front wheel and the fork, and shook it violently.

I said: 'Don't do that; you'll hurt it.'

I did not see why he should shake it; it had not done anything to him. Besides, if it wanted shaking, I was the proper person to shake it. I felt much as I should had he started whacking my dog.

He said: 'This front wheel wobbles.'

I said: 'It doesn't if you don't wobble it.' It didn't wobble, as a matter of fact – nothing worth calling a wobble.

He said: 'This is dangerous; have you got a screw-hammer?'

I ought to have been firm, but I thought that perhaps he really did know something about the business. I went to the tool shed to see what I could find. When I came back he was sitting on the ground with the front wheel between his legs. He was playing with it, twiddling it round between his fingers; the remnant of the machine was lying on the gravel path beside him.

He said: 'Something has happened to this front wheel of yours.'

'It looks like it, doesn't it?' I answered. But he was the sort of man that never understands satire.

He said: 'It looks to me as if the bearings were all wrong.'

I said: 'Don't you trouble about it any more; you will make yourself tired. Let us put it back and get off.'

He said: 'We may as well see what is the matter with it, now it is out.' He talked as though it had dropped out by accident.

Before I could stop him he had unscrewed something somewhere, and out rolled all over the path some dozen or so little balls.

'Catch 'em!' he shouted; 'catch 'em! We mustn't lose any of them.' He was quite excited about them.

We grovelled round for half an hour, and found sixteen. He said he hoped we had got them all, because, if not, it would make a serious difference to the machine. He said there was nothing you should be more careful about in taking a bicycle to pieces than seeing you did not lose any of the balls. He explained that you ought to count them as you took them out, and see that exactly the same number went back in each place. I promised, if ever I took a bicycle to pieces I would remember his advice.

I put the balls for safety in my hat, and I put my hat upon the doorstep. It was not a sensible thing to do, I admit. As a matter of fact; it was a silly thing to do. I am not as a rule addle-headed; his influence must have affected me.

He then said that while he was about it he would see to the chain for me, and at once began taking off the gearcase. I did try to persuade him from that. I told him what an experienced friend of mine once said to me solemnly:

'If anything goes wrong with your gearcase, sell the machine and buy a new one; it comes cheaper.'

He said: 'People talk like that who understand nothing about machines. Nothing is easier than taking off a gearcase.'

I had to confess he was right. In less then five minutes he had the gearcase in two pieces, lying on the path, and was grovelling for screws. He said it was always a mystery to him the way screws disappeared.

We were still looking for screws when Ethelbertha came out. She seemed surprised to find us there; she said she thought we had started hours ago.

He said: 'We shan't be long now. I'm just helping your husband to overhaul this machine of his. It's a good machine; but they all want going over occasionally.'

Ethelbertha said: 'If you want to wash yourselves when you have done you might go into the back kitchen, if you don't mind; the girls have just finished the bedrooms.'

She told me that if she met Kate they would probably go for a sail; but that in any case she would be back to lunch. I would have given a sovereign to be going with her. I was getting heartily sick of standing about watching this fool breaking up my bicycle.

Common sense continued to whisper to me: 'Stop him, before he does any more mischief. You have a right to protect your own property from the ravages of a lunatic. Take him by the scruff of the neck, and kick him out of the gate!'

But I am weak when it comes to hurting other people's feelings, and I let him muddle on.

He gave up looking for the rest of the screws. He said screws had a knack of turning up when you least expected them, and that now he would see to the chain. He tightened it till it would not move; next he loosened it until it was twice as loose as it was before. Then he said we had better think about getting the front wheel back into its place again.

I held the fork open, and he worried with the wheel. At the end of ten minutes I suggested he should hold the forks, and that I should handle the wheel; and we changed places. At the end of his first minute he dropped the machine, and took a short walk round the croquet lawn, with his hands pressed together between his thighs. He explained as he walked that the thing to be careful about was to avoid getting your fingers pinched between the forks and the spokes of the wheel. I replied I was convinced, from my own experience, that there was much truth in what he said. He wrapped himself up in a couple of dusters, and we commenced again. At length we did get the thing into position; and the moment it was in position he burst out laughing.

I said: 'What's the joke?'

He said: 'Well, I am an ass!'

It was the first thing he had said that made me respect him. I asked him what had led him to the discovery.

He said: 'We've forgotten the balls!'

I looked for my hat; it was lying topsyturvy in the middle of the path, and Ethelbertha's favourite hound was swallowing the balls as fast as he could pick them up.

'He will kill himself,' said Ebbson – I have never met him since that day, thank the Lord; but I think his name was Ebbson – 'they are solid steel.'

I said: 'I am not troubling about the dog. He has had a bootlace and a packet of needles already this week. Nature's the best guide; puppies seem to require this kind of stimulant. What I am thinking about is my bicycle.'

He was of a cheerful disposition. He said: 'Well, we must put back all we can find, and trust to providence.'

We found eleven. We fixed six on one side and five on the other, and half an hour later the wheel was in its place again. It need hardly be added that it really did wobble now; a child might have noticed it. Ebbson said it would do for the present. He appeared to be getting a bit tired himself. If I had let him, he would, I believe, at this point have gone home. I was determined now, however, that he should stop and finish; I had abandoned all thoughts of a ride. My pride in the machine he had killed. My only interest lay now in seeing him scratch and bump and pinch himself. I revived his drooping spirits with a glass of beer and some judicious praise: I said:

'Watching you do this is of real use to me. It is not only your skill and dexterity that fascinates me, it is your cheery confidence in yourself, your inexplicable hopefulness, that does me good.'

Thus encouraged, he set to work to refix the gearcase. He stood the bicycle against the house, and worked from the off side. Then he stood it against a tree, and worked from the near side. Then I held it for him, while he lay on the ground with his head between the wheels, and worked at it from below, and dropped oil upon himself. Then he took it away from me, and doubled himself across it like a pack-saddle, till he lost his balance and slid over on to his head. Three times he said:

'Thank heaven, that's right at last!'

And twice he said:

'No, I'm damned if it is after all!'

What he said the third time I try to forget.

Then he lost his temper and tried bullying the thing. The bicycle, I was glad to see, showed spirit; and the subsequent proceedings degenerated into little else than a rough-and-tumble fight between him and the machine. One moment the bicycle would be on the gravel path, and he on top of it; the next, the position would be reversed – he on the gravel path, the bicycle on him. Now he would be standing flushing with victory, the bicycle firmly fixed between his legs. But his triumph would be short-lived. By a sudden, quick movement it would free itself, and, turning upon him, hit him sharply over the head with one of its handles.

At a quarter to one, dirty and dishevelled, cut and bleeding, he said: 'I think that will do'; and rose and wiped his brow.

The bicycle looked as if it also had had enough of it. Which had received most punishment it would have been difficult to say. I took him into the back kitchen, where, so far as was possible without soda and proper tools, he cleaned himself, and sent him home.

The bicycle I put into a cab and took round to the nearest repairing shop. The foreman of the works came up and looked at it.

'What do you want me to do with that?' said he.

'I want you,' I said, 'so far as is possible, to restore it.'

'It's a bit far gone,' said he; 'but I'll do my best.'

He did his best, which came to two pounds ten. But it was never the same machine again; and at the end of the season I left it in an agent's hands to sell. I wished to deceive nobody; I instructed the man to advertise it as a last year's machine. The agent advised me not to mention any date. He said:

'In this business it isn't a question of what is true and what isn't; it's a question of what you can get people to believe. Now, between you and me, it don't look like a last year's machine; so far as looks are concerned, it might be a ten-year-old. We'll say nothing about date; we'll just get what we can.'

I left the matter to him, and he got me five pounds, which he said was more than he had expected.

There are two ways you can get exercise out of a bicycle: you can 'overhaul' it, or you can ride it. On the whole, I am not sure that a man who takes his pleasure overhauling does not have the best of the bargain. He is independent of the weather and the wind; the state of the roads troubles him not. Give him a screw-hammer, a bundle of rags, an oil-can, and something to sit down upon, and he is happy for the day. He has to put up with certain disadvantages, of course; there is no joy without alloy. He himself always looks like a tinker, and his machine always suggests the idea that, having stolen it, he has tried to disguise it; but as he rarely gets beyond the first milestone with it, this perhaps, does not much matter. The mistake some people make is in thinking they can get both forms of sport out of the same machine. This is impossible; no machine will stand for the double strain. You must make up your mind whether you are going to be an 'overhauler' or a rider. Personally, I prefer to ride, therefore I take care to have near me nothing that can tempt me to overhaul. When anything happens to my machine I wheel it to the nearest repairing shop. If I am too far from the town or village to walk, I sit by the roadside and wait till a cart comes along. My chief danger, I always find, is from the wandering overhauler. The sight of a broken-down machine is to the over-hauler as a wayside corpse to a crow, he swoops down upon it with a friendly yell of triumph. At first I used to try politeness. I would say:

'It's nothing; don't you trouble. You ride on, and enjoy yourself, I beg it of you as a favour; please go away.'

Experience has taught me, however, that courtesy is of no use in such an extremity. Now I say:

'You go away and leave the thing alone, or I will knock your silly head off.'

And if you look determined, and have a good stout cudgel in your hand, you can generally drive him off.

George came in later that day. He said:

'Well, do you think everything will be ready?'

I said: 'Everything will be ready by Wednesday, except, perhaps, you and Harris.'

He said: 'Is the tandem all right?'

'The tandem,' I said, 'is well.'

He said: 'You don't think it wants overhauling?'

I replied: 'Age and experience have taught me that there are few matters concerning which a man does well to be positive. Consequently, there remain to me now but a limited number of questions upon which I feel any degree of certainty. Among such still-unshaken beliefs, however, is the conviction that that tandem does not want overhauling. I also feel a presentiment that, provided my life is spared, no human being between now and Wednesday morning is going to ovehaul it.'

George said: 'I should not show temper over the matter, if I were you. There will come a day, perhaps not far distant, when that bicycle, with a couple of mountains between it and the nearest repairing shop, will, in spite of your chronic desire for rest, *have* to be overhauled. Then you will clamour for people to tell you where you put the oil-can, and what you have done with the screw-hammer. Then, while you exert yourself holding the thing steady against a tree, you will suggest that somebody else should clean the chain and pump the back wheel.'

I felt there was justice in George's rebuke – also a certain amount of prophetic wisdom. I said:

'Forgive me if I seemed unresponsive. The truth is, Harris was round here this morning . . .'

George said: 'Say no more; I understand. Besides, what I came to talk to you about was another matter. Look at that.'

He handed me a small book bound in red cloth. It was a guide to English conversation for the use of German travellers. It commenced 'On a Steamboat,' and terminated 'At the Doctor's'; its longest chapter being devoted to conversation in a railway carriage, among, apparently, a compartment load of quarrelsome and ill-mannered lunatics: 'Can you not get farther away from me, sir?' – 'It is impossible, madam; my neighbour, here, is very stout' – 'Shall we not endeavour to arrange our legs?' – 'Please have the goodness to keep your elbows down' – 'Pray do not inconvenience yourself, madam, if my shoulder is of any accommodation to you,' whether intended to be said sarcastically or not, there was nothing to indicate – 'I really must request you to move a little, madam, I can hardly breathe,' the author's idea being, presumably, that by this time the whole party was mixed up together on the floor. The chapter concluded with the phrase: 'Here we are at our destination, God be thanked! (*Gott sei dank!*)' a pious exclamation, which under the circumstances must have taken the form of a chorus.

At the end of the book was an appendix, giving the German traveller hints concerning the preservation of his health and comfort during his sojourn in English towns; chief among such hints being advice to him to always travel with a supply of disinfectant powder, to always lock his bedroom door at night, and to always carefully count his small change.

'It is not a brilliant publicaiton,' I remarked, handing the book back to George; 'it is not a book that personally I would recommend to any German about to visit England; I think it would get him disliked. But I have read books published in

London for the use of English travellers abroad every whit as foolish. Some educated idiot, misunderstanding seven languages, would appear to go about writing these books for the misinformation and false guidance of modern Europe.'

'You cannot deny,' said George, 'that these books are in large request. They are bought by the thousand, I know. In every town in Europe there must be people going about talking this sort of thing.'

'Maybe,' I replied; 'but fortunately, nobody understands them. I have noticed, myself, men standing on railway platforms and at streets corners reading aloud from such books. Nobody knows what language they are speaking; nobody has the slightest knowledge of what they are saying. This is, perhaps, as well; were they understood they would probably be assaulted.'

George said: 'Maybe you are right; my idea is to see what would happen if they were understood. My proposal is to get to London early on Wednesday morning, and spend an hour or two going about and shopping with the aid of this book. There are one or two little things I want – a hat and a pair of bedroom slippers, among other articles. Our boat does not leave Tilbury till twelve, and that just gives us time. I want to try this sort of talk where I can properly judge of its effect. I want to see how the foreigner feels when he is talked to in this way.'

It struck me as a sporting idea. In my enthusiasm I offered to accompany him, and wait outside the shop. I said I thought that Harris would like to be in it, too – or rather outside.

George said that was not quite his scheme. His proposal was that Harris and I should accompany him into the shop. With Harris, who looks formidable, to support him, and myself at the door to call the police if necessary, he said he was willing to adventure the thing.

We walked round to Harris's, and put the proposal before him. He examined the book, especially the chapter dealing with the purchase of shoes and hats. He said:

'If George talks to any bootmaker or any hatter the things that are put down here, it is not support he will want; it is carrying to the hospital that he will need.'

That made George angry.

'You talk,' said George, 'as though I were a foolhardy boy without any sense. I shall select from the more polite and less irritating speeches; the grosser insults I shall avoid.'

This being clearly understood, Harris gave in his adhesion; and our start was fixed for early Wednesday morning.

George came down on Tuesday evening, and slept at Harris's place. We thought this a better arrangement than his own suggestion, which was that we should call for him on our way and 'pick him up.' Picking George up in the morning means picking him out of bed to begin with, and shaking him awake – in itself an exhausting effort with which to commence the day; helping him find his things and finish his packing; and then waiting for him while he eats his breakfast, a tedious entertainment from the spectators point of view, full of wearisome repetition.

I knew that if he slept at Beggarbush he would be up in time; I have slept there myself, and I know what happens. About the middle of the night, as you judge, though in reality it may be somewhat later, you are startled out of your first sleep by what sounds like a rush of cavalry along the passage, just outside your door. Your half-awakened intelligence fluctuates between burglars, the Day of Judgment, and a gas explosion. You sit up in bed and listen intently. You are not kept waiting long; the next moment the door is violently slammed, and somebody, or something, is evidently coming downstairs on a tea-tray.

'I told you so,' said a voice outside, and immediately some hard substance, a head one would say from the ring of it, rebounds against the panel of your door.

By this time you are charging madly round the room for your clothes. Nothing is where you put it overnight; the articles most essential have disappeared entirely; and meanwhile the murder, or revolution, or whatever it is, continues unchecked. You pause for a moment, with your head under the wardrobe, where you think you can see your slippers, to listen to a steady, monotonous thumping upon a distant door. The victim, you presume, has taken refuge there; they mean to have him out and finish him. Will you be in time? The knocking ceases, and a voice, sweetly reassuring in its gentle plaintiveness, asks merely:

'Pa, may I get up?'

You do not hear the other voice, but the responses are:

'No, it was only the bath – no, she ain't really hurt – only wet, you know. Yes, ma, I'll tell 'em what you say. No, it was a pure accident. Yes; good night, papa.'

Then the same voice, exerting itself so as to be heard in a distant part of the house, remarks:

'You've got to come upstairs again. Pa says it isn't time yet to get up.'

You return to bed, and lie listening to somebody being dragged upstairs, evidently against her will. By a thoughtful arrangement the spare rooms at Beggarbush are exactly underneath the nurseries. The same somebody, you conclude, still offering the most credible opposition, is being put back into bed. You can follow the contest with much exactitude, because every time the body is flung down upon the spring mattress, the bedstead, just above your head, makes a sort of jump; while every time the body succeeds in struggling out again, you are aware by the thud upon the floor. After a time the struggle wanes, or maybe the bed collapses; and you drift back into sleep. But the next moment, or what seems to be the next moment, you again open your eyes under the consciousness of a presence. The door is being held ajar, and four solemn faces, piled one on top of the other, are peering at you, as though you were some natural curiosity kept in this particular room. Seeing you awake, the top face, walking calmly over the other three, comes in and sits on the bed in a friendly attitude.

Oh!' it says, 'we didn't know you were awake. I've been awake some time.'

'So I gather,' you reply shortly.

'Pa doesn't like us to get up too early,' he continues. 'He says everybody else in the house is liable to be disturbed if we get up. So, of course, we mustn't.'

The tone is that of gentle resignation. It is instinct with the spirit of virtuous pride, arising from the consciousness of self-sacrifice.

'Don't you call this being up?' you suggest.

'Oh, no; we're not really up, you know, because we're not properly dressed.' The fact is self-evident. 'Pa's always very tired in the morning,' the voice continues; 'of course, that's because he works hard all day. Are you ever tired in the morning?'

At this point he turns and notices, for the first time, that the three other children have also entered, and are sitting in a semicircle on the floor. From their attitude it is clear they have mistaken the whole thing for one of the slower forms of entertainment, some comic lecture or conjuring exhibition, and are waiting patiently for you to get out of bed and do something. It shocks him, the idea of their being in the guest's bedchamber. He peremptorily orders them out. They do not answer him, they do not argue; in dead silence, and with one accord they fall upon him. All you can see from the bed is a confused tangle of waving arms and legs, suggestive of an intoxicated octopus trying to find bottom. Not a word is spoken; that seems to be the etiquette of the thing. If you are sleeping in your pyjamas, you spring from the bed, and only add to the confusion; if you are wearing a less showy garment, you stop where you are and shout commands, which are utterly unheeded. The simplest plan is to leave it to the eldest boy. He does get them out after a while, and closes the door upon them. It reopens immediately, and one, generally Muriel, is shot back into the room. She enters as from a catapult. She is handicapped by having long hair, which can be used as a convenient handle. Evidently aware of this natural disadvantage, she clutches it herself tightly in one hand, and punches with the other. He opens the door again, and cleverly uses her as a battering-ram against the wall of those without. You can hear the dull crash as her head enters among them, and scatters them. When the victory is complete, he comes back and resumes his seat on the bed. There is no bitterness about him; he has forgotten the whole incident.

'I like the morning,' he says, 'don't you?'

'Some mornings,' you agree, 'are all right; others are not so peaceful.'

He takes no notice of your exception; a far-away look steals over his somewhat ethereal face.

'I should like to die in the morning,' he said: 'everything is so beautiful then.'

'Well,' you answer, 'perhaps you will, if your father ever invites an irritable man to come and sleep here, and doesn't warn him beforehand.'

He descends from his contemplative mood, and becomes himself again.

'It's jolly in the garden,' he suggests; 'you wouldn't like to get up and have a game of cricket, would you?'

It was not the idea with which you went to bed, but now, as things have turned out, it seems as good a plan as lying there hopelessly awake; and you agree.

You learn, later in the day, that the explanation of the proceeding is that you, unable to sleep, woke up early in the morning, and thought you would like a game of cricket. The children, taught to be ever courteous to guests, felt it their duty to humour you. Mrs Harris remarks at breakfast that at least you might have seen to it that the children were properly dressed before you took them out; while Harris points out to you, pathetically, how by your one morning's example and encouragement, you have undone his labour of months.

On this Wednesday morning, George, it seems, clamoured to get up at a quarter past five, and persuaded them to let him teach them cycling tricks round the cucumber frames on Harris's new wheel. Even Mrs Harris, however, did not blame George on this occasion; she felt intuitively the idea would not have been entirely his.

It is not that the Harris children have the faintest notion of avoiding blame at the expense of a friend and comrade. One and all they are honesty itself in accepting responsibility for their own misdeeds. It simply is, that is how the thing presents itself to their understanding. When you explain to them that you had no original intention of getting up at five o'clock in the morning to play cricket on the croquet lawn, or to mimic the history of the early Church by shooting with a crossbow at dolls tied to a tree; that as a matter of fact, left to your own initiative, you would have slept peacefully till roused in Christian fashion with a cup of tea at eight, they are firstly astonished, secondly apologetic; and thirdly sincerely contrite. In the present instance, waiving the purely academic question whether the awakening of George at a little before five was due to natural instinct on his part, or to the accidental passing of a homemade boomerang through his bedroom window, the dear children frankly admitted that the blame for his uprising was their own. As the eldest boy said:

'We ought to have remembered that Uncle George had a long day before him, and we ought to have dissuaded him from getting up. I blame myself entirely.'

But an occasional change of habit does nobody any harm; and besides, as Harris and I agreed, it was good training for George. In the Black Forest we should be up at five every morning; that we had determined on. Indeed, George himself had suggested half past four, but Harris and I had argued that five would be early enough as an average; that would enable us to be on our machines by six, and to break the back of our journey before the heat of the day set in. Occasionally, we might start a little earlier, but not as a habit.

I myself was up that morning at five. This was earlier than I had intended. I had said to myself on going to sleep, 'Six o'clock, sharp!'

There are men I know who can wake themselves at any time to the minute. They say to themselves literally, as they lay their heads upon the pillow, 'Four-thirty,' Four-forty-five,' or 'Five-fifteen,' as the case may be; and as the clock strikes they open their eyes. It is very wonderful this; the more one dwells upon it, the greater the mystery grows. Some Ego within us, acting quite independently of our conscious self, must be capable of counting the hours while we sleep. Unaided by clock or sun, or any other medium known to our five senses, it keeps watch through the darkness. At the exact moment it whispers 'Time!' and we awake. The work of an old riverside fellow I once talked with called him to be out of bed each morning half an hour before high tide. He told me that never once had he overslept himself by a minute. Latterly, he never even troubled to work out the tide for himself. He would lie down tired, and sleep a dreamless sleep, and each morning at a different hour this ghostly watchman, true as the tide itself, would silently call him. Did the man's spirit haunt through the darkness the muddy river stairs; or had it knowledge of the ways of Nature? Whatever the process, the man himself was unconscious of it.

In my own case my inward watchman is, perhaps, somewhat out of practice. He does his best; but he is over-anxious; he worries himself, and loses count. I say to him, maybe, 'Five-thirty, please'; and he wakes me with a start at half past two. I look at my watch. He suggests that, perhaps, I forgot to wind it up. I put it to my ear; it is still going. He thinks, maybe, something has happened to it; he is confident himself it is half past five, if not a little later. To satisfy him, I put on a pair of slippers and go downstairs to inspect the dining-room clock. What happens to a man when he wanders about the house in the middle of the night, clad in a dressing-gown and a pair of slippers, there is no need to recount; most men know by experience. Everything – especially everything with a sharp corner – takes a cowardly delight in hitting him. When you are wearing a pair of stout boots, things get out of your way; when you venture among furniture in woolwork slippers and no socks, it comes out and kicks you. I return to bed bad tempered, and refusing to listen to his further absurd suggestion that all the clocks in the house have entered into a conspiracy against me, take half an hour to get to sleep again. From four to five he wakes me every ten minutes. I wish I had never said a word to him about the thing. At five o'clock he goes to sleep himself, worn out, and leaves it to the girl, who does it half an hour later than usual.

On this particular Wednesday he worried me to such an extent, that I got up at five simply to rid of him. I did not know what to do with myself. Our train did not leave till eight; all our luggage had been packed and sent on the night before, together with the bicycles, to Fenchurch Street station. I went into my study; I thought I would put in an hour's writing. The early morning, before one has breakfasted, is not, I take it, a good season for literary effort. I wrote three paragraphs of a story, and then read them over to myself. Some unkind things have been said about my work; but nothing has yet been written which would have done justice to those three paragraphs. I threw them into the waste-paper basket, and sat trying to remember what, if any, charitable institutions provided pensions for decayed authors.

To escape from this train of reflection, I put a golf-ball in my pocket, and selecting a driver, strolled out into the paddock. A couple of sheep were browsing there, and they followed and took a keen interest in my practice. The one was a kindly, sympathetic old party. I do not think she understood the game; I think it was my doing this innocent thing so early in the morning that appealed to her. At every stroke I made she bleated:

'Go – o – o – d, go – o – o – d ind – e – e – d!'

She seemed as pleased as if she had done it herself.

As for the other one, she was a cantankerous, disagreeable old thing, as discouraging to me as her friend was helpful.

'Ba – a – a – d, da – a – a – m ba – a – a – d!' was her comment on almost every stroke. As a matter of fact, some were really excellent strokes; but she did it just to be contradictory, and for the sake of irritating, I could see that.

By a most regrettable accident, one of my swiftest balls struck the good sheep on the nose. And at that the bad sheep laughed – laughed distinctly and undoubtedly, a husky, vulgar laugh; and, while her friend stood glued to the ground, too astonished to move, she changed her note for the first time and bleated.

'Go – o – o –d, ve – e – ry go – o – o – d! Be – e – e – est sho – o – – – ot he – e – e's ma – a – a – de!'

I would have given half a crown if it had been she I had hit instead of the other one. It is ever the good and amiable who suffer in this world.

I had wasted more time than I had intended in the paddock, and when Ethelbertha came to tell me it was half past seven, and the breakfast was on the table, I remember that I had not shaved. It vexes Ethelbertha my shaving quickly. She fears that to outsiders it may suggest a poor-spirited attempt at suicide, and that in consequence it may get about the neighbourhood that we are not happy together. As a further argument, she has also hinted that my appearance is not of the kind that can be trifled with.

On the whole, I was just as glad not to be able to take a long farewell of Ethelbertha; I did not want to risk her breaking down. But I should have liked more opportunity to say a few farewell words of advice to the children, especially as regards my fishing-rod, which they will persist in using for cricket stumps; and I hate having to run for a train. Quarter of a mile from the station I overtook George and Harris; they were also running. In their case – so Harris informed me, jerkily, while we trotted side by side – it was the new kitchen stove that was to blame. This was the first morning they had tried it, and from some cause or other it had blown up the kidneys and scalded the cook. He said he hoped that by the time we returned they would have got more used to it.

We caught the train by the skin of our teeth, as the saying is, and reflecting upon the events of the morning, as we sat gasping in the carriage, there passed vividly before my mind the panorama of my Uncle Podger, as on two hundred and fifty days in the year he would start from Ealing Common by the nine-thirteen train to Moorgate Street.

From my Uncle Podger's house to the railway station was eight minutes' walk. What my uncle always said was:

'Allow yourself a quarter of an hour, and take it easily.'

What he always did was to start five minutes before the time and run. I do not know why, but this was the custom of the suburb. Many stout City gentlemen lived at Ealing in those days – I believe some live there still – and caught early trains to Town. They all started late; they all carried a black bag and a newspaper in one hand, and an umbrella in the other; and for the last quarter of a mile to the station, wet or fine, they all ran.

Folks with nothing else to do, nursemaids chiefly and errand boys, with now and then a perambulating costermonger added, would gather on the common on a fine morning to watch them pass, and cheer the most deserving. It was not a showy spectacle. They did not run well, they did not even run fast; but they were earnest, and they did their best. The exhibition appealed less to one's sense of art than one's natural admiration for conscientious effort.

Occasionally a little harmless betting would take place among the crowd.

'Two to one agin the old gent in the white weskit!'

'Ten to one on old Blowpipes, bar he don't roll over hisself 'fore 'e gets there!'

'Heven money on the Purple Hemperor!' – a nickname bestowed by a youth of entomological tastes upon a certain retired military neighbour of my uncle's – a gentleman of imposing appearance when stationary, but apt to colour highly under exercise.

My uncle and the others would write to the *Ealing Press* complaining bitterly concerning the supineness of the local police; and the editor would add spirited leaders upon the Decay of Courtesy among the Lower Orders, especially throughout the western suburbs. But no good ever resulted.

It was not that my uncle did not rise early enough; it was that troubles came to him at the last moment. The first thing he would do after breakfast would be to lose his newspaper. We always knew when Uncle Podger had lost anything, by the expression of astonished indignation with which, on such occasions, he would regard the world in general. It never occurred to my Uncle Podger to say to himself:

'I am a careless old man. I lose everything: I never know where I have put anything. I am quite incapable of finding it again for myself. In this respect I must be a perfect nuisance to everybody about me. I must set to work and reform myself.'

On the contrary, by some peculiar course of reasoning, he had convinced himself that whenever he lost a thing it was everybody else's fault in the house but his own.

'I had it in my hand here not a minute ago!' he would exclaim.

From his tone you would have thought he was living surrounded by conjurers, who spirited away things from him merely to irritate him.

'Could you have left it in the garden?' my aunt would suggest.

'What should I want to leave it in the garden for? I don't want the paper in the garden; I want the paper on the train with me.'

'You haven't put it in your pocket?'

'God bless the woman! Do you think I should be standing here at five minutes to nine looking for it if I had it in my pocket all the while? *Do* you think I'm a fool?'

Here somebody would explain. 'What's this?' and hand him from somewhere a paper neatly folded.

'I do wish people would leave my things alone,' he would growl, snatching at it savagely.

He would open his bag to put it in, and then glancing at it, he would pause, speechless with sense of injury.

'What's the matter?' aunt would ask.

'The day before yesterday's!' he would answer, too hurt even to shout, throwing the paper down upon the table.

If only sometimes it had been yesterday's it would have been a change. But it was always the day before yesterday's; except on Tuesday; then it would be Saturday's.

We would find it for him eventually; as often as not he was sitting on it. And then he would smile, not genially, but with the weariness that comes to a man who feels that fate has cast his lot among a hand of hopeless idiots.

'All the time, right in front of your noses . . .!' He would not finish the sentence; he prided himself on his self-control.

This settled, he would start for the hall, where it was the custom of my Aunt Maria to have the children gathered, ready to say goodbye to him.

My aunt never left the house herself, if only to make a call next door, without taking a tender farewell of every inmate. One never knew, she would say, what might happen.

One of them, of course, was sure to be missing, and the moment this was noticed all the other six, without an instant's hesitation, would scatter with a whoop to find it. Immediately they were gone it would turn up by itself from somewhere quite near, always with the most reasonable explanation for its absence; and would at once start off after the others to explain to them that it was found. In this way, five minutes at least would be taken up in everybody's looking for everybody else, which was just sufficient time to allow my uncle to find his umbrella and lose his hat. Then, at last, the group assembled in the hall, the drawing-room clock would commence to strike nine. It possessed a cold, penetrating chime that always had the effect of confusing my uncle. In his excitement he would kiss some of the children twice over, pass by others, forget whom he had kissed and whom he hadn't, and have to begin all over again. He used to say he believed they mixed themselves up on purpose, and I am not prepared to maintain that the charge was altogether false. To add to his troubles, one child always had a sticky face and that child would always be the most affectionate.

If things were going too smoothly, the eldest boy would come out with some tale about all the clocks in the house being five minutes slow, and of his having been late for school the previous day in consequence. This would send my uncle rushing impetuously down to the gate, where he would recollect that he had with him neither his bag nor his umbrella. All the children that my aunt could not stop would charge after him, two of them struggling for the umbrella, the others surging round the bag. And when they returned we would discover on the hall table the most important thing of all that he had forgotten, and wondered what he would say about it when he came home.

We arrived at Waterloo a little after nine, and at once proceeded to put George's experiment into operation. Opening the book at the chapter entitled 'At the Cab Rank,' we walked up to a hansom, raised our hats, and wished the driver 'Good morning.'

This man was not to be outdone in politeness by any foreigner, real or imitation. Calling to a friend named 'Charles' to 'hold the steed', he sprang from his box, and returned to us a bow that would have done credit to Mr Turveydrop himself. Speaking apparently in the name of the nation, he welcomed us to England, adding a regret that Her Majesty was not at the moment in London.

We could not reply to him in kind. Nothing of this sort had been anticipated by the book. We called him 'coachman,' at which he again bowed to the pavement, and asked him if he would have the goodness to drive us to the Westminster Bridge Road.

He laid his hand upon his heart, and said the pleasure would be his.

Taking the third sentence in the chapter, George asked him what his fare would be.

The question, as introducing a sordid element into the conversation, seemed to hurt his feelings. He said he never took money from distinguished strangers; he suggested a souvenir – a diamond scarf pin, a gold snuffbox, some little trifle of that sort by which he could remember us.

As a small crowd had collected, and as the joke was drifting rather too far in the cabman's direction, we climbed in without further parley, and were driven away amid cheers. We stopped the cab at a boot shop a little past Astley's Theatre that looked the sort of place we wanted. It was one of those overfed shops that the moment their shutters are taken down in the morning disgorge their goods all round them. Boxes of boots stood piled on the pavement or in the gutter opposite. Boots hung in festoons about its doors and windows. Its sunblind was as some grimy vine, bearing bunches of black and brown boots. Inside, the shop was a bower of boots. The man, when we entered, was busy with a chisel and hammer opening a new crate full of boots.

George raised his hat, and said 'Good morning.'

The man did not even turn round. He struck me from the first as a disagreeable man. He grunted something which might have been 'Good morning,' or might not, and went on with his work.

George said: 'I have been recommended to your shop by my friend, Mr X.'

In response, the man should have said: 'Mr X is a most worthy gentleman; it will give me the greatest pleasure to serve any friend of his.'

What he did say was: 'Don't know him; never heard of him.'

This was disconcerting. The book gave three or four methods of buying boots. George had carefully selected the one centred round 'Mr X,' as being of all the most courtly. You talked a good deal with the shopkeeper about this 'Mr X,' and then, when by this means friendship and understanding had been established, you slid naturally and gracefully into the immediate object, of your coming, namely, your desire for boots, 'cheap and good.' This gross, material man cared, apparently, nothing for the niceties of retail dealing. It was necessary with such a one to come to business with brutal directness. George abandoned 'Mr X,' and turning back to a previous page, took a sentence at random. It was not a happy selection; it was a speech that would have been superfluous made to any bootmaker. Under the present circumstances, threatened and tifled as we were on every side by boots, it possessed the dignity of positive imbecility. It ran: 'One has told me that you have here boots for sale.'

For the first time the man put down his hammer and chisel, and looked at us. He spoke slowly, in a thick and husky voice. He said:

'What d'ye think I keep boots for – to smell 'em?'

He was one of those men that begin quietly and grow more angry as they proceed, their wrongs apparently working within them like yeast.

'What d'ye think I am,' he continued, 'a boot collector? What d'ye think I'm running this shop for – my health? D'ye think I love the boots, and can't bear to part with a pair. D'ye think I hand 'em about here to look at 'em? Ain't there enough of 'em? Where d'ye think you are – in an international exhibition of boots? What d'ye think these boots are – a historical collection? Did you ever hear of a man keeping a boot shop and not selling boots? D'ye think I decorate the shop with 'em to make it look pretty? What d'ye take me for – a prize idiot?'

I have always maintained that these conversation books are never of any real use. What we wanted was some English equivalent for the well-known German idiom: 'Behalten Sie Ihr Haar auf.'

Nothing of the sort was to be found in the book from beginning to end. However, I will do George the credit to admit he chose the very best sentence that was to be found therein and applied it. He said:

'I will come again, when, perhaps, you will have some more boots to show me. Till then, adieu!'

With that we returned to our cab and drove away, leaving the man standing in the centre of his boot-bedecked doorway addressing remarks to us. What he said, I did not hear, but the passersby appeared to find it interesting.

George was stopping at another boot shop and trying the experiment afresh; he said he really did want a pair of bedroom slippers. But we persuaded him to postpone their purchase until our arrival in some foreign city, where the tradespeople are no doubt more inured to this sort of talk, or else more naturally amiable. On the subject of the hat, however, he was adamant. He maintained that without that he could not travel, and, accordingly, we pulled up at a small shop in the Blackfriars Road.

The properietor of this shop was a cheery, bright-eyed little man, and helped us rather than hindered us.

When George asked him in the words of the book: 'Have you any hats?' he did not get angry; he just stopped and thoughtfully scratched his chin.

'Hats,' said he. 'Let me think. Yes' – here a smile of positive pleasure broke over his genial countenance – 'yes, now I come to think of it, I believe I have a hat. But, tell me, why do you ask me?'

George explained to him that he wished to purchase a cap, a travelling cap, but the essence of the transaction was that it was to be a 'good cap.'

The man's face fell.

'Ah,' he remarked, 'there, I am afraid, you have me. Now, if you had wanted a bad cap, not worth the price asked for it; a cap good for nothing but to clean windows with, I could have found you the very thing. But a good cap – no; we don't keep them. But wait a minute,' he continued, on seeing the disappointment that spread over George's expressive countenance, 'don't be in a hurry. I have a cap here' – he went to a drawer and opened it – 'it's not a good cap, but it is not so bad as most of the caps I sell.'

He brought it forward, extended on his palm.

'What do you think of that?' he asked. 'Could you put up with that?'

George fitted it on before the glass, and, choosing another remark from the book, said:

'This hat fits me sufficiently well, but, tell me, do you consider that it becomes me?'

The men stepped back and took a bird's-eye view.

'Candidly,' he replied, 'I can't say that it does.'

He turned from George, and addressed himself to Harris and myself.

'Your friend's beauty,' said he, 'I should describe as elusive. It is there, but you can easily miss it. Now, in that cap, to my mind, you do miss it.'

At that point it occurred to George that he had had sufficient fun with this particular man. He said:

'That is all right. We don't want to lose the train. How much?'

Answered the man: 'The price of that cap, sir, which, in my opinion, is twice as much as it is worth, is four-and-six. Would you like it wrapped up in brown paper, sir, or in white?'

George said he would take it as it was, paid the four-and-six in silver, and went out. Harris and I followed.

At Fenchurch Steet we compromised with our cabman for five shillings. He made us another courtly bow, and begged us to remember him to the Emperor of Austria.

Comparing views in the train, we agreed that we had lost the game by two points to one; and George, who was evidently disappointed, threw the book out of the window.

We found our luggage and the bicycles safe on the boat, and with the tide at twelve dropped down the river.

●

Q: Why do Jews answer a question with a question?
A: Why shouldn't Jews answer a question with a question?

**Anon.**

# *Turn Back the Clock*

## Joyce Grenfell

### *Opera Interval*

Bravo . . . Bravo.

(*Applauding*) Oh, how lovely.

Wasn't it heavenly?

Bravo . . . Bravo.

Isn't she marvellous? That voice. It really is celestial. And he was *so* good, wasn't he? The one in the middle. The one in blue. You know, the main man. *Lovely* voice.

(*Gets up to let people pass*) Can you manage?

Do you want to go out and mingle a little and see who is here – or shall we stay here and digest what we've just heard? All right – let's digest now and mingle later.

Do you know, I think that when I was very very young I heard Belushkin sing that part, only he sang it lower.

I must confess I got a little confused in the story, did you? I know she's a twin and there was a muddle, but I can't *quite* remember why she starts off in that pretty white dress, and then when she comes in again later she's dressed as a Crusader. It's probably a disguise. But one wonders why?

She's the daughter of the man in black, I suppose. The one who sang at the top of the stairs with that lovely voice. Let's look it up and see who is who.

'Don Penzalo, a wealthy landowner.' (That's probably her father.) 'Mildura . . .' that's her I think . . . 'daughter to the Duke of Pantilla.' Oh, not Don Penzalo then. No . . . 'The Duke of Pantilla, father of Mildura.' Well, there we are.

'Zelda, an old nurse.' Yes, we have seen her. She's the

one with two sticks and rather a rumbly voice, remember?

'Fedora, a confidante.'

'Boldoni, a bodyguard.'

'Don Alfredo, a general in the Crusaders.' Ah, Crusaders.

'Chorus of Fisherfolk, Villagers, Haymakers, Courtiers and Crusaders.' We haven't seen the Courtiers and Crusaders yet, but we've seen the fisherfolk, villagers and haymakers – yes, we have. They were the ones with fishing-nets and rakes and things.

You know, one ought to do one's homework before one goes to the opera. I've got a little book that tells you all the stories, but I never can remember to look it up till I get home, then it's too late.

Let's see what we have just seen:

Oh, it was a market place – I thought so.

'Act I. The Market Place of Pola.

'As dawn breaks over the sleepy village of Pola in Pantilla fisherfolk on their way to work join with villagers and haymakers to express their concern over the Royalist cause.'

Oh . . . *that's* what they were doing.

'Mildura pines for her lover, Don Alfredo, who is preparing to leave for the Crusades' . . . ah, there you are . . . 'and disguises herself in order to join him in Malta.'

Oh, Malta. Dear Malta. How I love it.

Do you know it well?

I used to go there a great deal when I was a gel, and one had such fun. I used to go and stay with darling old Admiral Sir Cardington Dexter and his wife Nadia. Did you know Nadia? She was a *little* strange! He met her in Casablanca! Yes, exactly. But I won't hear a word against her, because she was always very kind to me. Oh, it was such fun in those days. So gay. Parties, parties and more parties. Heavenly young men in uniform – white naval uniform, quite irresistible, and you know, honestly, one hardly noticed the Maltese at all.

Now. 'Mildura disguises herself in order to join Don Alfredo, but Don Panzalo' (I'm sure he's the one in blue) 'seeks revenge for a slight done him by the Duke and plans to abduct Mildura, whom he suspects of political duplicity, and flee with her to

Spain.' Oh, Spain. Very *mouvementé*! Do you know Spain well?

No, Italy is my passion. *Bella Italia*. I always feel very hard done by if I don't get my annual ration of *Bella Italia*. It's so nourishing.

'Zelda, an old nurse, reads warnings in the stars and begs Mildura to delay her departure until the harvest is gathered in. Don Penzalo does not recognise Mildura and challenges her to a duet.' That's what it says: 'Challenges her to a du—' Oh, I am idiotic. The light's so bad in here.

(*Gets up to let people pass back to their seats*)

I'm so sorry. Can you get by? Ow – No, it's all right, only a *tiny* little ladder . . .

One really ought to come to the opera more often. I do love it so. My mother used to go a great deal. She loved it, and, of course, she was very musical. Oh, very. She had a most enchanting gift, she played the piano entirely by heart, well I suppose you could call it by ear. She never had a lesson in her life. She would go to the opera, hear it, and then come home and play the entire thing (oh, I'm so sorry, did I hit you?). She'd play the entire thing from memory without a note of music. So, of course, I grew up knowing all the lovely, lovely tunes one knows so well. It is such an advantage – one step ahead of everyone else.

*No, alas, I don't play*.

(*Sighs*) Now, let's see what the next act holds in store for us. 'Act II. The Cloisters of San Geminiani Cathedral.'

I wonder if I've been there. So many lovely *Cathedrale* all over *Bella Italia*.

'Mildura, no longer disguised (oh, good), is on her way to Mass with her confidante, Fedora, and Boldoni, a faithful bodyguard. Playfully she takes off her chaplet of roses and puts it on Boldoni, who laughs.' That sounds rather fun.

'Don Alfredo, forewarned of Penzalo's plot, arrives unannounced at the Cathedral with a band of Crusaders, ostensibly to celebrate the Feast of Saint Ogiano.'

Are you getting hungry?

It's a very long opera, three more acts. Are you sure you

aren't hungry? I should have fed you better. A boiled egg isn't enough for opera. I do hope you won't wilt.

No, I *love* it. I'm afraid it's all food and drink to me. Oh, there the lights are going down – it's too exciting – I'm like a child at the theatre.

(*Applauds*) I don't know who the conductor is, but he's supposed to be very well known.

Oh, dear, we don't know where we are, do we. Well, we do. We're in the Cloisters of the Cathedral of St. Geminiano. (*Turns to hush other talkers*) Sh. Sh. Sh.

●

From the moment I picked it [a book] up until I laid it down I was convulsed with laughter. Some day I intend reading it.

**Groucho Marx**

# *Esmé*

## Saki

'All hunting stories are the same,' said Clovis; 'just as all Turf stories are the same, and all—'

'My hunting story isn't a bit like any you've ever heard,' said the Baroness. 'It happened quite a while ago, when I was about twenty-three. I wasn't living apart from my husband then; you see, neither of us could afford to make the other a separate allowance. In spite of everything that proverbs may say, poverty keeps together more homes than it breaks up. But we always hunted with different packs. All this has nothing to do with the story.'

'We haven't arrived at the meet yet. I suppose there was a meet,' said Clovis.

'Of course there was a meet,' said the Baroness; 'all the usual crowd were there, especially Constance Broddle. Constance is one of those strapping florid girls that go so well with autumn scenery or Christmas decorations in church. "I feel a presentiment that something dreadful is going to happen," she said to me; "am I looking pale?"

'She was looking about as pale as a beetroot that has suddenly heard bad news.

'"You're looking nicer than usual," I said, "but that's so easy for you." Before she had got the right bearings of this remark we had settled down to business; hounds had found a fox lying out in some gorse-bushes.'

'I knew it,' said Clovis; 'in every fox-hunting story that I've ever heard there's been a fox and some gorse-bushes.'

'Constance and I were well mounted,' continued the Baroness serenely, 'and we had no difficulty in keeping ourselves in the first flight, though it was a fairly stiff run. Towards the finish, however, we must have held rather too independent a line, for we lost the hounds, and found ourselves plodding aimlessly along miles away from anywhere. It was fairly exasperating, and my temper was beginning to let itself go by inches, when on pushing our way through an accommodating hedge we were gladdened by the sight of hounds in full cry in a hollow just beneath us.

'"There they go," cried Constance, and then added in a gasp, "In Heaven's name, what are they hunting?"

'It was certainly no mortal fox. It stood more than twice as high, had a short, ugly head, and an enormous thick neck.

'It's a hyæna,' I cried; "it must have escaped from Lord Pabham's Park."

'At that moment the hunted beast turned and faced its pursuers, and the hounds (there were only about six couple of them) stood round in a half-circle, and looked foolish. Evidently they had broken away from the rest of the pack on the trail of this alien scent, and were not quite sure how to treat their quarry now they had got him.

'The hyæna hailed our approach with unmistakable relief and demonstrations of friendliness. It had probably been accustomed to uniform kindness from humans, while its first experience of a pack of hounds had left a bad impression. The hounds looked more than ever embarrassed as their quarry paraded its sudden intimacy with us, and the faint toot of a horn in the distance was seized on as a welcome signal for unobtrusive departure. Constance and I and the hyæna were left alone in the gathering twilight.

'"What are we to do?" asked Constance.

'"What a person you are for questions," I said.

'"Well, we can't stay here all night with a hyæna," she retorted.

'"I don't know what your ideas of comfort are," I said; "but I shouldn't think of staying here all night even without a hyæna. My home may be an unhappy one, but at least it has hot and cold water laid on, and domestic service, and other conveniences which we shouldn't find here. We had better make for that ridge of trees to the right; I imagine the Crowley road is just beyond."

'We trotted off slowly along a faintly marked cart-track, with the beast following cheerfully at our heels.

'"What on earth are we to do with the hyæna?" came the inevitable question.

'"What does one generally do with hyænas?" I asked crossly.

'"I've never had anything to do with one before," said Constance.

'"Well, neither have I. If we even knew its sex we might give it a name. Perhaps we might call it Esmé. That would do in either case.'

'There was still sufficient daylight for us to distinguish wayside objects, and our listless spirits gave an upward perk as we came upon a small half-naked gipsy brat picking blackberries from a low-growing bush. The sudden apparition of two horsewomen and a hyæna set it off crying, and in any case we should scarcely have gleaned any useful geographical information from that source; but there was a probability that we might strike a gipsy encampment somewhere along our route. We rode on hopefully but uneventfully for another mile or so.

'"I wonder what that child was doing there," said Constance presently.

'"Picking blackberries. Obviously."

'"I don't like the way it cried," pursued Constance; "somehow its wail keeps ringing in my ears."

'I did not chide Constance for her morbid fancies; as a matter of fact the same sensation, or being pursued by a persistent fretful wail, had been forcing itself on my rather over-tired nerves. For company's sake I hulloed to Esmé, who had lagged somewhat behind. With a few springy bounds he drew up level, and then shot past us.

'The wailing accompaniment was explained. The gipsy child was firmly, and I expect painfully, held in its jaws.

'"Merciful Heaven!" screamed Constance, "what on earth shall we do? What are we to do?"

'I am perfectly certain that at the Last Judgement Constance will ask more questions than any of the examining Seraphs.

'"Can't we do something?" she persisted tearfully, as Esmé cantered easily along in front of our tired horses.

'Personally I was doing everything that occurred to me at the moment. I stormed and scolded and coaxed in English and French and gamekeeper language; I made absurd, ineffectual cuts in the air with my thongless hunting-crop; I hurled my sandwich case at the brute; in fact, I really don't know what more I could have done. And still we lumbered on through the deepening dusk, with that dark uncouth shape lumbering ahead of us, and a drone of lugubrious music floating in our ears. Suddenly Esmé bounded aside into some thick bushes, where we could not follow; the wail rose to a shriek and then stopped altogether. This part of the story I always hurry over, because it is really rather horrible. When the beast joined us again, after an absence of a few minutes, there was an air of patient understanding about him, as though he knew that he had done something of which we disapproved, but which he felt to be thoroughly justifiable.

'"How can you let that ravening beast trot by your side?" asked Constance. She was looking more than ever like an albino beetroot.

'"In the first place, I can't prevent it," I said; "and in the second place, whatever else he may be, I doubt he's ravening at the present moment."

'Constance shuddered. "Do you think the poor little thing suffered much?" came another of her futile questions.

'"The indications were all that way," I said; "on the other hand, of course, it may have been crying from sheer temper. Children sometimes do."

'It was nearly pitch-dark when we emerged suddenly into the high road. A flash of lights and the whir of a motor went past us at the same moment at uncomfortably close quarters. A thud and a sharp screeching yell followed a second later. The car drew up, and when I had ridden back to the spot I found a young man bending over a dark motionless mass lying by the roadside.

'"You have killed my Esmé," I exclaimed bitterly.

'"I'm so awfully sorry," said the young man; "I keep dogs

myself, so I know what you must feel about it. I'll do anything I can in reparation."

'"Please bury him at once," I said; "that much I think I may ask of you."

'"Bring the spade, William," he called to the chauffeur. Evidently hasty roadside interments were contingencies that had been povided against.

'The digging of a sufficiently large grave took some little time. "I say, what a magnificent fellow," said the motorist as the corpse was rolled into over into the trench. "I'm afraid he must have been rather a valuable animal."

'"He took a second in the puppy class at Birmingham last year," I said resolutely.

'Constance snorted loudly.

'"Don't cry, dear," I said brokenly; "it was all over in a moment. He couldn't have suffered much."

'"Look here," said the young fellow desperately, "you simply must let me do something by way of reparation."

'I refused sweetly, but as he persisted I let him have my address.

'Of course, we kept our own counsel as to the earlier episodes of the evening. Lord Pabham never advertised the loss of his hyæna; when a strictly fruit-eating animal strayed from his park a year or two previously he was called upon to give compensation in eleven cases of sheep-worrying and practically to restock his neighbours' poultry-yards, and an escaped hyæna would have mounted up to something on the scale of a Government grant. The gipsies were equally unobtrusive over their missing offspring; I don't suppose in large encampments they really know to a child or two how many they've got.'

The Baroness paused reflectively, and then continued:

'There was a sequel to the adventure, though. I got through the post a charming little diamond brooch, with the name Esmé set in a sprig of rosemary. Incidentally, too, I lost the friendship of Constance Broddle. You see, when I sold the brooch I quite properly refused to give her any share of the proceeds. I pointed out that the Esmé part of the affair was my own invention, and the hyæna part of it belonged to Lord Pabham, if it really was his hyæna, of which, of course, I've no proof.'

•

*'Oh, I just got kinda fed up with the flying around alone.'*

# *Tobin's Palm*

## O. Henry

Tobin and me, the two of us, went down to Coney one day, for there was four dollars between us, and Tobin had need of distractions. For there was Katie Mahorner, his sweetheart, of County Sligo, lost since she started for America three months before with two hundred dollars, her own savings, and one hundred dollars from the sale of Tobin's inherited estate, a fine cottage and pig on the Bog Shannaugh. And since the letter that Tobin got saying that she had started to come to him not a bit of news had he heard or seen of Katie Mahorner. Tobin advertised in the papers, but nothing could be found of the colleen.

So, to Coney me and Tobin went, thinking that a turn at the chutes and the smell of popcorn might raise the heart in his bosom. But Tobin was a hard-headed man, and the sadness stuck in his skin. He ground his teeth at the crying balloons; he cursed the moving pictures; and, though he would drink whenever asked, he scorned Punch and Judy, and was for licking the tintype men as they came.

So I gets him down a side way on a board walk where the attractions were some less violent. At a little six by eight stall Tobin halts, with a more human look in his eye.

''Tis here,' says he, 'I will be diverted. I'll have the palm of me hand investigated by the wonderful palmist of the Nile, and see if what is to be will be.'

Tobin was a believer in signs and the unnatural in nature. He possessed illegal convictions in his mind along the subject of black cats, lucky numbers, and the weather predictions in the papers.

We went into the enchanted chicken coop, which was fixed

mysterious with red cloth and pictures of hands with lines crossing 'em like a railroad centre. The sign over the door says it is Madame Zozo the Egyptian Palmist. There was a fat woman inside in a red jumper with pothooks and beasties embroidered upon it. Tobin gives her ten cents and extends one of his hands. She lifts Tobin's hand, which is own brother to the hoof of a drayhorse, and examines it to see whether 'tis a stone in the frog or a cast shoe he has come for.

'Man,' says this Madame Zozo, 'the line of your fate shows—'

''Tis not me foot at all,' says Tobin, interrupting. 'Sure, 'tis no beauty, but ye hold the palm of me hand.'

'The line shows,' says the Madame, 'that ye've not arrived at your time of life without bad luck. And there's more to come. The mount of Venus – or is that a stone bruise? – shows that ye've been in love. There's been trouble in your life on account of your sweetheart.'

''Tis Katie Mahorner she has references with,' whispers Tobin to me in a loud voice to one side.

'I see,' says the palmist, 'a great deal of sorrow and tribulation with one whom ye cannot forget. I see the lines of designation point to the letter K and the letter M in her name.'

'Whist!' says Tobin to me; 'do ye hear that?'

'Look out,' goes on the palmist, 'for a dark man and a light woman; for they'll both bring ye trouble. Ye'll make a voyage upon the water very soon, and have a financial loss. I see one line that brings good luck. There's a man coming into your life who will fetch ye good fortune. Ye'll know him when ye see him by his crooked nose.'

'Is his name set down?' asks Tobin. ''Twill be convenient in the way of greeting when he backs up to dump off the good luck.'

'His name,' says the palmist, thoughtful-looking, 'is not spelled out by the lines, but they indicate 'tis a long one, and the letter "o" should be in it. There's no more to tell. Good evening. Don't block up the door.'

''Tis wonderful how she knows,' says Tobin as we walk to the pier.

As we squeezed through the gates a nigger man sticks his lighted cigar against Tobin's ear, and there is trouble. Tobin hammers his neck, and the women squeal, and by presence of mind I drag the little man out of the way before the police comes. Tobin is always in an ugly mood when enjoying himself.

On the boat going back, when the man calls 'Who wants the good-looking waiter?' Tobin tried to plead guilty, feeling the desire to blow the foam off a crock of suds, but when he felt in his pocket he found himself discharged for lack of evidence. Somebody had disturbed his change during the commotion. So we sat, dry, upon the stools, listening to the Dagoes fiddling on deck. If anything, Tobin was lower in spirits and less congenial with his misfortunes than when we started.

On a seat against the railing was a young woman dressed suitable for red automobiles, with hair the colour of an unsmoked meerschaum. In passing by, Tobin kicks her foot without intentions, and, being polite to ladies when in drink, he tries to give his hat a twist while apologising. But he knocks it off, and the wind carries it overboard.

Tobin came back and sat down, and I began to look out for him, for the man's adversities were becoming frequent. He was apt, when pushed so close by hard luck, to kick the best dressed man he could see, and try to take command of the boat.

Presently Tobin grabs my arm and says, excited: 'Jawn,' says he, 'do ye know what we're doing? We're taking a voyage upon the water.'

'There now,' says I; 'subdue yeself. The boat'll land in ten minutes more.'

'Look,' says he, 'at the light lady upon the bench. And have ye forgotten the nigger man that burned me ear? And isn't the money I had gone – a dollar sixty-five it was?'

I thought he was no more than summing up his catastrophes so as to get violent with good excuse, as men will do, and I tried to make him understand such things was trifles.

'Listen,' says Tobin. 'Ye've no ear for the gift of prophecy or the miracles of the inspired. What did the palmist lady tell ye out of me hand? 'Tis coming true before your eyes. "Look out," says she "for a dark man and a light woman; they'll bring ye trouble." Have ye forgot the nigger man, though he got some of it back from me fist? Can ye show me a lighter woman than the blonde lady that was the cause of me hat falling in the water? And where's the dollar sixty-five I had in me vest when we left the shooting gallery?'

The way Tobin put it, it did seem to corroborate the art of prediction, though it looked to me that these accidents could happen to anyone at Coney without the implication of palmistry.

Tobin got up and walked around on deck, looking close at the passengers out of his little red eyes. I asked him the interpretation of his movements. Ye never know what Tobin has in his mind until he begins to carry it out.

'Ye should know,' says he, 'I'm working out the salvation promised by the lines in me palm. I'm looking for the crooked-nose man that's to bring the good luck. 'Tis all that will save us. Jawn, did ye ever see a straighter-nosed gang of hellions in the days of your life?'

'Twas the nine-thirty boat, and we landed and walked uptown, through Twenty-second Street, Tobin being without his hat.

On a street corner, standing under a gas-light and looking over the elevated road at the moon, was a man. A long man he was, dressed decent, with a cigar between his teeth, and I saw that his nose made two twists from bridge to end, like the wriggle of a snake. Tobin saw it at the same time, and I heard him breathe hard like a horse when you take the saddle off. He went straight up to the man, and I went with him.

'Good night to ye,' Tobin says to the man. The man takes out his cigar and passes the compliments, sociable.

'Would ye hand us your name,' asks Tobin, 'and let us look at the size of it? It may be our duty to become acquainted with ye.'

'My name,' says the man, polite, 'is Friedenhausman – Maximus G. Friedenhausman.'

''Tis the right length,' says Tobin. 'Do you spell it with an "o" anywhere down the stretch of it?'

'I do not,' said the man.

'*Can* ye spell it with an "o"?' inquires Tobin, turning anxious.

'If your conscience,' says the man with the nose, is indisposed toward foreign idioms ye might, to please yourself, smuggle the letter into the penultimate syllable.'

''Tis well,' says Tobin. 'Ye're in the presence of Jawn Malone and Daniel Tobin.'

''Tis highly appreciated,' says the man, with a bow. 'And now since I cannot conceive that ye would hold a spelling bee upon the street corner, will ye name some reasonable excuse for being at large?'

'By the two signs,' answers Tobin, trying to explain, 'which ye display according to the reading of the Egyptian palmist from the sole of me hand, ye've been nominated to offset with good luck the lines of trouble leading to the nigger man and the blonde lady with her feet crossed in the boat, besides the financial loss of a dollar sixty-five, all so far fulfilled according to Hoyle.'

The man stopped smoking and looked at me.

'Have ye any amendments,' he asks, 'to offer to that statement, or are ye one too? I thought by the looks of ye ye might have him in charge.'

'None,' says I to him, 'except that as one horse-shoe resembles another so are ye the picture of good luck as predicted by the hand of me friend. If not, then the lines of Danny's hand may have been crossed, I don't know.'

'There's two of ye,' says the man with the nose, looking up and down for the sight of a policeman. 'I've enjoyed your company immense. Good-night.'

With that he shoves his cigar in his mouth and moves across the street, stepping fast. But Tobin sticks close to one side of him and me at the other.

'What!' says he, stopping on the opposite sidewalk and pushing back his hat; 'do ye follow me? I tell ye,' he says, very loud, 'I'm proud to have met ye. But it is my desire to be rid of ye. I am off to me home.'

'Do,' says Tobin, leaning against his sleeve. 'Do be off to your home. And I will sit at the door of it till ye come out in the morning. For the dependence is upon ye to obviate the curse of the nigger man and the blonde lady and the financial loss of the one-sixty-five.'

''Tis a strange hallucination,' says the man, turning to me as a more reasonable lunatic. 'Hadn't ye better get him home?'

'Listen, man,' says I to him. 'Daniel Tobin is as sensible as he ever was. Maybe he is a bit deranged on account of having drunk enough to disturb but not enough to settle his wits, but he is no more than following out the legitimate path of his superstitions and predicaments, which I will explain to you.' With that I relates the facts about the palmist lady and how the finger of suspicion points to him as an instrument of good fortune. 'Now, understand,' I concludes, 'my position in this riot. I am the friend of me friend Tobin, according to me interpretations. 'Tis easy to be a friend to the prosperous, for it pays; 'tis not hard to be a friend to the poor, for ye get puffed up by gratitude and have your picture printed standing in front of a tenement with a scuttle of coal and an orphan in each hand. But it strains the art of friendship to be a true friend to a born fool. And that's what I'm doing,' says I, 'for, in my opinion, there's no fortune to be read from the palm of me hand that wasn't printed there with the handle of a pick. And, though ye've got the crookedest nose in New York City, I misdoubt that all the fortune-tellers doing business could milk good luck from ye. But the lines of Danny's hand pointed to ye fair, and I'll assist him to experiment with ye until he's convinced ye're dry.'

After that the man turns, sudden, to laughing. He leans against a corner and laughs considerable. Then he claps me and Tobin on the backs of us and takes us by an arm apiece.

''Tis my mistake,' says he. 'How could I be expecting anything so fine and wonderful to be turning the corner upon me? I came near being found unworthy. Hard by,' says he, 'is a café, snug and suitable for the entertainent of idiosyncrasies. Let us go there and have drink while we discuss the unavailability of the categorical.'

So saying, he marched me and Tobin to the back room of a saloon, and ordered the drinks, and laid the money on the table. He looks at me and Tobin like brothers of his and we have the cigars.

'Ye must know,' says the man of destiny, 'that me walk in life is one that is called the literary. I wander abroad be night seeking idiosyncrasies in the masses and truth in the heavens above. When ye came upon me I was in contemplation of the elevated road in conjunction with the chief luminary of night. The rapid transit is poetry and art: the moon but a tedious, dry body, moving by rote. But these are private opinions, for, in the business of literature, the conditions are reversed. 'Tis me hope to be writing a book to explain the strange things I have discovered in life.'

'Ye will put me in a book,' says Tobin, disgusted; 'will ye put me in a book?'

'I will not,' says the man, 'for the covers will not hold ye. Not yet. The best I can do is to enjoy ye meself, for the time is not ripe for destroying the limitations of print. Ye would look fantastic in type. All alone my meself must I drink this cup of joy. But, I thank ye, boys; I am truly grateful.'

'The talk of ye,' says Tobin, blowing through his moustache and pounding the table with his fist, 'is an eyesore to me patience. There was good luck promised out of the crook of your nose, but ye bear fruit like the bang of a drum. Ye resemble, with your choice of books, the wind blowing through a crack. Sure, now, I would be thinking the palm of me hand lied but for the coming true of the nigger man and the blonde lady and—'

'Whist!' says the long man; 'would ye be led astray by physiognomy? Me nose will do what it can within the bounds. Let us have these glasses filled again, for 'tis good to keep idiosyncrasies well moistened, they being subject to deterioration in a dry moral atmosphere.'

So, the man of literature makes good, to my notion, for he pays, cheerful, for everything, the capital of me and Tobin being exhausted by prediction. But Tobin is sore, and drinks quiet, with the red showing in his eye.

By and by we moved out, for 'twas eleven o'clock, and stands a bit upon the sidewalk. And then the man says he must be going home, and invites me and Tobin to walk that way. We arrives on a side street two blocks away where there is a stretch of brick houses with high stoops and iron fences. The man stops at one of them and looks up at the top windows which he finds dark.

''Tis me humble dwelling,' says he, 'and I begin to perceive by the signs that me wife has retired to slumber. Therefore I will venture a bit in the way of hospitality. 'Tis me wish that ye enter the basement-room, where we dine, and partake of a reasonable refreshment. There will be some fine cold fowl and cheese and a bottle or two of ale. Ye will be welcome to enter and eat, for I am, indebted to ye for diversions.'

The appetite and conscience of me and Tobin was congenial to the proposition, though 'twas sticking hard in Danny's superstitions to think that a few drinks and a cold lunch should represent the good fortune promised by the palm of his hand.

'Step down the steps,' says the man with the crooked nose, 'and I will enter by the door above and let ye in. I will ask the new girl we have in the kitchen,' says he, 'to make ye a pot of coffee to drink before ye go. 'Tis fine coffee Katie Mahorner makes for a green girl just landed three months. Step in,' says the man, 'and I'll send her down to ye.'

●

An Englishman, even if he is alone, forms an orderly queue of one.

**George Mikes**, *How to be an Alien*, 1946

*The Test*

*He is not drunk who, from the floor*
*Can rise again and drink some more;*
*But he is drunk who prostrate lies*
*And cannot drink, and cannot rise.*

**Anon.**

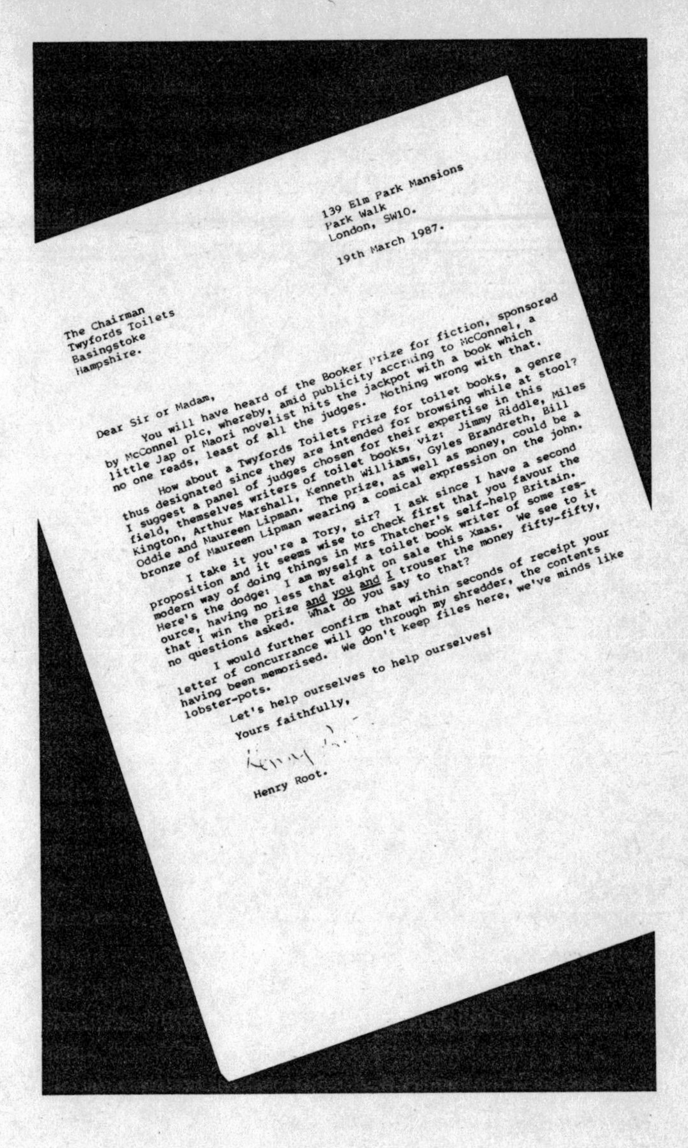

139 Elm Park Mansions
Park Walk
London, SW10.

19th March 1987.

The Chairman
Twyfords Toilets
Basingstoke
Hampshire.

Dear Sir or Madam,

You will have heard of the Booker Prize for fiction, sponsored by McConnel plc, whereby, amid publicity accruing to McConnel, a little Jap or Maori novelist hits the jackpot with a book which no one reads, least of all the judges. Nothing wrong with that.

How about a Twyfords Toilets Prize for toilet books, a genre thus designated since they are intended for browsing while at stool? I suggest a panel of judges chosen for their expertise in this field, themselves writers of toilet books, viz: Jimmy Riddle, Miles Kington, Arthur Marshall, Kenneth Williams, Gyles Brandreth, Bill Oddie and Maureen Lipman. The prize, as well as money, could be a bronze of Maureen Lipman wearing a comical expression on the john.

I take it you're a Tory, sir? I ask since I have a second proposition and it seems wise to check first that you favour the modern way of doing things in Mrs Thatcher's self-help Britain. Here's the dodge: I am myself a toilet book writer of some resource, having no less that eight on sale this Xmas. We see to it that I win the prize and you and I trouser the money fifty-fifty, no questions asked. What do you say to that?

I would further confirm that within seconds of receipt your letter of concurrance will go through my shredder, the contents having been memorised. We don't keep files here, we've minds like lobster-pots.

Let's help ourselves to help ourselves!

Yours faithfully,

Henry Root.

*A letter from Mr Henry Root to Twyfords Toilets from* The Soap Letters.

# *The £1,000,000 Bank-Note*

## Mark Twain

When I was twenty-seven years old, I was a mining broker's clerk in San Francisco, and an expert in all the details of stock traffic. I was alone in the world, and had nothing to depend upon but my wits and a clean reputation; but these were setting my feet in the road to eventual fortune, and I was content with the prospect.

My time was my own after the afternoon board, Saturdays, and I was accustomed to put it in on a little sailboat on the bay. One day I ventured too far, and was carried out to sea. Just at nightfall, when hope was about gone, I was picked up by a small brig which was bound for London. It was a long and stormy voyage, and they made me work my passage without pay, as a common sailor. When I stepped ashore in London my clothes were ragged and shabby, and I had only a dollar in my pocket. This money fed and sheltered me twenty-four hours. During the next twenty-four I went without food and shelter.

About ten o'clock on the following morning, seedy and hungry, I was dragging myself along Portland Place, when a child that was passing, towed by a nursemaid, tossed a luscious big pear – minus one bite –into the gutter. I stopped, of course, and fastened my desiring eye on that muddy treasure. My mouth watered for it, my stomach craved it, my whole being begged for it. But every time I made a move to get it some passing eye detected my purpose, and of course I straightened up, then, and looked indifferent, and pretended that I hadn't been thinking about the pear at all. This same thing kept happening and happening, and I couldn't get the pear. I was just getting desperate enough to brave the shame, and to seize it, when a window behind me was raised, and a gentleman spoke out of it, saying:

'Step in here, please.'

I was admitted by a gorgeous flunky, and shown into a sumptuous room where a couple of elderly gentlemen were sitting. They sent away the servant, and made me sit down. They had just finished their breakfast, and the sight of the remains of it almost overpowered me. I could hardly keep my wits together in the presence of that food, but as I was not asked to sample it, I had to bear my trouble as best I could.

Now, something had been happening there a little before, which I did not know anything about until a good many days afterward, but I will tell you about it now. Those two old brothers had been having a pretty hot argument a couple of days before, and had ended by agreeing to decide it by a bet, which is the English way of settling everything.

You will remember that the Bank of England once issued two notes of a million pounds each, to be used for a special purpose connected with some public transaction with a foreign country. For some reason or other only one of these had been used and cancelled; the other still lay in the vaults of the Bank. Well, the brothers, chatting along, happened to get to wondering what might be the fate of a perfectly honest and intelligent stranger who should be turned adrift in London without a friend, who had no money but that million-pound bank-note, and no way to account for his being in possession of it. Brother A said he would starve to death; Brother B said he wouldn't. Brother A said he couldn't offer it at a bank or anywhere else, because he would be arrested on the spot. So they went on disputing till Brother B said he would bet twenty thousand pounds that the man would live thirty days, *anyway*, on that million, and keep out of jail, too. Brother A took him up. Brother B went down to the Bank and bought the note. Just like an Englishman, you see; pluck to the backbone. Then he dictated a letter, which one of his clerks wrote out in a beautiful round hand, and then the two brothers sat at the window a whole day for the right man to give it to.

They saw many honest faces go by that were not intelligent

enough; many that were intelligent, but not honest enough; many that were both, but the possessors were not poor enough, or, if poor enough, were not strangers. There was always a defect, until I came along; but they agreed that I filled the bill all around; so they elected me unanimously, and there I was, now, waiting to know why I was called in. They began to ask me questions about myself, and pretty soon they had my story. Finally they told me I would answer their purpose. I said I was sincerely glad, and asked what it was. Then one of them handed me an envelope, and said I would find the explanation inside. I was going to open it, but he said no; take it to my lodgings, and look it over carefully, and not be hasty or rash. I was puzzled, and wanted to discuss this matter a little further, but they didn't; so I took my leave, feeling hurt and insulted to be made the butt of what was apparently some kind of practical joke, and yet obliged to put up with it, not being in circumstances to resent affronts from rich and stong folk.

I would have picked up the pear, now, and eaten it before all the world, but it was gone; so I had lost that by this unlucky business, and the thought of it did not soften my feeling toward those men. As soon as I was out of sight of that house I opened my envelope, and saw that it contained money! My opinion of those people changed, I can tell you! I lost not a moment, but shoved the note and money into my vest-pocket, and broke for the nearest cheap eating house. Well, how I did eat! When at last I couldn't hold any more, I took out my money and unfolded it, took one glimpse and nearly fainted. Five million of dollars! Why, it made my head swim.

I must have sat there stunned and blinking at the note as much as a minute before I came rightly to myself again. The first thing I noticed, then, was the landlord. His eye was on the note, and he was petrified. He was worshiping, with all his body and soul, but he looked as if he couldn't stir hand or foot. I took my cue in a moment, and did the only rational thing there was to do. I reached the note toward him, and said carelessly:

'Give me the change, please.'

Then he was restored to his normal condition, and made a thousand apologies for not being able to break the bill, and I couldn't get him to touch it. He wanted to look at it, and keep on looking at it; he couldn't seem to get enough of it to quench the thirst of his eye, but he shrank from touching it as if it had been something too sacred for poor common clay to handle. I said:

'I am sorry if it is an inconvenience, but I must insist. Please change it; I haven't anything else.'

But he said that wasn't any matter; he was quite willing to let the trifle stand over till another time. I said I might not be in his neighbourhood again for a good while; but he said it was of no consequence, he could wait, and, moreover, I could have anything I wanted any time I chose, and let the account run as long as I pleased. He said he hoped he wasn't afraid to trust as rich a gentleman as I was, merely because of a merry disposition, and chose to play larks on the public in the matter of dress. By this time another customer was entering, and the landlord hinted to me to put the monster out of sight; then he bowed me all the way to the door, and I started straight for that house and those brothers, to correct the mistake which had been made before the police should hunt me up, and help me do it. I was pretty nervous, in fact pretty badly frightened, though, of course, I was no way in fault; but I knew men well enough to know that when they find they've given a tramp a million-pound bill when they thought it was a one-pounder, they are in a frantic rage against *him* instead of quarreling with their own nearsightedness, as they ought. As I approached the house my excitement began to abate, for all was quiet there, which made me feel pretty sure the blunder was not discovered yet. I rang. The same servant appeared. I asked for those gentlemen.

'They are gone.' This in the lofty, cold way of that fellow's tribe.

'Gone? Gone where?'

'On a journey.'

'But whereabouts?'

'To the continent, I think.'

'The continent?'

'Yes, sir.'

'Which way – by what route?'

'I can't say, sir.'

'When will they be back?'

'In a month, they said.'

'A month! Oh, this is awfu;l! Give me *some* sort of idea how to get word to them. It's of the last importançe.'

'I can't indeed. I've no idea where they've gone, sir.'

Then I must see some member of the family.'

'Family's away too; been abroad months – in Egypt and India, I think.'

'Man, there's been an immense mistake made. They'll be back before night. Will you tell them I've been here, and that I will keep coming till it's all made right, and they needn't be afraid?'

'I'll tell them, if they come back, but I am not expecting them. They said you would be here in an hour to make inquiries, but I must tell you it's all right, they'll be here on time and expect you.'

So I had to give it up and go away. What a riddle it all was! I was like to lose my mind. They would he here 'on time'. What could that mean? Oh, the letter would explain, maybe. I had forgotten the letter; I got it out and read it. This is what it said:

> You are an intelligent and honest man, as one may see by your face. We conceive you to be poor and a stranger. Enclosed you will find a sum of money. It is lent to you for thirty days, without interest. Report at this house at the end of that time. I have a bet on you. If I win it you shall have any situation that is in my gift – any, that is, that you shall be able to prove yourself familiar with and competent to fill.

No signature, no address, no date.

Well, here was a coil to be in! You are posted on what had preceded all this, but I was not. It was just a deep, dark puzzle to me. I hadn't the least idea what the game was, nor whether harm was meant me or kindness. I went into a park, and sat down to try to think it out, and to consider what I had best do.

At the end of an hour, my reasonings had crystallised into this verdict.

Maybe those men mean me well, maybe they mean me ill; no way to decide that – let it go. They've got a game, or a scheme, or an experiment, of some kind on hand; no way to determine what it is – let it go. There's a bet on me; no way to find out what it is – let it go. That disposes of the indeterminable quantities; the remainder of the matter is tangible, solid, and may be classed and labeled with certainty. If I ask the Bank of England to place this bill to the credit of the man it belongs to, they'll do it, for they know him, although I don't; but they will ask me how I came in possession of it, and if I tell the truth, they'll put me in the asylum, naturally, and a lie will land me in jail. The same result would follow me if I tried to bank the bill anywhere or to borrow money on it. I have got to carry this immense burden around until those men come back, whether I want to or not. It is useless to me, as useless as a handful of ashes, and yet I must take care of it, and watch over it, while I beg my living. I couldn't *give* it away, if I should try, for neither honest citizen nor highwayman would accept it or meddle with it for anything. Those brothers are safe. Even if I lose their bill, or burn it, they are still safe, because they can stop payment, and the Bank will make them whole; but meantime, I've got to do a month's suffering without wages or profit – unless I help win that bet, whatever it may be, and get that situation that I am promised. I *should* like to get that; men of their sort have situations in their gift that are worth having.

I got to thinking a good deal about that situation. My hopes began to rise high. Without doubt the salary would be large. It would begin in a month; after that I should be all right. Pretty soon I was feeling first rate. By this time I was tramping the streets again. The sight of a tailor shop gave me a sharp longing to shed my rags, and to clothe myself decently once more. Could I afford it? No; I had nothing in the world but a million pounds. So I forced myself to go on by. But soon I was drifting back again. The temptation persecuted me cruelly. I must have passed that shop back and forth six times during that manful struggle. At last I gave in; I had to. I asked if they had a misfit suit that had been thrown on their hands. The fellow I spoke to nodded his head toward another fellow, and gave me no answer. I went to the indicated fellow, and he indicated another fellow with *his* head, and no words. I went to him, and he said:

''Tend to you presently.'

I waited till he was done with what he was at, then he took me into a back room, and overhauled a pile of rejected suits, and selected the rattiest one for me. I put it on. It didn't fit, and wasn't in any way attractive, but it was new, and I was anxious to have it; so I didn't find any fault, but said with some diffidence:

'It would be an accommodation to me if you could wait some days for the money. I haven't any small change about me.'

The fellow worked up a most sarcastic expression of countenance, and said:

'Oh, you haven't? Well, of course, I didn't expect it. I'd only expect gentlemen like you to carry large change.'

I was nettled, and said:

'My friend, you shouldn't judge a stranger always by the clothes he wears. I am quite able to pay for this suit; I simply didn't wish to put you to the trouble of changing a large note.'

He modified his style a little at that, and said, though still with something of an air:

'I didn't mean any particular harm, but as long as rebukes are going, I might say it wasn't quite your affair to jump to the conclusion that we couldn't change any note that you might happen to be carrying around. On the contrary, we *can*.'

I handed the note to him, and said:

'Oh, very well; I apologise.'

He received it with a smile, one of those large smiles which goes all around over, and has folds in it, and wrinkles, and spirals, and looks like the place where you have thrown a brick in a pond; and then in the act of his taking a glimpse at the bill this smile froze solid, and turned yellow, and looked like those wavy, wormy spreads of lava which you find hardened on little levels on the side of Vesuvius. I never before saw a smile caught like that, and perpetuated. The man stood there holding the bill, and looking like that, and the proprietor hustled up to see what was the matter, and said briskly:

'Well, what's up? what's the trouble? what's wanting?'

I said: 'There isn't any trouble. I'm waiting for my change.'

'Come, come; get him his change, Tod; get him his change.'

Tod retorted: 'Get him his change! It's easy to say, sir; but look at the bill yourself.'

The proprietor took a look, gave a low, eloquent whistle, then made a dive for the pile of rejected clothing, and began to snatch it this way and that, talking all the time excitedly, and as if to himself:

'Sell an eccentric millionaire such an unspeakable suit as that! Tod's a fool – a born fool. Always doing something like this. Drives every millionaire away from the place, because he can't tell a millionaire from a tramp, and never could. Ah, here's the thing I'm after. Please get those things off, sir, and throw them in the fire. Do me the favor to put on this shirt and this suit; it's just the thing, the very thing – plain, rich, modest, and just ducally nobby; made to order for a foreign prince – you may know him, sir, his serene Highness the Hospodar of Halifax; had to leave it with us and take a mourning suit because his mother was going to die – which she didn't. But that's all right; we can't always have things the way we – that is, the way they – there! trousers all right, they fit you to a charm, sir; now the waistcoat; aha, right again! now the coat – Lord! look at that, now! Perfect – the whole thing! I never saw such a triumph in all my experience.'

I expressed my satisfaction.

'Quite right, sir, quite right; it'll do for a makeshift, I'm bound to say. But wait till you see what we'll get up for you on your own measure. Come, Tod, book and pen; get at it. Length of leg, 32' – and so on. Before I could get in a word he had measured me, and was giving orders for dress suits, morning suits, shirts, and all sorts of things. When I got a chance I said:

'But, my dear sir, I *can't* give these orders, unless you can wait indefinitely, or change the bill.'

'Indefinitely! It's a weak word, sir, a weak word. Eternally – *that's* the word, sir. Tod, rush these things through, and send them to the gentleman's address without any waste of time. Let the minor customers wait. Get down the gentleman's address and—'

'I'm changing my quarters. I will drop in and leave the new address.'

'Quite right, sir, quite right. One moment – let me show you out, sir. There – good day, sir, good day.'

Well don't you see what was bound to happen? I drifted naturally into buying whatever I wanted, and asking for change. Within a week I was sumptuously equipped with all the needful comforts and luxuries, and was housed in an expensive private hotel in Hanover Square. I took my dinners there, but for breakfast I stuck by Harris's humble feeding house, where I had got my first meal on my million-pound bill. I was the making of Harris. The fact had gone all abroad that the foreign crank who carried million-pound bills in his vest-pocket was the patron saint of the place. That was enough. From being a poor, struggling, little hand-to-mouth enterprise, it had become celebrated, and overcrowded with customers. Harris was so grateful that he forced loans upon me, and would not be denied; and so, pauper as I was, I had money to spend, and was living like the rich and great. I judged that there was going to be a crash by and by, but I was in, now, and must swim across or drown. You see there was just that element of impending disaster to give a serious side, a sober side, yes, a tragic side, to a state of things which would otherwise have been purely ridiculous. In the night, in the dark, the tragedy part was always to the front, and always warning, always threatening; and so I moaned and tossed, and sleep was hard to find. But in the cheerful daylight the tragedy element faded out and disappeared, and I walked on air, and was happy to giddiness, to intoxication, you may say.

And it was natural; for I had become one of the notorieties of the metropolis of the world, and it turned my head, not just a little, but a good deal. You could not take up a newspaper, English, Scotch, or Irish, without finding in it one or more references to the 'vest-pocket million-pounder' and his latest doings and sayings. At first, in these mentions, I was at the bottom of the personal gossip column; next, I was listed above the knights; next, above the baronets; next, above the barons, and so on, and so on, climbing steadily as my notoriety augmented, until I reached the highest altitude possible, and there I remained, taking precedence of all dukes not royal, and of all ecclesiastics except the primate of all England. But mind, this was not fame; as yet I had achieved only notoriety. Then came the climaxing stroke – the accolade, so to speak – which in a single instant transmuted the perishable dross of notoriety into the enduring gold of fame: *Punch* caricatured me! Yes, I was a made man, now; my place was established. I might be joked about still, but reverently, not hilariously, not rudely; I could be smiled at, but not laughed at. The time for that had gone by. *Punch* pictured me all a-flutter with rags, dickering with a beefeater for the Tower of London. Well, you can imagine how it was with a young fellow who had never been taken notice of before, and now all of a sudden couldn't say a thing that wasn't taken up and repeated everywhere; couldn't stir abroad without constantly overhearing the remark flying from lip to lip. 'There he goes; that's him!' couldn't take his breakfast without a crowd to look on; couldn't appear in an opera box without concentrating there the fire of a thousand lorgnettes. Why, I just swam in glory all day long – that is the amount of it.

You know, I even kept my old suit of rags, and every now and then appeared in them, so as to have the old pleasure of buying trifles, and being insulted, and then shooting the scoffer dead with the million-pound bill. But I couldn't keep that up. The illustrated papers made the outfit so familiar that when I went out in it I was at once recognised and followed by a crowd, and if I attempted to purchase the man would offer me his whole shop on credit before I could pull my note on him.

About the tenth day of my fame I went to fulfill my duty to my flag by paying my respects to the American minister. He received me with the enthusiasm proper in my case, upbraided me for being so tardy in my duty, and said that there was only one way to get his forgiveness, and that was to take the seat at his dinner party that night made vacant by the illness of one of his guests. I said I would, and we to got to talking. It turned out that he and my father had been schoolmates in boyhood, Yale students together later, and always warm friends up to my father's death. So then he required me to put in at his house all the odd time I might have to spare, and I was very willing, of course.

In fact I was more than willing; I was glad. When the crash should come, he might somehow be able to save me from total destruction; I didn't know how, but he might think of a way, maybe. I couldn't venture to unbosom myself to him at this late date, a thing which I would have been quick to do in the beginning of this awful career of mine in London. No, I couldn't venture it now; I was in too deep; that is, too deep for me to be risking revelations to so new a friend, though not yet clear beyond my depth, as *I* looked at it. Because, you see, with all my borrowing, I was carefully keeping within my means – I mean within my slary. Of course I couldn't *know* what my salary was going to be, but I had a good enough basis for an estimate in the fact that, if I won the bet, I was to have *choice* of any situation in that rich old gentleman's gift provided I was competent – and I should certainly prove competent; I hadn't any doubt about that. And as to the bet, I wasn't worrying about that; I had always been lucky. Now my estimate of the salary was six hundred to a thousand a year; say, six hundred for the first year, and so on up year by year, till I struck the upper figure by proved merit. At present I was only in debt for my first year's salary. Everybody had been trying to lend me money, but I had fought off the most of them on one pretext or another; so this indebtedness represented only £300 borrowed money, the other £300 represented my keep and my purchases. I believed my second year's salary would carry me through the rest of the month if I went on being cautious and economical, and I intended to look sharply out for that. My month ended, my employer back from his journey, I should be all right once more, for I should at once divide the two years' salary among my creditors by assignment, and get right down to my work.

It was a lovely dinner party of fourteen. The Duke and Duchess of Shoreditch, and their daughter the Lady Anne-Grace-Eleanor-Celeste-and-so-forth-and-so-forth-de-Bohun, the Earl and Countess of Newgate, Viscount Cheapside, Lord and Lady Blatherskite, some untitled people of both sexes, the minister and his wife and daughter, and this daughter's visiting friend, an English girl of twenty-two, named Portia Langham, whom I fell in love with in two minutes, and she with me – I could see it without glasses. There was still another guest, an American – but I am a little ahead of my story. While the people were still in the drawing room, whetting up for dinner, and coldly inspecting the late-comers, the servant announced:

'Mr Lloyd Hastings.'

The moment the usual civilities were over, Hastings caught sight of me, and came straight with cordially outstretched hand; then stopped short when about to shake; and said with an embarrassed look:

'I beg your pardon, sir, I thought I knew you.'

'Why, you do know me, old fellow.'

'No! Are *you* the – the—'

'Vest-pocket monster? I am, indeed. Don't be afraid to call me by my nickname; I'm used to it.'

'Well, well, well, this is a surprise. Once or twice I've seen your own name coupled with the nickname, but it never occurred to me that *you* could be the Henry Adams referred to. Why, it isn't six months since you were clerking away for Blake Hopkins in Frisco on a salary, and sitting up nights on an extra allowance, helping me arrange and verify the Gould and Curry Extension papers and statistics. The idea of your being in London, and a vast millionaire, and a colossal celebrity! Why, it's the Arabian Nights come again. Man, I can't take it in at all; can't realise it; give me time to settle the whirl in my head.'

'The fact is, Lloyd, you are no worse off than I am. I can't realise it myself.'

'Dear me, it *is* stunning, now isn't it? Why, it's just three months today since we went to the Miners' restaurant—'

'No; the What Cheer.'

'Right, it *was* the What Cheer, went there at two in the morning, and had a chop and coffee after a hard six hours' grind over those Extension papers, and I tried to persuade you to come to London with me, and offered to get leave of absence for you and pay all your expenses, and give you something over if I succeeded in making the sale; and you would not listen to me, said I wouldn't succeed, and you couldn't afford to lose the run of business and be no end of time getting the hang of things again when you got back home. And yet here you are. How odd it all is! How did you happen to come, and whatever *did* give you this incredible start?'

'Oh, just an accident. It's a long story – a romance, a body may say. I'll tell you all about it, but not now.'

'When?'

'The end of this month.'

'That's more than a fortnight yet. It's too much of a strain on a person's curiosity. Make it a week.'

'I can't. You'll know why, by and by. But how's the trade getting along?'

His cheerfulness vanished like a breath, and he said with a sigh:

'You were a true prophet, Hal, a true prophet. I wish I hadn't come. I didn't want to talk about it.'

'But you must. You must come and stop with me tonight, when we leave here, and tell me all about it.'

'Oh, may I? Are you in earnest?' and the water showed in his eyes.

'Yes; I want to hear the whole story, every word.'

'I'm so grateful! Just to find a human interest once more, in some voice and in some eye, in me and affairs of mine, after what I've been through here – Lord! I could go down on my knees for it!'

He gripped my hand hard, and braced up, and was all right and lively after that for the dinner – which didn't come off. No; the usual thing happened, the thing that is always happening under the vicious and aggravating English system – the matter of precedence couldn't be settled, and so there was no dinner. Englishmen always eat dinner before they go out to dinner, because *they* know the risks they are running; but nobody ever warns the stranger, and so he walks placidly into the trap. Of course nobody was hurt this time, because we had all been to dinner, none of us being novices except Hastings, and he having been informed by the minister at the time that he invited him that in deference to the English custom he had not provided any dinner. Everybody took a lady and processioned down to the dining room, because it is usual to go through the motions; but there the dispute began. The Duke of Shoreditch wanted to take precedence, and sit at the head of the table, holding that he outranked a minister who represented merely a nation and not a monarch; but I stood for my rights, and refused to yield. In the gossip column I ranked all dukes not royal, and said so, and claimed precedence of this one. It couldn't be settled, of course, struggle as we might and did, he finally (and injudiciously) trying to play birth and antiquity, and I 'seeing' his Conqueror and 'raising' him with Adam, whose direct posterity I was, as shown by his name, while *he* was of a collateral branch, as shown by *his*, and by his recent Norman origin; so we all processioned back to the drawing room again and had a perpendicular lunch – plate of sardines and a strawberry, and you group yourself and stand up and eat it. Here the religion of precedence is not so strenuous; the two persons of highest rank chuck up a shilling, the one that wins has first go at his strawberry, and the looser gets the shilling. The next two chuck up, then the next two, and so on. After refreshments, tables were brought, and we all played cribbage, sixpence a game. The English never play any game for amusement. If they can't make something or lose something – they don't care which – they won't play.

We had a lovely time; certainly two of us had, Miss Langham and I. I was so bewitched with her that I couldn't count my hands if they went above a double sequence; and when I struck home I never discovered it, and started up the outside row again, and would have lost the game every time, only the girl did the same, she being in just my conditon, you see; and consequently neither of us ever got out, or cared to wonder why we didn't; we only just knew we were happy, and didn't wish to know anything else, and didn't want to be interrupted. And I *told* her – I did indeed – told her I loved her; and she – well, she blushed till her turned red, but she liked it; she *said* she did. Oh, there was never such an evening! Every time I pegged I put on a postscript; every time she pegged she acknowledged receipt of it, counting the hands the same. Why, I couldn't even say 'Two for his heels' without adding, '*My*, how sweet you do look!' and she would say, 'Fifteen two, fifteen four, fifteen six, and a pair are eight, and eight are sixteen – *do* you think so?' – peeping out aslant from under her lashes, you know, so sweet and cunning. Oh, it was just *too*-too!

Well, I was pefectly honest and square with her; told her I hadn't a cent in the world but just the million-pound note she'd heard so much talk about, and *it* didn't belong to me; and that started her curiosity, and then I talked low, and told her the whole history right from the start, and it nearly killed her, laughing. What in the nation she could find to laugh about, I couldn't see, but there it was; every half minute some new detail would fetch her, and I would have to stop as much as a minute and a half to give her a chance to settle down again. Why, she laughed herself lame, she did indeed; I never saw anything like it. I mean I never saw a painful story – a story of a person's troubles and worries and fears – produce just *that* kind of effect before. So I loved her all the more, seeing she could be so cheerful when there wasn't anything to be cheerful about; for I might soon need that kind of wife, you know, the way things looked. Of course I told her we should have to wait a couple of years, till I could catch up on my salary; but she didn't mind that, only she hoped I would be as careful as possible in the matter of expenses, and not let them run the least risk of trenching on our third year's pay. Then she began to get a little worried, and wondered if we were making any mistake, and starting the salary on a higher figure for the first year than I would get. This was good sense, and it made me feel a little less confident than I had been feeling before; but it gave me a good business idea, and I brought it frankly out.

'Portia, dear, would you mind going with me that day, when I confront those old gentlemen?'

She shrank a little, but said:

'N-o; if my being with you would help hearten you. But – would it be quite proper, do you think?'

'No, I don't know that it would; in fact I'm afraid it wouldn't;

but you see, there's so *much* dependent upon it that—'

'Then I'll go anyway, proper or improper,' she said, with a beautiful and generous enthusiasm. 'Oh, I shall be so happy to think I am helping.'

'Helping, dear? Why, you'll be doing it all. You're so beautiful and so lovely and so winning, that with you there I can pile our salary up till I break those good old fellows, and they'll never have the heart to struggle.'

Sho! you should have seen the rich blood mount, and her happy eyes shine!

'You wicked flatterer! There isn't a word of truth in what you say, but still I'll go with you. Maybe it will teach you not to expect other people to look with your eyes.'

Were my doubts dissipated? Was my confidence restored? You may judge by this fact: privately I raised my salary to twelve hundred the first year on the spot. But I didn't tell her; I saved it for a surprise.

All the way home I was in the clouds, Hastings talking, I not hearing a word. When he and I entered my parlor, he brought me to myself with his fervent appreciation of my manifold comforts and luxuries.

'Let me just stand here a little and look my fill! Dear me, it's a palace; it's just a palace! And in it everything a body *could* desire, including cozy coal fire and supper standing ready. Henry, it doesn't merely make me realise how rich you are; it makes me realise, to the bone, to the marrow, how poor I am – how poor I am, and how miserable, how defeated, routed, annihilated!'

Plague take it! this language gave me the cold shudders. It scared me broad awake, and made me comprehend that I was standing on a half-inch crust, with a crater underneath. *I* didn't know I had been dreaming – that is, I hadn't been allowing myself to know it for a while back; but *now* – oh, dear! Deep in debt, not a cent in the world, a lovely girl's happiness or woe in my hands, and nothing in front of me but a salary which might never – oh, *would* never – materialise! Oh, oh, oh, I am ruined past hope; nothing can save me!

'Henry, the mere unconsidered drippings of your daily income would—'

'Oh, my daily income! Here, down with this hot Scotch, and cheer up your soul. Here's with you! Or, no – you're hungry; sit down—'

'Not a bite for me; I'm past it. I can't eat, these days; but I'll drink with you till I drop. Come!'

'Barrel for barrel, I'm with you! Ready? Here we go! Now, then, Lloyd, unreel your story while I brew.'

'Unreel it? What, again?'

'Again? What do you mean by that?'

'Why, I mean do you want to hear it *over* again?'

'Do I want to hear it *over* again? This *is* a puzzler. Wait; don't take any more of that liquid. You don't need it.'

'Look here, Henry, you alarm me. Didn't I tell you the whole story on the way here?'

'You?'

'Yes, I.'

'I'll be hanged if I heard a word of it.'

'Henry, this is a serious thing. It troubles me. What did you take up yonder at the minister's?'

Then it all flashed on me, and I owned up, like a man.

'I took the dearest girl in this world – prisoner!'

So then he came with a rush, and we shook, and shook, and shook till our hands ached; and he didn't blame me for not having heard a word of a story which lasted while we walked three miles. He just sat down then, like the patient, good fellow he was, and told it all over again. Synopsised, it amounted to this: He had come to England with what he thought was a grand opportunity; he had an 'option' to sell the Gould and Curry Extension for the 'locators', of it, and keep all he could get over a million dollars. He had worked hard, had pulled every wire he knew of, had left no honest expedient untried, had spent nearly all the money he had in the world, had not been able to get a solitary capitalist to listen to him, and his option would run out at the end of the month. In a word, he was ruined. Then he jumped up and cried out:

'Henry, you can save me! You can save me, and you're the only man in the universe that can. Will you do it? *Won't* you do it!'

'Tell me how. Speak out, my boy.'

'Give me a million and my passage home for my 'option'! Don't *don't* refuse!'

I was in a kind of agony. I was right on the point of coming out with the words. 'Lloyd, I'm a pauper myself – absolutely penniless, and in *debt*!' But a white-hot idea came flaming through my head, and I gripped my jaws together, and calmed myself down till I was as cold as a capitalist. Then I said, in a commercial and self-possessed way:

'I will save you, Lloyd—'

'Then I'm already saved! God be merciful to you forever! If ever I—'

'Let me finish, Lloyd. I will save you, but not in that way; for that would not be fair to you, after your hard work, and the risks you've run. I don't need to buy mines; I can keep my capital moving, in a commercial center like London without that; it's what I'm at, all the time; but here is what I'll do. I know all about that mine, of course; I know it's immense value, and can swear to it if anybody wishes it. You can sell out inside of the fortnight for three million cash, using my name freely, and we'll divide, share and share alike.'

Do you know, he would have danced the furniture to kindling wood in his insane joy, and broken everything on the place, if I hadn't tripped him up and tied him.

Then he lay there, perfectly happy, saying:

'I may use your name! Your name – think of it ! Man, they'll flock in droves, these rich Londoners; they'll *fight* for that stock! I'm a made man, I'm a made man forever, and I'll never forget you as long as I live!'

In less than twenty-four hours London was abuzz! I hadn't anything to do, day after day, but sit at home, and say to all comers:

'Yes; I told him to refer to me. I know the man, and I know the mine. His character is above reproach, and the mine is worth far more than he asks for it.'

Meantime I spent all my evenings at the minister's with Portia. I didn't say a word to her about the mine; I saved it for a surprise. We talked salary; never anything but salary and love;

sometimes love, sometimes salary, sometimes love and salary together. And my! the interest the minister's wife and daughter took in our little affair, and the endless ingenuities they invented to save us from interruption, and to keep the minister in the dark and unsuspicious – well, it was just lovely of them!

When the month was up, at last, I had a million dollars to my credit in the London and County bank, and Hastings was fixed in the same way. Dressed at my level best, I drove by the house in Portland Place, judged by the look of things that my birds were home again, went on toward the minister's and got my precious, and we started back, talking salary with all our might. She was so excited and anxious that it made her just intolerably beautiful. I said:

'Dearie, the way you're looking it's a crime to strike for a salary a single penny under three thousand a year.'

'Henry, Henry, you'll ruin us!'

'Don't you be afraid. Just keep up those looks, and trust to me. It'll all come out right.'

So as it turned out, I had to keep bolstering up *her* courage all the way. She kept pleading with me, and saying:

'Oh, please remember that if we ask too much we may get no salary at all; and then what will become of us, with no way in the world to earn our living?'

We were ushered in by that same servant, and there they were, the two gentlemen. Of course they were surprised to see that wonderful creature with me, but I said:

'It's all right, gentlemen; she is my future stay and helpmate.'

And I introduced them to her, and called them by name. It didn't surprise them; they knew I would know enough to consult the directory. They seated us, and were very polite to me, and very solicitious to relieve her from embarrassment, and put her as much at her ease as they could. Then I said:

'Gentlemen, I am ready to report.'

'We are glad to hear it,' said *my* man, 'for now we can decide the bet which my brother Abel and I made. If you have won for me, you shall have any situation in my gift. Have you the million-pound note?'

'Here it is, sir,' and I handed it to him.

'I've won!' he shouted, and slapped Abel on the back. '*Now* what do you say, brother?'

'I say he *did* survive, and I've lost twenty thousand pounds. I never would have believed it.'

'I've a further report to make,' I said, 'and a pretty long one. I want you to let me come soon, and detail my whole month's history; and I promise you it's worth hearing, Meantime, take a look at that.'

'What, man! Certificate of deposit for £200,000? Is it yours?'

'Mine, I earned it by thirty days' judicious use of that little loan you let me have. And the only use I made of it was to buy trifles and offer the bill in change.'

'Come, this is astonishing! It's incredible, man!'

'Never mind, I'll prove it. Don't take my word unsupported.'

But now Portia's turn was come to be surprised. Her eyes were spread wide, and she said:

'Henry, is that really your money? Have you been fibbing to me?'

'I have indeed, dearie. But you'll forgive me, *I* know.'

She put up an arch pout, and said:

'Don't you be so sure. You are a naughty thing to deceive me so!'

'Oh, you'll get over it, sweetheart, you'll get over it; it was only fun, you know. Come, let's be going.'

'But wait, wait! The situation, you know. I want to give you the situation,' said my man.

'Well,' I said, 'I'm just as grateful as I can be, but really I don't want one.'

'But you can have the very choicest one in my gift.'

'Thanks again, with all my heart; but I don't even want *that* one.'

'Henry, I'm ashamed of you. You don't half thank the good gentleman. May I do it for you?'

'Indeed you shall, dear, if you can improve it. Let us see you try.'

She walked to my man, got up in his lap, put her arm round his neck, and kissed him right on the mouth. Then the two old gentlemen shouted with laughter, but I was dumbfounded, just petrified, as you may say. Portia said:

'Papa, he has said you haven't a situation in your gift that he'd take; and I feel just as hurt as—'

'My darling! – Is that your papa?'

'Yes; he's my steppapa, and the dearest one that ever was. You understand now, don't you, why I was able to laugh when you told me at the minister's, not knowing my relationships, what trouble and worry papa's and Uncle Abel's scheme was giving you?'

Of course I spoke right up, now, without any fooling, and went straight to the point.

'Oh, my dearest dear sir, I want to take back what I said. You *have* got a situation open that I want.'

'Name it.'

'Son-in-law.'

'Well, well, well! But you know, if you haven't ever served in that capacity, you of course can't furnish recommendations of a sort to satisfy the conditions of the contract, and so—'

'Try me – oh, do, I beg of you! Only just try me thirty or forty years, and if—'

'Oh, well, all right; it's but a little thing to ask. Take her along.'

Happy, we two? There're not words enough in the unabridged to describe it. And when London got the whole story, a day or two later, of my month's adventures with that bank-note, and how they ended, did London talk, and have a good time? Yes.

My Portia's papa took that friendly and hospitable bill back to the Bank of England and cashed it; then the Bank canceled it and made him a present of it, and he gave it to us at our wedding, and it has always hung in its frame in the sacredest place in our home, ever since. For it gave me my Portia. But for it I could not have remained in London, would not have appeared at the minister's, never should have met her. And so I always say, 'Yes, it's a million-pounder, as you see; but it never made but one purchase in its life, and *then* got the article for only about a tenth part of its value.'

●

There was a young lady of Florence
Who for kissing professed great abhorrence;
But when she'd been kissed,
And found what she'd missed,
She cried till her tears came in torrents.

**Anon**

# *The Truth About Pyecraft*

## H.G. Wells

He sits not a dozen yards away. If I glance over my shoulder I can see him. And if I catch his eye – and usually I catch his eye – it meets me with an expression—

It is mainly an imploring look – and yet with suspicion in it.

Confound his suspicion! If I wanted to tell on him I should have told long ago. I don't tell and I don't tell, and he ought to feel at his ease. As if anything so gross and fat as he could feel at ease! Who would believe me if I did tell?

Poor old Pyecraft! Great, uneasy jelly of substance! The fattest clubman in London.

He sits at one of the little club tables in the huge bay by the fire, stuffing. What is he stuffing? I glance judiciously and catch him biting at a round of hot buttered teacake, with his eyes on me. Confound him – with his eyes on me!

That settles it, Pyecraft! Since you *will* be abject, since you *will* behave as though I was not a man of honour, here, right under your embedded eyes, I write the thing down – the plain truth about Pyecraft. The man I helped, the man I shielded, and who has requited me by making my club unendurable, absolutely unendurable, with his liquid appeal, with the perpetual 'don't tell' of his looks.

And, besides, why does he keep on eternally eating?

Well, here goes for the truth, the whole truth, and nothing but the truth!

Pyecraft – I made the acquaintance of Pyrcraft in this very smoking-room. I was a young, nervous new member, and he saw it. I was sitting all alone, wishing I knew more of the members, and suddenly he came, a great rolling front of chins and abdomina, towards me, and grunted and sat down in a chair close by me and wheezed for a space, and scraped for a space with a match and lit a cigar, and then addressed me. I forgot what he said – something about the matches not lighting properly, and afterwards as he talked he kept stopping the waiters one by one as they went by, and telling them about the matches in that thin, fluty voice he has. But, anyhow, it was in some such way we began our talking.

He talked about various things and came round to games. And thence to my figure and complexion. 'You ought to be a good cricketer,' he said. I suppose I am slender, slender to what some people would call lean, and I suppose I am rather dark, still – I am not ashamed of having a Hindu great-grandmother, but, for all that, I don't want casual strangers to see through me at a glance to *her*. So that I was set against Pyecraft from the beginning.

But he only talked about me in order to get to himself.

'I expect,' he said, 'you take no more exercise than I do, and probably you eat no less.' (Like all excessively obese people he fancied he ate nothing.) 'Yet' – and he smiled an oblique smile – 'we differ.'

And then be began to talk about his fatness and his fitness; all he did for his fatness and all he was going to do for his fatness; what people had advised him to do for his fatness and what he had heard of people doing for fatness similar to his. '*A priori*,' he said, 'one would think a question of nutrition could be answered by dietary and a question of assimilation by drugs.' It was stifling. It was dumpling talk. It made me feel swelled to hear him.

One stands that sort of thing once in a way at a club, but a time came when I fancied I was standing too much. He took to me altogether too conspicuously. I could never go in the smoking-room but he would come wallowing towards me, and sometimes he came and gormandised round and about me while I had my lunch. He seemed at times to be clinging to me. He was a bore, but not so fearful a bore as to be limited to me; and from the first there was something in his manner – almost as though he knew, almost as though he penetrated to the fact that

I *might* – that there was a remote, exceptional chance in me that no one else presented.

'I'd give anything to get it down,' he would say – 'anything,' and peer at me over his vast cheeks and pant.

Poor old Pyecraft! He has just gonged, no doubt to order another buttered teacake!

He came to the actual thing one day. 'Our Pharmacopaeia,' he said, 'our Western Pharmacopaeia, is anything but the last word of medical science. In the East, I've been told—

He stopped and stared at me. It was like being at an aquarium.

I was quite suddenly angry with him. 'Look here,' I said, 'who told you about my great-grandmother's recipes?'

'Well,' he fenced.

'Every time we've met for a week,' I said '—and we've met pretty often – you've given me a broad hint or so about that little secret of mine.'

'Well,' he said, 'now the cat's out of the bag, I'll admit, yes, it is so. I had it—'

'From Pattison?'

'Indirectly,' he said, which I believe was lying, 'yes.'

'Pattison,' I said, 'took that stuff at his own risk.'

He pursed his mouth and bowed.

'My great-grandmother's recipes,' I said, 'are queer things to handle. My father was near making me promise—'

'He didn't?'

'No. But he warned me. He himself used one – once.'

'Ah! . . . But, do you think – ? Suppose – suppose there did happen to be one—'

'The things are curious documents,' I said. 'Even the smell of 'em . . . No!'

But after going so far Pyecraft was resolved I should go farther. I was always a little afraid that if I tried his patience too much he would fall on me suddenly and smother me. I own I was weak. But I was also annoyed with Pyecraft. I had got to that state of feeling for him that disposed me to say: 'Well, *take* the risk!' The little affair of Pattison to which I have alluded was a different matter altogether. What it was doesn't concern us now, but I knew, anyhow, that the particular recipe I used then was safe. The rest I didn't know so much about, and, on the whole, I was inclined to doubt their safety pretty completely.

Yet even if Pyecraft got poisoned—

I must confess the poisoning of Pyecraft struck me as an immense undertaking.

That evening I took that queer odd-scented sandal-wood box out of my safe and turned the rustling skins over. The gentleman who wrote the recipes for my great-grandmother evidently had a weakness for skins of a miscellaneous origin, and his handwriting was cramped to the last degree. Some of the things are quite unreadable to me – though my family, with its Indian Civil Service associations, has kept up a knowledge of Hindustani from generation to generation – and none are absolutely plain sailing. But I found the one that I knew was there soon enough, and sat on the floor by my safe for some time looking at it.

'Look here,' said I to Pyecraft next day, and snatched the slip away from his eager grasp.

'So far as I can make it out, this is a recipe for Loss of Weight.' ('Ah!' said Pyecraft.) 'I'm not absolutely sure, but I think it's that. And if you take my advice you'll leave it alone. Because, you know – I blacken my blood in your interest, Pyecraft – my ancestors on that side were, so far as I can gather, a jolly queer lot. See?'

'Let me try it,' said Pyecraft.

I leant back in my chair. My imagination made one mighty effort and fell flat within me. 'What in Heaven's name, Pyecraft,' I asked, 'do you think you'll look like when you get thin?'

He was impervious to reason. I made him promise never to say a word to me about his disgusting fatness again whatever happened – never, and then I handed him that little piece of skin.

'It's nasty stuff,' I said.

'No matter,' he said, and took it.

He goggled at it. 'But – but –' he said.

He had just discovered that it wasn't English.

'To the best of my ability,' I said, 'I will do you a translation.'

I did my best. After that we didn't speak for a fortnight. Whenever he approached me I frowned and motioned him away, and he respected our compact, but at the end of the fortnight he was as fat as ever. And then he got a word in.

'I must speak,' he said. 'It isn't fair. There's something wrong. It's done me no good. You're not doing your great-grandmother justice.'

'Where's the recipe?'

He produced it gingerly from his pocket-book.

I ran my eye over the items. 'Was the egg addled?' I asked.

'No. Ought it to have been?'

'That,' I said, 'goes without saying in all my poor dear great grandmother's recipes. When condition or quality is not specified you must get the worst. She was drastic or nothing . . . And there's one or two possible alternatives to some of these other things. You got *fresh* rattlesnake venom?'

'I got a rattlesnake from Jamrach's. It cost – it cost—'

'That's you affair, anyhow. This last item—'

'I know a man, who—'

'Yes. H'm. Well, I write the alternatives down . So far as I know the language, the spelling of this recipe is particularly atrocious. By the by, dog here probably means pariah dog.'

For a month after that I saw Pyecraft constantly at the club, and as fat and as anxious as ever. He kept our treaty, but at times he broke the spirit of it by shaking his head despondently. Then one day in the cloakroom he said: 'Your great-grandmother—'

'Not a word against her,' I said; and he held his peace.

I could have fancied he had desisted, and I saw him one day talking to three new members about his fatness as though he was in search of other recipes. And then, quite unexpectedly his telegram came.

'Mr Formalyn!' bawled a page-boy under my nose, and I took the telegram and opened it at once.

*'For Heaven's sake come. – Pyecraft'*

'H'm,' said I, and to tell the truth I was so pleased at the rehabilitation of my great-grandmother's reputation this evidently promised that I made a most excellent lunch.

I got Pyecraft's address from the hall porter. Pyecraft inhabited the upper half of a house in Bloomsbury, and I went there as soon as I had done my coffee and Trappistine. I did not wait to finish my cigar.

'Mr Pyecraft?' said I, at the front door.

They believed he was ill; he hadn't been out for two days.

'He expects me,' said I, and they sent me up.

I rang the bell at the lattice door upon the landing.

'He shouldn't have tried it, anyhow,' I said to myself. 'A man who eats like a pig ought to look like a pig.'

An obviously worthy woman, with an anxious face and a carelessly placed cap, came and surveyed me through the lattice.

I gave my name and she opened his door for me in a dubious fashion.

'Well?' said I, as we stood together inside Pyecraft's piece of the landing.

''E said you was to come in if you came,' she said; and regarded me, making no motion to show me anywhere. And then, confidentially: ''E's locked in, sir.'

'Locked in?'

'Locked himself in yesterday morning and 'asn't let anyone in since, sir. And ever and again *swearing*. Oh, my!'

I stared at the door she indicated by her glances. 'In there?' I said.

'Yes, sir.'

'What's up?'

She shook her head sadly. ''E keeps on calling for vittles, sir. '*Eavy* vittles 'e wants. I get 'im what I can. Pork 'e's 'ad, sooit puddin', sossiges, noo bread. Everythink like that. Left outside, if you please, and me go away. 'E's eatin', sir, somethink *awful*.'

There came a piping bawl from inside the door: 'That Formalyn?'

'That you, Pyecraft?' I shouted, and went and banged the door.

'Tell her to go away.'

I did.

Then I could hear a curious pattering upon the door, almost like someone feeling for the handle in the dark, and Pyecraft's familiar grunts.

'It's all right,' I said, 'she's gone.'

But not for a long time did the door open.

I heard the key turn. Then Pyecraft's voice said: 'Come in.'

I turned the handle and opened the door. Naturally I expected to see Pyecraft.

Well, you know, he wasn't there!

I never had such a shock in my life. There was his sitting-room in a state of untidy disorder, plates and dishes among the books and writing things, and several chairs overturned, but Pyecraft—

'It's all right, o' man; shut the door,' he said, and then I discovered him.

There he was right up close to the cornice in the corner by the door, as though someone had glued him to the ceiling. His face was anxious and angry. He panted and gesticulatd. 'Shut the door,' he said. 'If that women gets hold of it—'

I shut the door, and went and stood away from him and stared.

'If anything gives away and you tumble down,' I said, 'you'll break your neck, Pyecraft.'

'I wish I could,' he wheezed.

'A man of your age and weight getting up to kiddish gymnastics—'

'Don't,' he said, and looked agonised. 'Your damned great-grandmother—'

'Be careful,' I warned him.

'I'll tell you,' he said, and gesticulated.

'How the deuce,' said I, 'are you holding on up there?'

And then abruptly I realised that he was not holding on at all, that he was floating up there – just as a gas-filled bladder might have floated in the same position. He began to struggle to thrust himself away from the ceiling, and to clamber down the wall to me. 'It's that prescription,' he panted, as he did so. 'Your great-gran—'

'*No*!' I cried.

He took hold of a framed engraving rather carelessly as he spoke and it gave way, and he flew back to the ceiling again, while the picture smashed on to the sofa. Bump he went against the ceiling, and I knew then why he was all over white on the more salient curves and angles of his person. He tried again more carefully, coming down by way of the mantel.

It was really a most extraordinary spectacle, that great, fat, apopletic-looking man upside down and trying to get from the ceiling to the floor. 'That prescription,' he said. 'Too successful.'

'How?'

'Loss of weight – almost complete.'

And then of course, I understood.

'By Jove, Pyecraft,' said I, 'what you wanted was a cure for fatness! But you always called it weight. You would call it weight.'

Somehow I was extremely delighted. I quite liked Pyecraft for the time. 'Let me help you!' I said, and took his hand and pulled him down. He kicked about trying to get a foothold somewhere. It was very like holding a flag on a windy day.

'That table,' he said, pointing, 'is solid mahogany and very heavy. If you can put me under that—'

I did, and there he wallowed about like a captive balloon, while I stood on his hearthrug and talked to him.

I lit a cigar. 'Tell me,' I said, 'what happened.'

'I took it, he said.

'How did it taste?'

'Oh, *beastly*!'

I should fancy they all did. Whether one regards the ingredients or the probable compound or the possible results, almost all my great-grandmother's remedies appear to me at least to be extraordinarily uninviting. For my own part—

'I took a little sip first.'

'Yes?'

'And as I felt lighter and better after an hour, I decided to take the draught.'

'My dear Pyecraft!'

'I held my nose,' he explained. 'And then I kept on getting lighter and lighter – and helpless, you know.'

He gave way suddenly to a burst of passion. 'What the goodness am I to *do*?' he said.

'There's one thing pretty evident,' I said, 'that you mustn't do. If you go out of doors you'll go up and up.' I waved an arm upward. 'They'd have to send Santos-Dumont after you to bring you down again.'

'I suppose it will wear off?'

I shook my head. 'I don't think you can count on that,' I said.

And then there was another burst of passion, and he kicked out at adjacent chairs and banged the floor. He behaved just as I should have expected a great, fat, self-indulgent man to behave under trying circumstances – that is to say, very badly. He spoke of me and of my great-grandmother with an utter want of discretion.

'I never asked you to take the stuff,' I said.

And generously disregarding the insults he was putting upon me, I sat down in his armchair and began to talk to him in a sober, friendly fashion.

I pointed out to him that this was a trouble he had brought upon himself, and that it had almost an air of poetical justice. He had eaten too much. This he disputed, and for a time we argued the point.

He became noisy and violent, so I desisted from this aspect of his lesson. 'And then,' said I, 'you committed the sin of euphuism. You call it, not Fat, which is just and inglorious, but Weight. You—'

He interrupted me to say that he recognised all that. What was he to *do*?

I suggested he should adapt himself to his new conditions. So we came to the really sensible part of the business. I suggested that it would not be difficult for him to learn to walk about on the ceiling with his hands—

'I can't sleep,' he said.

But that was no great difficulty. It was quite possible, I pointed out, to make a shake-up under a wire mattress, fasten the under things on with tapes, and have a blanket, sheet, and coverlet to button at the side. He would have to confide in his housekeeper, I said; and after some squabbling he agreed to that. (Afterwards it was quite delightful to see the beautiful matter-of-fact way with which the good lady took all these amazing inversions.) He could have a library ladder in his room, and all his meals could be laid on the top of his bookcase. We also hit on an ingenious device by which he could get to the floor whenever he wanted, which was simply to put the *British Encyclopaedia* (tenth edition) on the top of his open shelves. He just pulled out a couple of volumes and held on, and down he came. And we agreed there must be iron staples along the skirting, so that he could cling to those whenever he wanted to get about the room on the lower level.

As we got on with the thing I found myself almost keenly interested. It was I who called in the housekeeper and broke matters to her, and it was I chiefly who fixed up the inverted bed. In fact, I spent two whole days at his flat. I am a handy, interfering sort of man with a screwdriver, and I made all sorts of ingenious adaptations for him – ran a wire to bring his bells within reach, turned all his electric lights up instead of down, and so on. The whole affair was extremely curious and interesting to me, and it was delightful to think of Pyecraft like some great, fat blowfly, crawling about on his ceiling and clambering round the lintel of his doors from one room to another, and never, never, never coming to the club any more . . .

Then, you know, my fatal ingenuity got the better of me. I was sitting by his fire drinking his whisky, and he was up in his favourite corner by the cornice, tacking a turkey carpet to the ceiling, when the idea struck me. 'By Jove, Pyecraft!' I said, 'all this is totally unnecessary.'

And before I could calculate the complete consequences of my notion, I blurted it out. 'Lead underclothing,' said I, and the mischief was done.

Pyecraft received the thing almost in tears. 'To be right ways up again—' he said.

I gave him the whole secret before I saw where it would take me. 'Buy sheet lead,' I said, 'stamp it into discs. Sew 'em all over your underclothes until you have enough. Have lead-soled boots, carry a bag of solid lead, and the thing is done! Instead of being a prisoner here you may go abroad again. Pyecraft; you may travel—'

A still happier idea came to me. 'You need never fear a shipwreck. All you need do is just slip off some or all of your clothes, take the necessary amount of luggage in your hand, and float up in the air—'

In his emotion he dropped the tack-hammer within an ace of my head. 'By Jove!' he said, 'I shall be able to come back to the club again.'

The thing pulled me up short. 'By Jove!' I said faintly. 'Yes. Of course – you will.'

He did. He does. There he sits behind me now, stuffing – as I live! – and a third go of buttered tea-cake. And no one in the whole world knows – except his housekeeper and me – that he weighs practically nothing; that he is a mere boring mass of assimilatory matter, mere clouds in clothing, *niente, nefas*, the most inconsiderable of men. There he sits watching until I have done this writing. Then, if he can, he will waylay me. He will come billowing up to me . . .

He will tell me over again all about it, how it feels, how it doesn't feel, how he sometimes hopes it is passing off a little. And always somewhere in that fat, abundant discourse he will say: 'The secret's keeping, eh? If anyone knew of it – I should be so ashamed . . . Makes a fellow look such a fool, you know. Crawling about on a ceiling and all that . . .'

And now to elude Pyecraft, occupying as he does, an admirable strategic position between me and the door.

●

When it's three o'clock in New York, it's still 1938 in London.

**Bette Midler**

Telegram to a consultant at a large hospital in the north-east on his appointment as Honorary Physician to the Queen:

CONGRATULATIONS. GOD SAVE THE QUEEN.

# *Puckoon*

## Spike Milligan

Dr Goldstein pulled the sheet over the face of Dan Doonan. Mrs Doonan took the news dry-eyed. She'd only stayed with him for the money. Twenty years before she had tried to get a separation. The solicitor listened to her attentively. 'But Mrs Doonan, just because you don't like him, that's no grounds for separation.'

'Well, make a few suggestions,' she said.

'Has he ever struck you?'

'No. I'd kill him if he did.'

'Has he ever been cruel to the children?'

'Never.'

'Ever left you short of money, then?'

'No, every Friday on the nail.'

'I see.' The solicitor pondered. 'Ah, wait, think hard now, Mrs Doonan, has he ever been unfaithful to you?'

Her face lit up. 'By God, I tink we got him there, I know for sure he wasn't the father of me last child!'

The solicitor had advised her acccordingly. 'Get out of my office,' he told her and charged six and eight-pence for the advice.

Now Dan was dead. 'I wonder how much he's left me,' the widow wondered. Money couldn't buy friends but you got a better class of enemy.

Messrs Quock, Murdle, Protts and Frigg, solicitors and Commissioners for Oaths, pondered dustily over the grey will papers; at 98, Dan Doonan had died leaving all his money to himself. The quartet of partners shook their heads, releasing little showers of legal dandruff. They had thumbed carefully through the 3,000 pages of *Morrell on Unorthodox Wills*, and no light was cast on the problem. Murdle took a delicate silver Georgian snuff box from his waistcoat, dusted the back of his hand with the fragrant mixture of Sandalwood and ground Sobrani, sniffed into each nostril, then blew a great clarion blast into a crisp white handkerchief.

'This will take years of work to unravel,' he told his companions, 'we must make sure of that,' he added with a sly smile, wink, and a finger on the nose. They were, after all, a reputable firm built up on impeccable business principles, carefully doctored books and sound tax avoidance.

Only the last paragraph of the said will was clear. Doonan wanted a hundred pounds spent on a grand 'Wake' in honour of himself. Senior partner, Mr Protts, stood up, drew a gold engraved pocket watch to his hand, snapped it closed, '4.32 exactly, gentlemen – Time for Popeye,' he said switching on the T.V.

The inebriated chanting of professional mourners came wailing from 44 Cloncarragah Terrace. Inside the front room, propped by the fireplace, was the flower-bedecked coffin of Dan Doonan. Grouped around admiringly, reverently clutching their drinks, were friends and foes alike, and with drink they were all very much alike. Funeral clichés were flying in the teeth of the dear departed.

'A fine man, ma'am, it's a great day for him.'

'You must be proud of him, Mrs Doonan.'

'One of the finest dead men ter ever walk the earth.'

'I was sorry ter see him go!'

'So was I – he owed me a pound.'

'It's hard to believe he's dead.'

'Oh he's *dead* is he?' said Foggerty, who'd been speaking to him all evening.

The corpse looked fine, fine. New suit, hair cut and greased, his boots highly polished and loaned by an anonymous donor were firmly nailed to the coffin for additional security. The tables in the next room were swollen high with the food. Two wooden tubs steamed with baked potatoes, their earthy jackets split and running with rivulets of melting butter. Hot pig slices, a quarter inch thick, were piled high on seventeen plates. In the middle, was one huge dish of brown pork sausages, and bacon, still bubbling from the pan. On the floor, floating in a bucket of vinegar, was a minefield of pickled onions. The temporary bar was serving drinks as fast as O'Toole could pour them.

'God. There hasn't been a night like this since the signing of the Treaty.'

Many people die of thirst but the Irish are born with one.

O'Connor the piper tucked his kilt between his legs, puffed the bladder of his pipes and droned them into life; soon the floor was lost in a sea of toiling, reeling legs. Uppity-hippity-juppity-ippity-dippity-dippity shook the house. The centre bulb danced like a freshly hanged man. There was a clapping a stamping-and-cries-of-encouragement. The faithful few in Dan's parlour soon deserted him for the dance. Alone in his room he stood, his body jerking to the rhythm now shaking the house. The party was swelled by the arrival of the victorious Puckoon Hurley team, many still unconscious from the game. These were dutifully laid on the floor beside Dan's coffin – the rest joined into the frenzied dance.

Three fights had broken out in the midst of the dancers but the difference was hard to tell. The whole house now trembled from roof to foundations. In the next room the great family bible shook from the shelf above the coffin and struck Dan Doonan, throwing him from the coffin and catapulting him from his boots. His wig, a life-long secret, shot from his head and slid under the table next to the cat. He fell among the unconscious members of the Hurley team, who were starting to recover. 'He's drunk as a lord,' they said, dragging him across the hall and tucking him in bed.

'Good God, look at the size of that rat,' one said, seeing the cat pass with a wig in its jaws. 'He mustha' put up a fight.'

Placing a bottle of whisky by the bed they drank it and stumbled from the room.

It was 4.32 in the morning as the crow flies. The last mourners had slobbered out their drunken farewells, their voices and great posterior blasts mingling into the night. Mrs

Doonan drained an empty bottle, scratched her belly, and made for her bed.

Somewhere in the night, Milligan, drunk and with lumps on his head, was wandering through the braille-black countryside; in his path a carefully written well. Splash! it went on receipt of his body.

At 4.56 in the morning, the quietly patrolling constable Oaf was reduced to a kneeling-praying holy man by a leg-weakening shriek. The door of number 33 burst open and out screamed Mrs Doonan in unlaced corsets.

'There's a man in me bed, get him out!' she yelled, restraining her abounding bosoms.

'Madame, if you can't frighten him in that get up, I certainly can't!'

'Do yer duty,' she said, ladelling her bosoms back.

The constable unclipped his torch, took a firm grip on his truncheon and entered the house.

'In that room,' she whispered.

'Leave him to me,' said Oaf, pushing her in front. He shone his torch on the bed. Mrs Doonan gasped and let fall her bosoms. 'Holy Mary!' she gasped, 'It's me husband.'

She fainted, clutching the policeman's legs as she fell, bringing his trousers to the ground. Now then, who would have thought a constable would use green knotted string for garters, and have red anchors tattooed on his knees? Ah, Ireland is still a land of mystery.

●

# *Acknowledgements*

The Publisher has made every effort to contact the Copyright holders but wishes to apologise to those he has been unable to trace. Grateful acknowledgement is made for permission to reprint the following:

*Part One* **The War between the Sexes**

Miles Kington 'The Dangerous World of Relationships'. Copyright © *Miles and Miles* 1982 by Miles Kington, published by Hamish Hamilton, courtesy of Anthony Sheil Associates.

Jilly Cooper, 'Is it Time for a Degree in Sex?' From *Jolly Super*. Copyright © Jilly Cooper 1969. Reprinted by permission of Methuen London Ltd.

P.G. Wodehouse *The Inimitable Jeeves*, 1973. Reprinted by permission of Century Hutchinson Publishing Group Ltd and A.P. Watt Ltd.

*Part Two* **Somebody Has to do it**

Tom Sharpe *The Great Pursuit.* Reprinted by permission of Martin Secker & Warburg Ltd.

Jonathan Lynn and Antony Jay 'Yes Minister'. Reproduction from *The Complete Yes Minister* 1981–84, edited by Jonathan Lynn and Antony Jay with the permission of BBC Enterprises Ltd.

Terry Wogan 'It's a Funny Business' from *The Day Job*. Copyright © Terry Wogan 1981. Courtesy Lennard Publishing.

Peter Ustinov 'Hollywood', from *Dear Me*. Copyright © Pavor S.A. 1977. Reprinted by permission of William Heinemann Ltd.

E.Œ. Somerville & M. Ross 'Occasional Licenses'. From *Some*

*Experiences of an Irish R.M.* Courtesy John Farquharson Ltd.

*Part Three* **Perfect Beasts**

Gerald Durrell 'A Wilderness of Monkeys' from *The Bafut Beagles*, 1954. Courtesy Grafton Books, a division of William Collins & Sons.

James Herriot *All Things Bright and Beautiful*, 1973/4. Published by Michael Joseph Ltd, reprinted by permission of David Higham Associates Ltd.

Groucho Marx *Groucho and Me*, 1959. Excerpted with the permission of the original publisher Bernard Geis Associates, New York, from *Groucho and Me* by Groucho Marx.

*Part Four* **Young Things**

Sue Townsend *The Growing Pains of Adrian Mole*, 1984. Reprinted by permission of Methuen London Ltd.

Clive James *Unreliable Memoirs*, 1980. Reprinted by permission of Peters, Fraser & Dunlop Group Ltd.

*Part Five* **Life Sentences**

David Niven 'Military Affairs' from *The Moon's a Balloon*, 1971. Reprinted by permission of Hamish Hamilton Ltd.

Ronnie Corbett 'On Being Small', from *Small Man's Guide*, 1976. Copyright © Ronnie Corbett, 1976. Published by Michael Joseph Ltd.

James Thurber 'The Night the Ghost Got In', from *My Life and Hard Times* (From Vintage Thurber Vol 2). Reprinted by permission of Hamish Hamilton Ltd and Rosemary A. Thurber and Lucy Kroll Agency, New York.

Groucho Marx 'My Best Friend is a Dog', from *Memoirs of a Mangy Lover*. Excerpted with the permission of the original publisher Bernard Geis Associates, New York, from *Memoirs of a Mangy Lover*, 1963, by Groucho Marx.

S.J. Perelman *The Most of S.J. Perelman*, 1959. Reprinted by permission of Peters, Fraser and Dunlop Group and Simon and Schuster, New York.

Peter Ustinov 'Army Days', from **Dear Me**. Copyright © Pavor

S.A. 1977. Reprinted by permission of William Heinemann Ltd.

Arthur Marshall *Life's Rich Pageant*, 1984. Reprinted by permission of Hamish Hamilton Ltd.

*Part Six* **Exit Laughter**

Joyce Grenfell *Turn Back the Clock*, 1977–83. Reprinted by permission of Richard Scott Simon Ltd.

H.G. Wells 'The Truth About Pyecraft' from *The Complete Short Stories of H.G. Wells*. Reprinted by permission of A.P. Watt Ltd on behalf of the Literary Executors of the Estate of H.G. Wells.

Spike Milligan *Puckoon*, 1963. Courtesy Spike Milligan Productions Ltd.

●

*Illustrations are taken from:*

*The Jokes of ffolkes (Private Eye Cartoon Library 8)* 1976, by permission of *Private Eye; Best of Heath,* 1984, by permission of David & Charles Publishers; *Vintage Thurber Volume One* by permission of Hamish Hamilton Ltd and Rosemary A. Thurber and Lucy Kroll Agency, New York; *Dogs Dogs Dogs*, 1985, edited by S. Gross, courtesy Henry R. Martin and Don Orehek.

# A selection of non-fiction from Headline

|  |  |  |
|---|---|---|
| THE DRACULA SYNDROME | Richard Monaco & William Burt | £5.99 ☐ |
| DEADLY JEALOUSY | Martin Fido | £5.99 ☐ |
| WHITE COLLAR KILLERS | Frank Jones | £4.99 ☐ |
| THE MURDER YEARBOOK 1994 | Brian Lane | £5.99 ☐ |
| THE PLAYFAIR CRICKET ANNUAL | Bill Frindall | £3.99 ☐ |
| ROD STEWART | Stafford Hildred & Tim Ewbank | £5.99 ☐ |
| THE JACK THE RIPPER A–Z | Paul Begg, Martin Fido & Keith Skinner | £7.99 ☐ |
| THE *DAILY EXPRESS* HOW TO WIN ON THE HORSES | Danny Hall | £4.99 ☐ |
| COUPLE SEXUAL AWARENESS | Barry & Emily McCarthy | £5.99 ☐ |
| GRAPEVINE: THE COMPLETE WINEBUYERS HANDBOOK | Anthony Rose & Tim Atkins | £5.99 ☐ |
| ROBERT LOUIS STEVENSON: DREAMS OF EXILE | Ian Bell | £7.99 ☐ |

*All Headline books are available at your local bookshop or newsagent, or can be ordered direct from the publisher. Just tick the titles you want and fill in the form below. Prices and availability subject to change without notice.*

Headline Book Publishing, Cash Sales Department, Bookpoint, 39 Milton Park, Abingdon, OXON, OX14 4TD, UK. If you have a credit card you may order by telephone – 0235 400400.

Please enclose a cheque or postal order made payable to Bookpoint Ltd to the value of the cover price and allow the following for postage and packing:
UK & BFPO: £1.00 for the first book, 50p for the second book and 30p for each additional book ordered up to a maximum charge of £3.00.
OVERSEAS & EIRE: £2.00 for the first book, £1.00 for the second book and 50p for each additional book.

Name ..............................................................................................

Address ..........................................................................................

.......................................................................................................

.......................................................................................................

If you would prefer to pay by credit card, please complete:
Please debit my Visa/Access/Diner's Card/American Express (delete as applicable) card no:

| | | | | | | | | | | | | | | | |
|---|---|---|---|---|---|---|---|---|---|---|---|---|---|---|---|

Signature .......................................................................... Expiry Date .........